ECO-FADS

How the rise of trendy environmentalism is harming the environment

ECO-FADS

How the rise of trendy environmentalism
is harming the environment

TODD MYERS

PO Box 3643
Seattle, WA 98124
(206) 937-9691
www.washingtonpolicy.org

Designed by Travis Andersen, Mindbogl Design

ISBN 978-0-615-48614-7

Contents

Acknowledgements

Since this is my first book, there are many people who have helped me come to the point where I could actually put these ideas down on paper. Special thanks go to my wife Maria who repeatedly asked me, "How's the book coming?" as a gentle reminder to stop watching baseball and make progress. Also, thanks to my parents who gave me the opportunities to learn and encouraged me to write even if I didn't fully absorb my father's English skills.

I would not be writing on environmental policy without the opportunity provided by former Washington State Lands Commissioner Doug Sutherland to join him at the Department of Natural Resources and learn about these issues firsthand. While at DNR, I benefitted from the teaching of many excellent scientists and public servants, including Bruce Mackey, Fran McNair, Bonnie Bunning, Pat McElroy, Angus Brodie and Vicki Christiansen. Thanks especially to my former DNR colleague Patty Henson, who provided comedy and therapy in the midst of the strangeness that often envelops environmental politics.

The Washington Policy Center has been a fantastic partner in my work. Thanks to Dann Mead-Smith for his support, and to Paul Guppy for his editing and thoughtful comments. There are many others on the staff who added key elements, including Brandon Houskeeper and John Barnes, who helped manage the process and keep things moving forward so I could focus on the book's content. I appreciate the support of the WPC Board whose enthusiasm helped keep me going and especially to Jim Day and Al Symington who were instrumental in the creation of the Center for Environmental Policy at the WPC. Thanks also to Susan Hutchison and the Charles Simonyi Fund for Arts and Sciences, whose financial support of the CEP helped us focus on ensuring that good science guided our thinking about environmental policy.

I'd also like to acknowledge the thinking and support of others in the policy community who gave me the opportunity to share my ideas and engage in the process that led to this book. Thinkers and activists like Bjørn Lomborg, Ann McElhinney, Phelim McAleer, Matt Manweller, Cliff Mass, Chris Horner, Sterling Burnett, James Taylor, Patrick Moore, Bob Kahn, Yoram Bauman and others, many of whom I have quoted in the book, helped mold my thinking and pushed me to be more rigorous.

Thanks also are due to my coworkers at my business, Todd Myers Communications, Marissa Dunn and Dianne Danowski Smith, who held down the fort while I focused on research and writing. They gave me the opportunity to put the necessary time and attention into the project.

Finally, I appreciate the help of those who offered edits and ideas along the way. Pat Coussens read every word of the book, made thoughtful comments and edits, and challenged my thinking. Thanks also to my sister Kim and to my sister-in-law Anna Moss who gave robust feedback even while admitting, "I kinda like eco-fads."

All these people, and others, made this book what it is. I hope they feel it is worth being associated with it.

Introduction to Part One

What kind of person would oppose the latest in environmentally friendly buildings – those built to meet "green" building standards? If they were honest with themselves, environmentalists.

"Green" buildings are all the rage among environmental activists who want to cut carbon emissions by making our lives more energy-efficient. Inefficient buildings, they argue, are a key cause of "climate pollution." They repeatedly note that buildings account for a significant share of energy use in the United States and the only way to cut our total carbon emissions is to take significant steps in making them more efficient.

The environmental community has even created a system they claim will achieve that important goal. LEED, short for Leadership in Energy and Environmental Design, is the creation of the U.S. Green Building Council (USGBC), which is the nation's most prominent green building advocate and a darling of the environmental community. Environmental activists across the country have not been satisfied with encouraging builders and owners to adopt LEED in their design process. They have actively lobbied numerous communities, states and federal agencies, to make achieving LEED certification a requirement for government, and sometimes private, buildings.

The goal is to dramatically reduce carbon emissions and the risks from climate change. After all, climate change (or global warming, whatever term suits you), environmentalists frequently tell us, is "the most important issue facing this generation." The stakes simply could not be higher, and environmental activists stress that without serious efforts to reduce the energy used in buildings, we will never achieve the aggressive carbon-emissions reductions needed to avoid the array of dangerous calamities that await us.

One might conclude that such an important, far-reaching policy would be extremely expensive. Not so, claim advocates of green buildings. Although "green" buildings do cost more, the added cost, about 2 percent more, is very small. Wouldn't you pay 6 cents more for an environmentally friendly cup of coffee? Who would claim that an extra $10 is too much to pay for a dishwasher that helps save the planet? What kind of person would mortgage their children's future by refusing to pay just 2 percent more for a green building?

After all, with such a small up-front cost, the energy savings will quickly pay for themselves. Green buildings, it is claimed, cut energy costs by up to 50 percent, allowing building owners to recover the additional cost in just a few years. After that, the savings are all planet-saving gravy.

As if that were not enough, green buildings also make you healthier and smarter.

Advocates claim green buildings provide more fresh air, reducing the potential for "sick buildings" and cutting sick days and absenteeism in green buildings. The benefits of improved health in these buildings adds up quickly, more than paying for the additional costs in reduction in lost worker time and reduction in health insurance costs – so the story goes.

As we are saving our children's environmental future with green buildings, we're also making them smarter. Green building supporters confidently claim the extra daylight available in green schools make children smarter, improving test scores and significantly improving their learning environment. Green schools alone increase test scores by 10 percent say the "studies."

If there were ever a win-win, we are assured, it is certainly this. And, even if the buildings don't live up to all the promises, they are still a positive step toward environmental sustainability and reducing the impact we have on the planet.

When I hear these kinds of claims, I immediately wonder, "If this is so great, why do we need politicians to force us to take these steps?" The answer, invariably, is that experts know best and politicians have access to information and expertise that you and I do not.

Living and working in a hotbed of environmental consciousness like the Pacific Northwest of the United States, I hear these arguments frequently. Environmental ideology is so ingrained in this part of the country that some refer to it as "Ecotopia."

It should not come as a surprise, then, that the Washington State Legislature and city of Seattle have both adopted rules favoring these trendy new environmental building standards. To great fanfare, the politicians behind these new requirements were quick to take credit for their courageous stand for the environment – a stand that would help save the planet and save us money.

Yet, it turned out that Seattle's newly constructed "green" City Hall, built to those green standards, actually used more energy than the decades-old building it replaced. Instead of saving energy, the new building saw a dramatic increase in energy use.

Such lessons, however, were lost on the state's legislature, who decided to make similar rules mandatory for all new state buildings and schools. Parading before the legislature were experts in architecture and engineering, promising that these new regulations would easily save money and reduce energy use. They pointed to a number of schools across the state that had already adopted these rules and were already "saving" about 30 percent in energy costs – money that would quickly pay back the additional construction costs.

When it turned out that one of the green schools was, in fact, not saving 30 percent but was actually using 30 percent *more* energy than a school built at the same time in the same school district, legislators were told that, while mistakes had been made, the building would soon be achieving those energy savings.

When it turned out that studies promising these savings were shoddy or inaccurate, the legislative lobbyist for the environmental community laughed it off, saying he "wasn't a big fan of studies in particular," without explaining how he did get the information he used to make decisions.

Time would tell the story, supporters insisted, that these new rules would be a real benefit for the environment.

Six years later, what is the verdict?

Among dozens of "green" schools in Washington state, only two use less energy than traditional schools built in those same districts. In more than one instance, the "green" schools use 30 percent more energy per square foot than schools built without the elements the politicians and environmental activists promised would so spectacularly cut energy use. Frustrated building managers in these districts are candid about the failures of these new rules even as they feel obliged to defend them in public, often standing next to the politicians who promised the rules would yield great savings.

While the building managers fretted over the failure of the promised energy savings, some teachers and principals praised the buildings for being lighter and cleaner. The data, however, show that green schools aren't healthier than new schools built without the "green" embellishments. Absentee rates among students are little different at green schools and, just like energy use, are actually worse in some of the green buildings.

Most revealing, perhaps, is the fact that when comparing the student achievement ratings provided by the state of Washington for 42 "green" schools compared to the 407 traditional schools in those same districts, the "green" schools ratings are actually worse.

Higher energy use. More sick days. Lower test scores. And all for a higher price.

Such failures do not deter politicians eager to portray themselves as environmentally responsible. After all, they are showing leadership in the fight against climate change. Even if the buildings are merely a symbol of that fight, they serve a purpose – just like the electric car charging station installed at one of the green schools more than a year ago that has never been used. Even if it is not useful in the traditional sense of providing an actual service, it serves as a monolith, a monument honoring those who care about the environment.

Of course, wasting money on efforts that produce no tangible environmental benefit should be condemned, especially if the stakes are as high as environmental advocates claim. Real environmentalism is based in a desire to use resources responsibly and reduce waste of money and resources.

Wasting money to save the environment should be an oxymoron. Increasingly, however, it is not. Wasting money on trendy environmental projects, what I call "eco-fads," has actually become commonplace for politicians and even green consumers. Rather than judging policies based on their results, eco-fads grow in popularity based on their ability to confer a green image to those who embrace them – just like the most recent fashion trends offer social benefits to those with the latest shoe style.

And those who have worked hard to cultivate an environmental self-image are aggressive about protecting it.

While presenting the data about the failure of green schools to save energy in front of a group in Seattle, one person simply couldn't take it anymore. Fed up, he pounded his fists on the table and yelled, "What you are saying is simply immoral!" He didn't say "inaccurate" or "unscientific." He chose "immoral." When asked by the leader of the group to be respectful of other opinions, he told the group that he was there to protect the planet, and if the others weren't, he "was in the wrong place."

But he wasn't saving the planet. He was defending policies that were actually doing damage to the environment. Yet he was more concerned about what he felt was an attack on a policy that is a central tenet of a particular brand of environmental ideology than the actual results. The social benefits of appearing green trumped the environmental benefits that were supposed to be the center of that image.

True environmentalism should not simply be a contest aimed at projecting a carefully crafted and appealing image that feels environmentally progressive. Yet, from green buildings, to reusable grocery bags, to biofuels and solar panels, environmental consciousness too often amounts to little more than a race to follow the latest environmental fad. They are the eco-fads that signal our peers that we are not simply thrifty and intelligent, but profoundly moral.

How Did We Get Here?

Truly, protecting the planet for future generations is an important goal. Understanding the ways in which we can do better is a critical part of that effort. Scientifically identifying the areas where humanity is doing environmental damage provides the important foundation of knowledge necessary to make good decisions. It is exactly the type of information that Bjørn Lomborg set out to discover.

As a professor of statistics at a Danish university, Lomborg set out to use statistics to show how humans are gradually harming the environment. His findings, however, turned out much different than he expected. He discovered the standard list of environmental threats, which he called "the litany," were either exaggerated or simply false. The data showed that, in many ways, the health of the planet was getting better, not worse.

Lomborg realized many of the environmental policies being pushed by politicians and advocates around the world were misplaced and that scarce public resources were being spent on the wrong problem. Working with Nobel-winning economists, Lomborg created the Copenhagen Consensus, an effort to use data, science and economics to prioritize the problems that most plagued humans and the planet. It then ranks the most effective solutions to each from best to worst.

The Copenhagen Consensus is an effort to put environmental policy back on track, focusing on policies that yield the greatest benefits to the environment and to humanity, in general.

Even Lomborg's critics acknowledge environmental policy has veered off track. Environmental groups that once opposed timber harvests now argue that wood is the most sustainable building material. Advocates of renewable fuels express concern that corn-based ethanol does more harm than good. Policies that offered hope have, instead, ended in costly failure. Environmental decisions are increasingly made by appealing to popular sentiment, leaving the complexities of science and unintended consequences behind.

Lomborg's work is an effort to highlight those failures and return to fact-based, scientifically sound environmental policy. It does not, however, explain why environmentalism got so far off track, or why people who claim they support environmental protection continue to promote failed policies even when the data are clear.

Put simply, scientific and economic information regarding environmental problems is increasingly taking a back seat to the social and personal value of being seen and perceived as "green." As environmental consciousness has become socially popular, eco-fads have supplanted objective data. Politicians pick the latest environmental agenda in the same way we choose the fall fashions – looking for signals about what will yield the largest benefit within our public and social circles.

This book is about the pressures that cause politicians, businesses, the media and even scientists to fall for trendy environmental fads. Each of these groups benefits from perpetuating the latest environmental fashion and encourages us to join them – all for the "sake of the environment," of course.

This book also discusses why we fall for such fads, even when we should know better. Who doesn't want to be seen as green? That natural desire can cloud our better judgment, causing us to place things that make us appear green ahead of actions that may be socially invisible but are environmentally responsible.

Much of recent public debate has been about whether the environmental threats emphasized in popular culture are real or not. This book addresses that question only peripherally. I do not discuss whether or not climate change is "real," and if so, how serious it is. My working assumption is that all of us, regardless of where we live or our political persuasion, value our planet's natural environment, even though we express that view in different ways.

I also assume that most people are sincere in their desire to help the environment, to protect fragile ecosystems, to save endangered animals and to preserve the remarkable natural diversity of our world. It is true that, like many of us, I know people who have ulterior motives, who use legitimate environmental concerns as a handy bludgeon to achieve other political goals. For most of us, however, public efforts to protect the environment are just that, even when mixed with other personal or political motivations.

My main purpose is to address how those sincere desires are sidetracked, leading to the result Lomborg describes in his book, *The Skeptical Environmentalist* – where we focus on the wrong environmental problems and advocate counterproductive solutions.

Many of the anecdotes and lessons in these pages are drawn from the Pacific Northwest of the United States. While the case studies and examples tend to be from this region, the lessons are widely applicable.

I have benefitted from spending a decade working on environmental policy in an area that has launched many of the eco-fads people everywhere now recognize. What may seem new or trendy in other parts of the world have been the norm in the Ecotopian Northwest for many years.

The purpose of this book is twofold – to help share an understanding of the range of forces that have taken us in the wrong direction and to show how we can begin to get back on track, creating a prosperous and sustainable legacy for our planet's future.

Chapter 1

The Rise of Eco-Fads

The photo takes more than a full page of the magazine and it is stark. It shows acre upon acre of decaying tree stumps, a vast barren area where a mighty forest once stood. Only a small patch of trees remains, sitting on top of a mound of dirt. The caption underneath the photo reads "Clear-cut land in Washington."[1] Those few dozen trees are all that is left in a large area of what was forest.

Published in 2002 by the technology magazine *Business 2.0*, it is the kind of arresting photo that is designed to imply scientific meaning by evoking an emotion. "How can something that ugly, that stark, be good for the environment?" is the question we are intended to ask. The photo is intended to demonstrate the real environmental damage humans are doing to the planet without having to scientifically support the claim. And there is no doubting that the view is ugly. It is not the type of thing people hike miles to see or desire as the view from the home of their dreams. That the view is undeniably ugly implies that the environmental impact of that scene must be undeniably negative.

The photo complemented an accompanying article that discussed a new forestry technology that would make such clear-cuts a thing of the past. A new breed of tree, hybrid poplars, which the article calls "supertrees," was created using biotechnology that, according to the photo caption, "could greatly reduce the need for such heavy logging."[2] The new trees, the article promised, are fast growing and obviate the need to harvest the large, old trees that are used in home and commercial construction today. Growing in less than half the time of conifer timber, hybrid poplars, the article asserts, could be grown as a crop without reducing wildlife habitat.

There are other purported benefits as well. Hybrid poplars soak up toxins in the soil. They can grow in soils that would harm other types of trees, but these bioengineered trees are able to remove toxins from the soil, harmlessly sequestering them inside the lumber for decades.

No more clear-cuts. Forests would be saved. Environmental cleanup would occur naturally. The idea represents the type of ingenuity Americans pride themselves on. The article presented the kind of technological solution that makes the world a better place: creating new jobs and enhancing our lifestyle and prosperity. It seemed to offer the best of all worlds.

At the time this article appeared, I was the Communications Director for the Department on Natural Resources, the chief forestry agency in Washington state. It intrigued me for a variety of reasons.

Forestry in Washington is extremely controversial. Nationwide the spotted owl is a symbol of the battle between timber communities and environmentalists, and Washington state was ground zero in that fight. Much of Western Washington was engaged in forestry at some point in the last 100 years, and there are still communities that are appropriately known as "timber towns" in several areas.

Choosing between ending people's jobs and protecting the environment is not an academic exercise at the Department of Natural Resources. The agency is involved literally in every timber harvest conducted in the state, either by issuing permits to private loggers or in planning harvests on state land. Revenues from timber sales go to the state's school construction fund. With every planned harvest, the impact on wildlife, the economy, salmon, jobs or simply the beautiful forest views we enjoy was subject to heated debate and discussion. The protracted process involved public meetings, letters to the editor, political speeches and, ultimately, since the head of the agency was elected by the public, a vote. Agency officials were always seeking ways to reduce the friction between these passionate and competing forces. Any new idea that could break the deadlock was always welcome.

Hybrid poplars, the *Business 2.0* article claimed, promised to do all of those things. The high-tech poplars, however, became my introduction to the phenomenon of eco-fads – the quick-fix environmental solution that relies more on its initial gut-level appeal as a simple, feel-good solution than proven scientific merit.

Despite the promises, hybrid poplars suffer from many limitations.

For instance, the very speed at which the tree grows is one of its main drawbacks. The strength of lumber is related to the distance between the growth rings of the tree it is cut from. This is why baseball players using wooden bats are told to hold the bat with the label up. At home plate, famed catcher Yogi

Berra supposedly once told home-run champion Hank Aaron to hold the bat so he could read the label, otherwise he would break his bat. Aaron replied, "I came up here to hit, not to read."[3]

The reason Berra gave the advice is bat makers place the label across the grain, ensuring that the ball will strike where the growth rings are closest. The tight grain there is the strongest part of the bat and prevents it from splintering when the ball is hit.

The same is true of structural lumber. A tight grain provides more structural integrity useful in building houses. In Washington state, more than 90 percent of the timber sold by the state is intended for structural use.

The problem with hybrid poplar, and similar fast-growing trees, is the growth rings are farther apart, significantly reducing the strength of the lumber. Anyone who has seen the way that poplars or cottonwoods bend dramatically in the wind can understand that, while these trees are very flexible, they are not very strong.

This is not to say that there isn't a market for these trees. They are used in furniture and other light uses that don't require the ability to support large amounts of weight. They are also used to make pulp, and some of the byproducts, like a residue of the pulping process called black liquor, can be used to produce energy.

The basic problem, however, is that they are not a substitute for slower-growing, but strong, softwood trees like Douglas fir, hemlock and pine. The very fact that these trees grow slowly makes them desirable. It also means that cutting them seems like more of an irretrievable environmental loss because it takes so long to replace the trees, the habitat and the scenic beauty they provide.

Put simply, the demand for slow-growing timber creates that very conflict that we at the Department of Natural Resources faced every day.

There are other problems as well. Poplars, like cottonwoods and other fast-growing species, consume a tremendous amount of water. In the few places in Washington state where poplars grow naturally, they are located near swampy land, in river bottoms, or next to dams that supply significant amounts of irrigation water. If there is an environmental conflict that is more controversial than forestry, it is the public debate over how to use water.

Water is claimed by communities, farmers, fish biologists, Indian tribes, hydroelectric energy producers and many others. Allocating that water is a politically charged process, and few are satisfied with the portion they receive. A dramatic expansion of hybrid poplar cultivation, as envisioned by the editors of *Business 2.0*, would mean adding to the heavy demands on water for irrigation, drinking, fish and carbon-free hydroelectric power.

Such tradeoffs are common in environmental debates. Sometimes reducing the use of one resource means increasing the use of others. In the case of hybrid poplars, it is a case of out of the frying pan and into the fire. As a result of the high demand for water, only a small percentage of the available land is suitable for the tree.

The search for easy environmental solutions is understandable. When faced with pictures of ugly clear-cuts, oil spills or similarly stark images that portray the impact human activity has on the environment, it is natural that we work to reduce that impact. There is a strong feeling that in a country as rich as ours we can afford to spend some of our disposable income to improve environmental sustainability. It is hard to feel good about living well when the cost of doing so results in such serious damage to the environment. Working to reduce our impact on the environment is the right thing to do and has the side benefit of making us feel good about ourselves. Girl Scouts and Boy Scouts are taught early on to leave their campsites cleaner than they found them. Protecting the environment is simply an extension of that principle.

Taking the right steps to protect the environment, therefore, seems fairly straightforward. Some actions are obviously destructive to the environment, and avoiding those actions should be clear enough. There may be some personal or social sacrifice, but the choice, at least, between what will help or harm the environment, is clear.

As we have seen in the case of hybrid poplars, however, that desire for simplicity can open the door to approaches that do little environmental good, or that actually damage the environment, because they ignore the complexity involved in environmental sustainability. But these simplistic ideas give people the feeling they are having a positive impact on the planet. Easy eco-fads are often substituted for real solutions, and once they become the current fashion they can be very hard to dislodge.

Embracing Eco-Fads

Eco-fads become widely accepted not simply because these simple ideas are attractive in themselves. A number of powerful people have a strong interest in promoting eco-fads.

Politicians and policymakers are some of the loudest proponents of eco-fads. Politicians know that protecting the environment is popular with the public, and advocating steps that appear to improve sustainability is an easy way to gain the support of organized green groups and of voters.

Moreover, politics is about creating contrasts among competing candidates. A candidate who can set up a choice between an opponent whom she says will increase the number of forest clear-cuts, oil spills or global warming and herself, who will protect pristine forests, create sparkling clean water and keep polar bears safe by stopping global warming, is likely to enjoy electoral success. No matter how much people realize that they use wood products, emit carbon dioxide or burn oil shipped in tankers, they still don't want to be associated with a politician who unapologetically defends the impacts that are associated with those modern economic activities.

Politicians also need to demonstrate progress. Environmental sustainability is, by its very nature, a long-term issue. Progress in protecting the environment is measured over decades, not months or years. As a result, quick and easy policies that show results in only a few years are very attractive, even if the true benefits of such policies are far less than long-term alternatives.

It shouldn't be surprising that some companies see business opportunity in the growth of eco-fads. Products that claim to be greener not only offer differentiation from similar products made by competitors, they also cater to consumers with greater disposable income. Shoppers willing to spend a little extra to buy products labeled as "green" are highly coveted by retailers and businesses that want to find new ways to reach them.

Businesses have always worked to reduce the amount of energy and resources they use in an effort to cut costs, lower prices and become more competitive. Now, these routine cost-cutting reductions are touted as "eco-friendly" because they also reduce the impact on the environment.

There is nothing wrong with reducing material and energy use as long as it doesn't cross the line between efforts that actually reduce environmental impact and products that become more profitable for their marketability as green products rather than for their actual environmental benefit. The fact that these improvements are being made is not different – only the way they are marketed changes.

The media readily embraces eco-fads that offer uncomplicated and compelling stories with the promise of environmental benefit. This effect is compounded when environmental reporters are chosen because of their commitment to a particular set of environmental policies rather than their undirected intellectual curiosity. Just as the editors of *Business 2.0* wanted to promote a story they felt would have a positive impact on environmental stewardship, environmental reporters at newspapers and other news media promote similar efforts.

Environmental groups offer awards to environmental reporters for stories these groups feel help the cause. News stories that highlight a potential environmental danger are much more likely to win these awards, particularly the more prestigious awards, than stories examining failed environmental policies or indicating that a potential environmental threat is not all that it is purported to be. Reporters who write stories about potential threats that never materialize are rarely questioned or criticized afterwards. There will be many more hard questions asked of a reporter who downplays a potential threat that turns out to be real. As a result, environmental reporters, especially those with a sympathetic ideological bent, are more likely to err on the side of exaggerating threats than to offer a mild or moderate assessment of environmental risks.

Frequently, the result of this exaggeration is not benign. The public and policymakers take cues from the media about what priorities are important and how they stack up against other issues of the day. Reporters who exaggerate environmental risks to compete for the attention of editors and the public can cause policymakers to waste money and resources on heavily reported, but minor, problems, leaving fewer resources to address more serious issues.

Scientists are also seduced by eco-fads. One of the most frequently heard appeals in the debate about environmental policy is to the credibility of scientists. The scientific method is rightly respected for its logical, detached and unemotional claim to truth. The claim of scientific validity is often used as the trump card in claiming support for particular public policies. Elected officials who disagree with "the science" are likely to find themselves on shaky political ground and will soon be answering questions about their belief in evolution, a helio-centric solar system, the moon landing and the like.

Difficulties arise, however, when scientists and others ignore real gaps in our knowledge and fill in the gray areas of uncertainty with personal, value-laden decisions. It is common to find scientists in an area of study disagreeing about the appropriate public policy. These disagreements are often portrayed as scientific, when they are actually differences in values and risk aversion. For instance, fish biologists are likely to have a very low tolerance for environmental risks to salmon, preferring very costly policies that save a few salmon over spending money on other areas of public policy, protecting private property rights or keeping taxes low.

This can be compounded when scientists overestimate the level of their own knowledge. Few scientists are rewarded for admitting that they still have much to learn about their area of expertise, even if that is true. Scientists who offer compelling explanations for observed phenomena, while minimizing areas of uncertainty, are more likely to rise to the top of their profession even when their explanations lead down the wrong path.

As a result, the average person who wishes to be environmentally responsible is bombarded by conflicting messages, encouraging them to embrace fads that offer solutions to environmental threats. Individuals have many reasons to embrace these fads unexamined. Few people have the time, interest or expertise to test every environmental claim they hear. In the midst of busy lives there is little incentive to ask: Do biofuels really reduce carbon dioxide emissions? Are polar bears really threatened by global warming? Are hybrid poplars really a solution to intensive forestry and clear-cuts? These are complicated questions that rarely have clear scientific answers. It is also difficult to determine the policy and economic consequences of these policies. Scientists, economists and others whose careers are built around answering these questions frequently disagree among themselves.

So how can we know what solutions make sense and what don't? To deal with these issues, people often have shorthand rules of thumb, called heuristics, to apply when weighing competing claims. The most common shorthand rule is the appeal to authority, where we ask ourselves "What do the experts say?" and then follow their lead. But what if politicians, businesses, the media, and even scientists, have strong incentives to exaggerate environmental threats and to offer simplistic eco-fads as solutions? How can we trust what we are hearing and know what information is real and what is embellishment?

This confusion is compounded by the natural desire of individuals to believe they are doing good without invoking much sacrifice. Eco-fads are emotionally satisfying because they offer easy solutions that cut through confusion, while allowing individuals to derive the emotional satisfaction of protecting the planet. When you add a social component to that, with peer pressure encouraging us to carry "green" shopping bags, replace incandescent light bulbs with easy to recognize compact fluorescent light bulbs or trade a traditional gas-guzzler for a hybrid vehicle, we find that we can receive social benefits in addition to that warm feeling in our hearts.

Deciding to reject an eco-fad means choosing to swim against the current of these various powerful forces. If you've ever seen a salmon at the end of its long migration, spawning to the place of its birth, you have an idea of how taxing this can be, emotionally and physically. At least salmon are rewarded with the continuation of their species at the end of their trip.

Environmental Fashion and Iconoclasm

The efforts to promote eco-fads set off claims and counter-claims that can lead believers and skeptics to engage in counterproductive policies.

Environmental activists understand that social pressure is a powerful force, and they openly cultivate the image that environmentalism is chic. They enlist movie actors to narrate ads for major environmental groups or pose (mostly) nude to support them. Who can ignore the plea that "animals have rights" when it is emblazoned across the chests of the Houston Rockets' dance team?

Professional actors, whose business is the very definition of trendsetting and fashion, feed the popularity of eco-fads by latching on to simple messages enhanced by their personal appeal. Who could oppose the reconstruction of New Orleans with "green" buildings when Brad Pitt is helping foot the bill? While few people actually watched Leonardo di Caprio's film about global warming, those who did were probably as attracted to the narrator as they were to the message.

Fashion magazines like *Vanity Fair* feature "green" issues, packed with celebrities announcing their commitment to the environment in a way that makes standing up for environmental values a fashion statement. It is rarely asked whether the lifestyles of celebrities and fashion moguls are, in fact, consistent with the values they proclaim. The reasons famous people subscribe to favored environmental policies are less important to activists than securing their vocal support. Come for the sex appeal, stay for the ideology.

Many on the right react to this confluence of the trendy and the ideological with another powerful, and trendy, approach: iconoclasm. Conservatives become rebels without a cause, basing their approach on opposition to whatever appeal is being offered by fashionable environmentalists.

When environmentalists like the World Wildlife Fund promoted Earth Hour, encouraging people to turn off their lights for one hour to emphasize the impact of energy use on the planet, conservatives did the opposite. The conservative grassroots organization Grassfire, announced "carbon belch day,"[4] encouraging people to use extra electricity, turning lights on, dialing their heaters up and generally wasting resources. This reaction may have had the visceral appeal of annoying the environmentally inclined, but it is not a productive reaction in any sense of the word. Who wants to expend additional energy simply to impoverish themselves? The only possible goal is to answer kind for kind – to protest a trendy ideology opponents see as meaningless with an opposite approach that is equally meaningless.

There are legitimate reasons thoughtful conservatives oppose the environmental approaches promoted through eco-fads. Such fads, and the policies they endorse, are perceived as Trojan horses for a larger goal. They argue there is legitimate concern that environmental causes are used merely as an excuse for expanding government control and infringements upon liberty. Prominent environmentalists themselves help promote this perception.

When Al Gore announced he had won the Nobel Prize for his work on climate change, he told the assembled audience that the issue, "...also provides us with opportunities to do a lot of things we ought to be doing for other reasons anyway." Such statements feed the legitimate concern of opponents and encourage those on the right to reject all things "green" out of fear they are being used to expand government control over the economy. This effect sometimes leads those on the right to reject environmental issues entirely, rather than addressing them within a more comfortable ideological framework.

Ideology Over Reality

The result of all these influences is that eco-fads, once established, are very difficult to dislodge. Who wants to believe that one's actions to save the planet don't actually promote the values one has publicly embraced? Who wants to replace clarity of action with the recognition that truly productive action is difficult? When was the last time you heard a politician say the policies he had long promoted are actually wrongheaded and counterproductive? It is always easier to say, "Even if this doesn't change the world, it is better than doing nothing."

Unfortunately, that is not always the case. With increasing frequency, eco-fads are worse than doing nothing. In some cases such fads are counterproductive, actually doing more damage to the environment than they prevent.

Even more often, eco-fads draw energy and resources away from solving real environmental problems. Politicians, business owners and people in the media find they gain more benefit from tackling dramatic problems with simple solutions than from broad, but amorphous, environmental risks that require a menu of solutions, each of which plays a small role. Public priorities, as a result, are set based not on the actual level of risk to the environment, but on the popular appeal of the solution and the drama of the images associated with the problem.

Stories like that published in *Business 2.0*, with dramatic photos of clear-cuts or other environmental impacts, are often intended to influence public policy decisions. But, if they don't tell the whole story or, worse, are actually misleading, they can make addressing environmental risks more difficult.

The picture caught my eye for a couple reasons. Working at Washington's forestry agency, I was attuned to any discussion and portrayal of forestry in the state.

More importantly, however, I had driven past the location where the photo was taken dozens of times. The photo was taken along Interstate 90 in the middle of the Cascade Mountains. The photographer, looking for a dramatic example of a clear-cut forest, had been seduced by such a stark image and pulled off the road to shoot the photo.

There is only one problem – it isn't a clear-cut. The *Business 2.0* image actually shows the bottom of Kechelus Lake, a mountain reservoir that stores water over the winter. The photo, taken in summer when the lake is low, depicts the decaying stumps leftover from decades before when the lake was created. The small clump of trees standing in the middle of the image actually sits on a small island during most of the year. Calling this image a clear-cut is no different than calling a city building a clear-cut, because once upon a time trees stood on the site.

What's more, the area depicted in the photo is many hundreds of acres, a much larger area than would ever be allowed to be logged by modern forest regulations in Washington state. Despite being portrayed as typical of forestry practice in Washington, the photo was neither a clear-cut nor representative of any logging that could have been done anywhere else in Washington, even under the most intensive regimen of harvest.

Knowing that the photo was falsely labeled, I emailed the editors, believing they would naturally want to issue a correction. At the very least they could ask for their money back from the photographer they hired to shoot the photo. The reaction I received demonstrates how difficult it is to dislodge established eco-fads.

The editors initially asked me to write a short letter, highlighting the error in the photo, noting that such a clear-cut would never be allowed under Washington's laws and explaining some of the limits of hybrid poplars. I submitted the requested letter and they thanked me for my constructive input.

When I received the next issue of *Business 2.0* I was surprised to see the note they included. Rather than publish my letter the editors wrote, at the very end of all the letters, the following correction:

"In a photo caption within our feature on bioengineered trees, we identified the shot as 'clear-cut land in Washington,' implying that it was indicative of current forestry practices in the state. In fact, the land had been cleared to build a reservoir. Although there are examples of land in Washington that has [sic] been similarly devastated by clear-cutting, current state regulations require that loggers leave at least eight trees per acre."[5]

This is tepid, to say the least. They didn't mention that rules going back decades prevented harvests anywhere near the size of that implied by the photo. In fact, there are no similar examples of present day clear-cutting.

While the editors were obliged to admit the photo was incorrect, they continued to claim that the substance of the photo was right, albeit without any proof. They admitted only the minimum they had to, holding tightly to the values and policies the photo implied. The photo fit the image of forestry they held in their minds, and they continued to embrace the message of the photo, even when the photo itself proved to be inaccurate.

In the end, the editors understood how powerful that picture was, and undermining its power was too much for them. To admit the truth would mean questioning the justification of the entire article and admitting not merely that the photo was a mistake, but that their position on the issue was not on firm footing. That is a key element of understanding the strength of eco-fads. The commitment to the policies or actions are, too frequently, based not on whether or not they help the environment, but on the personal, emotional feeling that taking these steps or supporting particular policies makes one a good person. Eco-fads help people to believe they are part of a large, important movement.

The basic question is, what incentive did the editors have to risk all of that over what they regarded a technical mislabeling of a powerful image?

Protecting the Environment or Gaining Emotional Satisfaction?

The challenge for those of us who care about the environment face is how to promote true environmental sustainability while rejecting emotionally satisfying but counterproductive eco-fads. It is a problem I have thought about over the decade I have worked in environmental policy.

When I began my work in environmental policy in 2000, I saw the issues in much the same way most people did. I believed the basic trade-off was between a strong economy and a healthy environment. The question was not, "How do we most effectively protect the environment?," but, "Are we as a society willing to pay the economic cost to achieve a higher goal?" The policies offered by environmental groups would achieve the goal they desired but were often very costly and undermined personal liberty, all so a few dedicated greens could satisfy their personal values.

Closely working day after day with foresters, biologists, geologists and others dramatically changed my thinking. I realized that while the threats to the environment were all too real, the most prominent policy options were not effective at making actual improvements in protecting the environment. Policies that claimed the mantle of scientific validity often had only a weak, tangential relationship to the full range of scientific options and knowledge.

Most enlightening was the understanding that environmental sustainability and economic sustainability are not in conflict but work hand-in-hand. That fact was key to the realization that we have an opportunity to continue making great strides in environmental sustainability without falling for eco-fads that are so frequently costly and ineffective.

The first step to understanding this crucial point is to recognize eco-fads for what they are and admit to ourselves that they often do not truly advance environmental sustainability. From global climate change to healthy local forests and reducing waste, eco-fads distract us from real efforts and an honest assessment of environmental risk and priorities.

Making an honest assessment of long-held beliefs is not an easy process. Rejecting eco-fads, and their emotional comfort, means we have to be more questioning of what we read, even when we don't have ready information about alternatives. We will have to give up some of the emotional comfort enjoyed by embracing eco-fads. Consumers will have to understand that businesses' commitment to "green" marketing is often more about profit than sustainability. Politicians will have to say that they do not have clear or even effective answers to all environmental problems and voters should scorn those who claim otherwise. Reporters will have to write stories with more nuance, contain fewer compelling, albeit misleading, images and watch as their gripping prose is invaded by careful caveats. Scientists will have to admit they are less certain about the state of environmental knowledge and will have to step out from behind the shield of scientific authority and argue on the unsteady ground of values.

Difficult as it is, shedding these pretenses is more honest. It offers more promise of real environmental sustainability, and it is more likely to leave an environmental legacy that we can all be proud of.

Chapter 2

What is an Eco-Fad?

Their very shape says "green." Al Gore made them a centerpiece of his campaign to cut carbon emissions. Now, they are not merely a tool in the effort to be more energy efficient – using them is the law.

Compact fluorescent light bulbs, known as CFLs, are, as much as anything else, the accepted symbol of environmental responsibility. They use about 75 percent less energy than incandescent light bulbs, and some advocates estimate that if each of us replaced just one incandescent light bulb with a CFL, we could save $700 million in annual energy costs.[1] When the city of Seattle launched its campaign against global warming, officials handed out CFLs at the city's Christmas tree-lighting ceremony. At the event, the mayor's staff, wearing buttons that said "Save Santa," told small children that global warming threatened to destroy Santa's home at the North Pole.

One car company even had its spokesman hold up one of the spiral bulbs in a TV commercial and tout the company's fuel efficient vehicles, in an obvious "green by association" message.

The bulb's distinctive look contributes to its power as a recognizable emblem. While it may be difficult to tell some "green" products from their "planet-killing" counterparts, there is no mistaking a CFL. Its twisting shape tells the story as does the type of light it emits – for better or worse. Replacing regular incandescent bulbs with CFLs is not just about saving energy, it is meant to be about saving the planet in a way that everyone can see. When people walk into your house, apartment or dorm room, CFLs are, almost literally, a neon sign proclaiming your commitment to the environment. This is not to say the bulbs do not save energy – they certainly do. They have, however, become more than that. They are a symbol as well.

But there is a problem. They also harm the planet.

CFLs contain mercury, a highly poisonous element that environmental activists have tried for years to eliminate. New government regulations limiting mercury emissions from coal-fired power plants are a key part of the Environmental Protection Agency (EPA) effort to close those plants and cut overall carbon emissions. There are even campaigns to remove mercury from the lights in car trunks. When the trunk lid is lifted, mercury moves within the switch, completing the circuit and activating the light. When it comes to CFLs, however, the risks are downplayed. Ask yourself what other consumer product comes with a long cautionary to-do list in case of breakage.

The EPA instructs that, when a CFL breaks, "Have people and pets leave the room, and don't let anyone walk through the breakage area on their way out …"[2] You should air out the room for fifteen minutes. After evacuating the room, people are instructed to:

- Carefully scoop up glass pieces and powder using stiff paper or cardboard and place them in a glass jar with metal lid (such as a canning jar) or in a sealed plastic bag.

- Use sticky tape, such as duct tape, to pick up any remaining small glass fragments and powder.

- Wipe the area clean with damp paper towels or disposable wet wipes. Place towels in the glass jar or plastic bag.

- Do not use a vacuum or broom to clean up the broken bulb on hard surfaces.

Given the steps involved in simply cleaning up after a broken CFL, it is a bit surprising they have become so popular. It is unlikely there is any other product in your home that requires this level of care simply to clean up when it breaks.

These health concerns, however, are overlooked because the power of the CFL as a symbol in the fight against climate change has pushed aside worries about releasing mercury into the environment. Climate change is the fashionable cause of the day, so previous concerns are suddenly less important.

This pattern is the essence of an eco-fad. Instead of judging a product by its real impact on the environment, eco-fads lead us to include other considerations. Is this product or policy popular? Will it symbolize my commitment to save the planet to myself and others? Does it send the right message to others in a visible way? Will it make me feel I am a good person, doing what is right for the environment and for future generations? When these personal considerations become a significant part of the reason we choose certain environmental actions, products or policies, it means we are reducing the role that data, fact and actual benefit to the environment play in the decisions we make. Our self-image starts to matter more to us, while the real-world impact of the products and policies means less.

These observations do not mean popular environmental policies are worthless. Being cool doesn't have to be incompatible with being sustainable. CFLs do save energy. But eco-fads lead us to ignore concerns or data that detract from the symbolic power of the statement we are trying to make. Being seen as earth-friendly is more than just a way of doing things. It is a statement about the type of individual we want to be and what we want others to believe we are.

Eco-fads combine three elements. First, they are personal, reflecting the worthiness of the consumer or policymaker choosing the fad. Second, they are popular, demonstrating to others that the person making the decision is environmentally responsible. The more visible the choice, the more powerful the enticement to follow the fad. Finally, eco-fads are, at some level, phony. They fail to achieve the goal supporters claim to want, creating more negative environmental effects than benefits. Not all popular or personal environmental choices are phony. When image outweighs impact, however, a choice crosses that line and becomes a fad.

Not all popular environmental policies are eco-fads. Dolphin-safe tuna legitimately addressed a real environmental concern – the needless killing of dolphins in tuna nets. In this instance, personal buying habits and popular pressure combined to encourage a sound environmental solution – sensible changes in net design that allow the capture of fish without drowning dolphins. Though taken entirely for granted, "dolphin-safe" labels now appear on all major brands of tuna.

Too many of today's environmental policies, however, do not have similar positive results. These policies substitute popularity and emotional satisfaction for sound science and responsible economics. By combining a sense of personal mission with public applause, eco-fads encourage environmental symbolism over environmental sustainability.

What It Says About Me

When driving in Seattle, it is hard to go very far without seeing a Toyota Prius. There is perhaps no more potent symbol of today's environmental movement. Since its introduction in the United States a decade ago, the Prius electric hybrid has become synonymous with environmental responsibility. Driving a Prius isn't just about comfort, cutting gas costs or other traditional consumer benefits. Hybrids make a clear public statement about the driver. Often, that statement is not subtle. Near my Seattle office, I passed a Prius every day with a vanity license plate that read "HIBRED." Not only did the driver care about the planet, the license plate made it clear that the owner considered himself intelligent and well-bred. Green is the new blue blood.

This is not an accident. Toyota designed the Prius with a distinctive body shape in order to confer the image benefits of the car to the driver. The design as image was so successful that in 2010 a Toyota competitor, Honda, made its flagship hybrid, the Insight, to look like the Prius. Honda executives understand they are marketing more than just the particular statistics of their car – fuel efficiency, safety, interior comfort. An essential part of the appeal of hybrid vehicles is the ability to make drivers feel good about themselves – and the effort has been effective. J.D. Power and Associates, a leading consumer research organization, found that image was the top reason people reported for purchasing a hybrid car. In an interview on National Public Radio in 2007, J.D. Powers' Michael Omotoso said, "A lot of people buy hybrids because of what it says about them, just like people buy sports cars to project a certain image. And with a hybrid, it's like, 'Look at me, I'm environmentally conscious.'"[3] Whatever environmental benefits hybrids may deliver, they are secondary to the sense of self conferred by a car that shows that the owner cares about the future of the planet.

The connection between an individual sense of self-worth and personal choice is an important reason that eco-fads have proliferated. Unlike top-down environmental regulations we all must abide by, products we buy and policies we support distinguish us from others. Politicians and activists say they are promoting policies that will protect the planet for future generations. The sense of personal sacrifice that results from these choices serves as evidence of strong moral character. This intensely personal element of environmental choices is why the personal values of the consumer or policymaker play as important a role as does science or economics in these decisions. This element is so strong that it infuses even the most straightforward environmental decisions with deep moral meaning.

Speaking to a group about environmental policy a few years ago, I highlighted the problems some "green" buildings were having in living up to their promised benefits. Using data from a number of buildings, I was pointing to data outlining the large amounts of energy being used by buildings that environmental activists claimed would be more energy efficient than their predecessors. I didn't have to worry about putting my audience to sleep with columns of statistics. The reaction to what appeared to be dry information ended up being electric.

Eventually the data was just too much for one person in the conference room where we were meeting. Pounding his fists on the table, he said in a raised voice that what I was saying was simply "immoral." He had come to the meeting still wearing his bicycle helmet and riding shorts, telling the rest of the room that he was trying to live his values. For him, questioning the validity of green building policies was about more than energy savings. When I asked him if it was moral to promote policies that didn't save energy, he simply said, "I'm not going to address that." Yet, that was the very issue at hand. If the buildings did not save energy, then what environmental justification could there be for supporting them?

For my angry audience member, the green building policy was inextricably intertwined with personal morality. The scientific or economic validity of the policy was trumped by the direction it set for society, and standing up for green buildings was an important part of living his values. Questioning the policy was not simply an issue of whether the math on the spreadsheet added up. It wasn't a question of the math at all. It was a question of maintaining his sense of self-worth. When I questioned a policy he supported, he heard an attack on his values and beliefs and responded in kind by questioning mine. When policies are personal, questioning them becomes personal. And eco-fads by their nature are intensely personal.

The sense that one is personally sacrificing for the greater good also helps explain why so many environmental policymakers emphasize policies that force lifestyle change. Michael Strong, who advocates "conscious capitalism" as a way to address many of the world's problems, including environmental challenges, argues that those who sacrifice for what they believe is the good of the community are more inclined to "punish" those who do not do the same. In his book, *Be the Solution*, Strong notes that the notion of punishing those who do not help the community, who instead choose to do their own thing and "free ride" on the sacrifices of others, has been bred into humans through evolution. Citing research on evolutionary trends, he writes, "If we had not developed the instinctive correlation between eagerness to contribute to the good of the community on the one hand, and eagerness to punish those who do not contribute to the good of the community on the other, the genes of those of us who are more genetically prone to contributing to the good of the community would have lost out to the genes of those who were more narrowly selfish."[4] As a result, he continues, "those who contribute most to the community good are the most motivated to punish" others who are not perceived to be pulling their weight.

Even if we set aside the question of whether this is evolutionarily determined, there is a simple issue of fairness at work here. Those committed to a particular policy who feel they are making personal sacrifices on behalf of the greater good can begin to feel that others who are living high on the hog, driving Hummers and eating steak, are simply being greedy and failing to appreciate the necessary sacrifices. Studies show that even dogs have a sense of fairness[5], so it is not surprising that humans with strongly held beliefs about the fair and proper way to act in society can easily begin to believe that if others don't follow, they should be forced to do so, for the sake of the greater good. This mitigates strongly toward policies that dictate a direction for individuals and society, backed up by regulations and enforcement that make people participate in shared sacrifice. The policies also work against the uncoordinated personal choice that is inherent in free choices and free markets.

The environment is not the only area where we base consumer and policy decisions with an eye to enhancing our self-worth. We receive tremendous psychological benefit from voting in what we believe is a responsible way. People regularly vote for a range of policies they hope will reflect well on them, even if they never reveal their choice to anyone but their own conscience. Many times, however, people make those choices public in the hope they will receive social benefits. After all, how many times have you seen a bumper sticker that says, "Don't blame me, I voted for_____."? The message is, "I was right. I am a good person." Whether voting a particular way makes us feel smarter or more compassionate, we all want to feel proud of how we vote.

In his book, *The Myth of the Rational Voter: Why Democracies Choose Bad Policies*, economist Bryan Caplan argues that since the cost of voting is very low, even if we happen to vote for a person or policy that does not deliver positive results, the ability to take personal pride in our vote weighs heavily on the decision we make. Elections are rarely decided by one vote, so the damage done if we happen to vote incorrectly is rather small. As a result, we gain the benefits we associate with our voting choices in other ways. If we can't take credit for a candidate's win or loss, what benefit do we receive from voting? The benefit comes, at least in part, by demonstrating to ourselves that we are good people, trying to do what is best for our community, our country and the world.

Caplan notes that voting is not merely instrumental, with a goal of achieving a particular policy outcome. Voting also says something about who we are. He notes that, "Citizens might vote not to help policies win, but to express their patriotism, their compassion, or their devotion to the environment."[6] He goes on to say that the impact of such voting could be serious, because bad-but-feel-good policies, "…might win because expressing support for them makes people feel good about themselves."[7] This mindset does not apply only to voting. It can affect the products we buy, as well. Why else would we pay more for expensive designer-name clothes, perfumes and other products that we know are similar in quality or style to lesser-known brands? This does not mean voters or consumers ignore other costs. Products or policies that have high economic or social costs may not be chosen, even if they do make us feel good. The view, however, that we make decisions based only on a clear-eyed and selfless assessment that calmly weighs costs and benefits is inaccurate.

A lack of information compounds the role that the sense of self-worth plays in making these decisions. If the costs of a particular decision are unclear, it is not unreasonable to believe we will look at which product makes us feel better. If all milk costs the same, we may decide to buy it from a local farmer. If all of the avocados are the same size and quality, we might well choose organic. If the way a decision makes us feel is the only clear piece of information we have, it is likely to be the key factor when we make choices about the products we buy.

Buying Green is Good for the Soul

There is good evidence that the emotional benefits we derive from making these kinds of environmental decisions are particularly strong.

A recent study found that when people buy products labeled "environmentally friendly," their personal sense of moral credit increases. Buying these products makes people feel they are doing good things for the planet and provides leeway for consumers to make moral compromises in other areas. This is like telling yourself while dieting that it's okay to eat a brownie because you had oatmeal for breakfast. In the grand scheme of things, you have done more good than bad, so what's a cookie now and then?

Nina Mazar and Chen-Bo Zhong of the University of Toronto ran a series of experiments with students to determine how buying "green" products affected an individual's morality and sense of self-worth. They argued that, "Consumer choices reflect not only price and quality preferences but also social and moral values, as witnessed in the remarkable growth of the global market for organic and environmentally friendly products."[8] Many who are cynical about politics or political motives argue that to understand why politicians or activists promote a particular policy, we need only "follow the money." As the study demonstrates, however, the opposite is often true. The things we spend money on yield personal rewards by making us feel good about ourselves. That feeling becomes the actual "product" we are buying: self-worth. The researchers found the desire for higher self-worth to be a very powerful force.

Mazar and Zhong created two groups of students. One group was given $25 to purchase from a conventional store that had mostly non-green products. The other group was given the same amount of money to allocate for purchases at a store selling primarily "green" products. After making their selections, the students were put through additional experiments they were told were unrelated. These experiments tested both their altruism and the effect buying "green" had on the students. The impact, they found, was significant.

While merely exposing students to "green" products increased their level of altruism in subsequent experiments, actually buying "green" products reduced their altruism significantly. The researchers concluded that the people in the experiment were "more likely to cheat and steal after purchasing green products than after purchasing conventional products."[9] Having committed an act they considered altruistic – helping the planet – the participants felt they had the moral license to cheat a bit elsewhere. The students seemed to reason, "After all, buying these products has already proven that I am a good person, so if I cut the corners elsewhere, I am still doing good for the planet." Ironically, buying green had become a selfish act.

It should be made clear that this result does not mean we should not buy environmentally friendly products. It also does not mean people who buy environmental products are immoral or, as one online magazine suggested in a tongue-in-cheek manner, "evil."[10] It is simply to say that there is a strong component to buying green, or supporting green policies, that is associated with how we feel about ourselves. Questioning someone's purchases or commitment to green policies is not simply about the merits or demerits of that particular policy – it is a question of their value as a human being. Telling someone that buying "organic" shampoo does not help the environment is not merely a consumer tip. Such advice says to the person, "You are not living up to your values and some part of your sense of self is based on a lie." When the issue at stake is who we are as people, it becomes clear why environmental debates about even simple behaviors quickly become extremely emotional. In such a charged environment, how can we make rational decisions about private purchasing decisions or about public policy?

To a significant extent, then, what we are really buying with some green products is emotional satisfaction. Often the difference in cost between a "green" product and a conventional one is small, and purchasing green products yields more in benefits to our self-esteem than it costs us in additional dollars. That is certainly the case with voting. The cost of voting is very small and the psychological benefits are significant. Since everyone likes a good deal, even when what we are receiving is intangible, this gives us an incentive to exaggerate the benefits of the decisions we are making. We aren't just reducing energy use, we are saving the planet. We aren't just buying solar panels, we are saving the polar bears. We are not just voting, we are showing we care.

This reasoning also motivates public policymakers. Speaking at an environmental breakfast, a board member of a clean water agency in Washington state told the audience, "We environmentalists can be a difficult group to deal with, but we make great ancestors." Not only was she claiming that her work was good for the environment today, but that people would be thanking her for generations to come. Supporting environmental policies is not just about doing what is right, but about how others, even future generations, see her. Unfortunately, this can mean judgments about public policies or consumer buying are heavily influenced not by whether a particular decision actually helps the environment, but whether people feel good about it and can highlight their meritorious work to others.

One result is people mentally filter out information that may call into question the effectiveness of environmental policies or purchases, and instead exaggerate the perceived benefits. This trend is becoming more obvious in environmental policy. Environmental advocates, like former Obama administration "green jobs czar" Van Jones, say that environmentalism promotes the larger goal of "social justice." In Jones' view our policies not only help the planet, they can help the economy prosper by creating "green jobs." And the chief lobbyist for the Washington Environmental Council told a Seattle Post-Intelligencer reporter that passing cap-and-trade legislation was about "remaking the economy of the nation, the whole globe."[11] All the benefits of green living can be ours, as Alex Steffen, of the blog "Worldchanging," told the Seattle City Council, for "absolutely no sacrifice whatsoever."[12] Each of these people emphasize the message that when you support their policies and products, you are not just being responsible, you are saving the planet and the world – and you are doing it at very low cost. Put this way, how could anyone say no? Given the low cost and high reward, the only reason one would say no, so this logic goes, is if you have some ulterior, selfish reason for opposing these worthy policies. The irony is that environmental advocates ignore the selfish benefits they themselves receive when people buy and vote "green."

The strong emotional benefit of environmental policies increases the appeal of eco-fads. For a very small cost, you can make a big difference in the world. It also makes potentially harmful eco-fads more difficult to dislodge. Even though we know everyone makes mistakes, coming clean is hard when we are actually confronted with our shortcomings. This is true even when we have made a factual error that is demonstrably incorrect. Adding an emotional component makes an honest self-assessment even more difficult because it means undermining what we see as the embodiment of our values. Questioning an eco-fad means more than just identifying logical flaws or unintended consequences. It means challenging, in part, the basis of an individual's self-worth. Telling a friend that buying local food does not really save energy can sound a lot like "you're living a lie."

Compounding this problem is the fact that there are often conflicting interpretations of what scientific data means, making it difficult to know where environmental truth lies. This gray area provides the opportunity to select the information that is most convenient to our viewpoint and steers us away from data that conflicts with the image of the person we are trying to be. Thus, information that threatens not only to show we are wrong about a particular fact, but about our self-image as well, is quickly set aside in favor of messages that reinforce our feeling we are saving the planet. In the end, it may be difficult to know what data to believe, but each of us knows what we want to believe. Ironically, intangible personal values actually become a more solid foundation for the way we understand environmental issues than scientific information that is subject to varied interpretations and threaten our emotional comfort.

Saving the Planet in Public

Improving one's self-esteem is not the only thing that makes eco-fads so appealing. There is a strong social aspect to eco-fads. That is what makes them fads. Instead of wearing the right clothes or carrying the right cell phone, we show off our commitment to the planet. Everyone can see that you have chosen CFLs just by looking. We can all spot a Prius a mile away, and hybrid cars with a less obvious shape display a large nameplate on the outside to indicate the driver inside is environmentally conscious. Not only do you get to feel good about living your values, you get credit for doing so. The credit builds on itself. Other people see you as a respected colleague, an environmental fellow traveler, and they reward you for your wise choices and good sense, reconfirming their own positive self-identity in the process.

The public aspect of eco-fads can be quite ostentatious. Students wear shirts with images of the earth that say "My God" or "Love Your Mother." Nothing very subtle there. If we are sending people a message about ourselves, why not make it clear? Politicians, business leaders and others know that this public element is an important part of creating a green identity. Reusable grocery bags are bright green with the recycling symbol printed prominently on the side. Politicians hand out stickers to kids with environmental messages on them. Direct mail from politicians carries symbols telling us that the mailing is made from recycled material, harvested according to "green" standards and printed with renewable soy ink. Soon there won't be room left for the words. The result is that environmental symbolism competes with real sustainability when making decisions about the policies and products we choose. Are designer jeans more comfortable or durable than less expensive brands? Often they are neither. That is what makes them fads. Are products that claim to be "environmentally friendly" actually better for the environment? Not always. That is what makes them eco-fads.

Like other fads, those who do not follow along are publically ostracized – often aggressively. After all, who wants to be viewed as anti-environment? If you are not pulling your weight, you must be freeloading. The pressure to support policies and trends that confirm your status as a friend of the environment can be intense. If you are uncertain about the impact humans are having on the climate by burning fossil fuels, you are not just undecided, you are a "denier." The term, of course, is specifically chosen to create a link to a group we all recognize as truly immoral – holocaust deniers. Social power becomes a key tool in the creation of eco-fads and promotion of particular policies. Instead of logically and gradually (and sometimes frustratingly slowly), offering arguments and logic to coax people, some activists choose the shortcut of applying social power to shame people into conformity. The result can only be counterproductive to formulating good public policy. As Voltaire said, "It is dangerous to be right when the government is wrong." Being right when proponents of an eco-fad are wrong carries a high social cost.

The Power and Cost of Eco-Fads

The point of all this is not to say that buying "green" products or supporting popular environmental policies is wrong. Some people do rebel against these fads and become reflexively anti-green because they reject the strong emotional element of popular environmentalism. But iconoclasm is no more logical or sound than being trendy. Neither approach is a sensible way to assess whether we are actually achieving the goals we intend: to promote environmental sustainability and a healthy planet for humans and wildlife. Recognizing these motivations is like taking the first step in the recovery process – admitting we have a problem with making sound, unemotional judgments about environmental policy and consumer products. Being aware of the strong emotional connection that exists between popular environmentalism, self-worth and public acceptance is a critical part of understanding why certain policies are chosen and endure, even when we find they are counterproductive.

Compact fluorescent light bulbs have become a popular symbol of environmental consciousness because they embody so many of the qualities that make eco-fads powerful. First, they are personal. We can feel good about buying them knowing we are reducing carbon emissions and fighting climate change. The cost is very low – and indeed we may even save money – but the emotional satisfaction is very high. Second, they offer strong public benefits. The distinctive spiral shape of CFLs makes them instantly recognizable to others. You do not need to show you care about the environment – your light bulbs say it for you. Finally, the potential downside to CFLs, the risk of releasing poisonous mercury into the environment, is hard to assess. It is difficult to weigh the benefit of reduced carbon emissions against the impact of harmful mercury. Presented with this choice, we err on the side of our personal values and what gives us the most personal satisfaction. We ignore the environmental risk and reap the reward, putting concerns about the health impacts of releasing mercury behind us in favor of the new and trendy effort to reduce energy-related carbon emissions.

Recognizing these influences helps us understand how we make environmental decisions and the potential flaws in the green policies and products we are constantly confronted with. It also helps us understand the frustrating tendency of environmental discussions to become highly emotional and personal. Eco-fads endure because they have adapted to appeal to some important human characteristics – the desire to feel good about the decisions we are making, a vision of the kind of person we want to become and our need for acceptance by those we want to be our peers. Appeals based in popular environmentalism pass a Darwinian test – they survive because they have adapted in response to human emotional needs. This does not mean, however, that we can't overcome the emotional appeal of eco-fads and find an approach that is more environmentally sustainable. By applying sound science and economics, we can judge which approaches truly make a positive difference. Choosing the right policies means we can do good for the environment and feel good about doing it.

Chapter 3

The Illogical Common Sense of Eco-Fads

Few things demonstrate the difficulty of applying sound science and economics to public policy more plainly than the environmental town meeting. Government agencies, considering some environmental project or permit, are often obliged to invite the public to hear the details of a proposal and receive feedback on the information they present. The result is rarely productive.

As a member of a government team, I visited a small community along the shores of Puget Sound in Washington state. The purpose of our visit was to host a town meeting to discuss the environmental permits needed to build a loading dock near a local gravel mine. Gravel mines are rarely popular with their residential neighbors, and this mine was no exception. At the meeting community members presented a long list of objections and made the arguments they felt were the most persuasive – scientific claims about the potential environmental impact of building the dock. Emphasizing the need for good science, one member of the public told our team we should complete a rigorous scientific analysis, follow wherever the facts lead, and draw our conclusions from the data. He paused a moment, and added without a hint of irony that if the science "doesn't make sense," we should use our own common sense and do what is right: deny the permit. Put simply, he knew what the outcome "should be." If the science did not agree with his policy position, the best thing to do was not to change his conclusion, but instead alter the standards of judgment leading to it. Ultimately he meant our team should do what he wanted, no matter what the science said. What's more, he seemed unaware of the inherent conflict in what he had said.

Making important policy decisions without a stable and objective standard is, of course, fraught with danger. Not only is it likely to lead to lawsuits, which are numerous in environmental policy, it is illogical. Making up the rules as you go in order to reach a pre-determined outcome is simply nonsensical. It is difficult, however, to blame people outside government agencies for the failure to set consistent and clear standards. The public is thrown into the middle of debates that are supposed to be based on science, and people have understandable difficulty adapting to rules of a game they play only on rare occasions. The science and information presented in detailed plans, written by government employees whose full-time jobs are to collect information and write plans, are well beyond the limited time and expertise of nearly every member of the public. This is not the fault of the average citizen who cares deeply about what goes on in his or her community. It does, however, shine a bright light on the disconnect between the type of objective scientific information we need to make good decisions and the public's ability to find, understand and apply that information.

This disconnect in the public process comes from the difficulty in judging what good science looks like. Without the time and expertise needed to understand the technical aspects of scientific documents, many of us are left trying to judge whether a policy proposal meets the amorphous test of "common sense." Economic analysis can be equally opaque. Trying to understand the dynamic interchange between costs and benefits involved in policies, including unintended consequences, becomes complex very rapidly. Both scientific and economic findings can be, although accurate, counterintuitive. In these cases, following our common sense actually leads us in illogical directions.

Despite these difficulties, the reason we appeal to science and economics is we understand that the underlying basis for each is, in the ideal, a systemic and objective logic. Disagreements exist among scientists and economists, but the process to work out these agreements is generally rigorous and tends to produce good conclusions. Science and economics offer powerful tools that help us distinguish the eco-fad from the eco-friendly. Like a jigsaw puzzle, we can often see where the picture is headed, even if we don't have every piece. We have the ability to use scientific and economic information to judge policies even when we don't have all the facts.

Sometimes the conclusions are, of course, hard to accept, especially when they challenge our desired outcomes. If discarding eco-fads was as simple as pointing out logical flaws, we would have many fewer environmental problems. Emotional insecurity is the price, however, of trying to get it right.

A Firm Foundation Under our Feet

Few phrases are uttered more frequently in environmental debates than "follow the science." Usually the people who utter these words think they already know what "the science" is and where it leads. Too often the phrase is used to advocate a predetermined policy position rather than an open commitment to truly follow the science. Even when we try to follow the science, the answers available are not always as clear as we hope. We want science to provide, more or less, a clear answer about what we should do. We treat science as a process that is, essentially, like solving a math problem. If you put in all the forces and factors, the equation will spit out a result. Map all the variables for a billiard table and you can determine where and how hard to hit the cue ball, thus accurately predicting which balls will end up in the pockets. Environmental issues, however, don't always work out this way.

We don't always have all the information and sometimes the calculations involved are quite complex, making it difficult to know what will happen when we choose a particular course. In these circumstances, science can provide us with an estimate of the risks involved with different policies. If we ask how wide a buffer is needed beside a stream to prevent soil erosion from harming fish, the answer will not be a definitive number like 150 feet. Science is more likely to indicate that with a 50-foot buffer the risk to fish will be moderate, with a 150-foot buffer it will be low and with a 250-foot buffer the risk will be virtually, but not quite, zero. This is because we can't predict the weather, wind and heavy rainstorms, or other variable factors that may overwhelm the odds. The difficulty is that most people believe the results speak for themselves. If something goes wrong, it must be because of poor planning. If nothing bad happens, there is nothing to argue about.

As anyone who has been to Las Vegas knows, however, the odds in any one particular instance do not reflect the odds overall. Some people do win at slot machines despite amazingly poor odds. Other people limit their gambling to games that are even chance or that favor them, and they still lose. Such is the case with environmental science. Even well-considered risks can go bad, and reckless approaches occasionally emerge unscathed.

Good science helps provide a foundation for decision-making. Without it, we would be making decisions based largely on wishes and prayers. It helps to understand the risks we are taking. The problem we face at the point of decision is how risk-averse we are. Answering that question has little to do with science. That is a question of values. Do we believe that a little risk today is acceptable if it is likely to make us better off in the long run? Should we minimize risk today even if that means we, and future generations, will be poorer? Are we more concerned about preserving opportunities for recreation in forests, or do we prefer to keep large areas of wilderness undisturbed for wildlife? Science can help us understand the risks involved if we choose one approach over another. But the decision about which way to choose is also impacted by our personal priorities.

Whether we should take those risks, however, and how to assess the tradeoffs when we do, is the domain of economics. Adding economic analysis to science can help us determine which environmental policies are likely to help the environment and which are firmly in the domain of eco-fads.

We often think of economics only in the context of money, jobs and prosperity. Economics does, of course, have much to say about each of those. Really, though, economics is a question of how we allocate resources. Lionel Robbins, who formerly headed the economics department at the London School of Economics, is famous for having said "Economics is a science which studies human behavior as a relationship between ends and scarce means which have alternative uses." How do we act when resources (whether those resources are wildlife habitat, raw materials or money) are scarce? And how do we judge one priority over another?

That is exactly the approach we need when addressing environmental concerns. After all, environmentalism was born out of a concern for scarce resources, so why not turn to the intellectual discipline that addresses that very question? Economics helps us take the scientific and values information and weigh our various options. It can guide us toward answers to some fairly difficult questions. Should we expend more money and effort on creating fish habitat or on developing clean energy? Should we save a tree or create a job? Economics doesn't set the values, it simply weighs the impact of trying to achieve various goals.

Economics can also help us determine which approach is best when we agree upon the goal. If we are trying to reduce emissions of sulfur dioxide, which approach does economic analysis indicate will work better – mandating the use of air scrubbers on smokestacks or implementing a cap-and-trade system? As economists had predicted, cap-and-trade proved to be much more efficient in reducing sulfur dioxide emissions. The acid rain it contributed to went away much more quickly and inexpensively than the previous law which mandated the use of particular technologies. This is an extremely important reason to use economic analysis in environmental policy. The response that "it's only money" ignores the fact that every dollar wasted is a dollar that could have been spent improving the environment or achieving some other important goal. Even if we decide our top priority is environmental protection, as opposed to tax cuts or other policy goals, we should want to get every bit of value we can for the money we spend. George Santayana[a], a Spanish-American philosopher is famous for saying, "Fanaticism consists of redoubling your efforts when you have forgotten your aim." Throwing good money after bad on a strategy that doesn't work is simply piling waste upon waste. Far too often the aim of improving the environment is forgotten when activists or others fixate on a particular strategy. The result is we cling to particular solutions long after they have failed because we don't complete a serious cost-benefit analysis that would guide us. In the end, we find we have spent lots of time and money, yet the problem persists.

Finally, we need to remember that none of this is static. What is important today is not always important tomorrow. We may decide that addressing the ozone hole in the atmosphere is the top environmental priority, but once we take steps to reduce the release of ozone-destroying chemicals into the environment, we move on to other priorities, environmental or otherwise. We can only increase forestland so much before each additional acre becomes staggeringly expensive and we reach a point of diminishing returns.

It is not easy to hit a target when we keep moving it. That change, however, can be a good thing. It means that as problems arise we address them, reducing their impact and then devoting our resources to other issues we feel are more important. If we fixate on one goal, there can be a very high cost in crowding out other things we feel are important. As famed psychiatrist Milton Saperstein says, "There is nobody as enslaved as the fanatic, the person in whom one impulse, one value, has assumed ascendancy over all others." The approaches that promise to protect the environment "at all costs" are virtually guaranteed to do more harm than good. This environmental approach not only does more harm to the lifestyles of families and to the economy, but to the environment itself, by spending an inordinate amount of resources on one problem that may have merited a high level of attention at one point, but no longer does.

Now we can understand why environmental issues can be so contentious. Often we don't agree on what goals are most important, making it hard to weigh them against each other. Even when we do agree on a goal, we often disagree about how to achieve it. And just when we find a solution to the problem, another problem emerges, eclipsing the previous one and distracting us from the combination of goals and tactics we had previously agreed on.

Of course there is no silver bullet to address these problems. If, however, we want to make a serious attempt at prioritizing environmental goals, heading into such stormy waters without some tools is foolhardy. A serious and honest

---

[a] He is most famous, perhaps, for saying, "Those who cannot remember the past are condemned to repeat it."

economic analysis of the costs and benefits of the various approaches and tradeoffs can help set some context, even if the analysis does not paint a perfectly clear picture of the best path to follow.

Cost-benefit analysis seeks to compare policies against each other, weighing them based on a common standard. Typically, this means comparing the outcome of each policy in dollar terms. But dollars are simply a useful unit of measurement. Measuring with dollars does not preclude measuring the value of free time, cleaner air and other goods we would not normally associate with a price tag. For example, we may decide that an hour of free time is worth $30 to us – meaning that if someone paid us $31 to work that hour, we would forego the free time and take the money. We may determine that dirty air will shorten our life by one year, and that the value of an additional year to us is $100,000 (or whatever price). So if it costs you $1 million to clean the air and add one year of life, you would probably rather have the money than take the costly steps needed to make the small improvement in air quality.

Of course this type of analysis does not solve all the problems (I imagine you are already wondering if you would take $1 million in exchange for a year of your life). But it is useful to compare the outcome of various policies and conduct a general weighing of different approaches. The other advantage of this approach is that even if we do not know what unintended consequences will arise, economic analysts have developed some rules of thumb based on experience that can tell us the types of factors that are likely to crop up. For instance, University of Chicago professor Cass Sunstein writes in his book, *Worst Case Scenarios*, that "any expensive regulation will have an adverse effect on life and health"[1] from consequences the regulators cannot foresee. He notes studies that show one statistical life will be lost for every $7 million to $15 million spent on regulations. If a driver spends an extra $500 a year on biofuel, he might not be able to spend that on a high-efficiency furnace that would actually do more good for the environment. If government agencies require manufacturers to spend $10 million on air scrubbers in smokestacks, companies might not have the money to improve workplace safety, leading to one additional job-related death a year. We might have cleaner air, but only at the cost of lower workplace safety. How these chain reactions occur is hard to predict, but a cost-benefit analysis provides an opportunity to see if estimated costs are at least in the ballpark.

Lastly, we can come up with an assessment of risk and add that to our understanding of the tradeoffs to be made. Each of us has a different level of risk tolerance, and we are more afraid of some things than of others. Nuclear power has seen an increase in support over the past few years because many people who fear the effects of high CO_2 emissions and climate change are now more comfortable with accepting the low risk of a nuclear accident. Other people do not share that opinion, and for them the risk of a nuclear accident like we saw in Japan after the March 2011 tsunami or the risk that nuclear waste may get into the wrong hands outweighs the benefit nuclear power offers by producing carbon-free energy. How much risk we are willing to accept helps guide our conclusions about which environmental problems we want to address first. This also means weighing certain risk today against uncertain risk in the future. How much are we willing to spend today to prevent an event from happening next month or in the next century? The answer depends on our level of risk tolerance, our current level of economic prosperity and a range of other factors.

Building risk tolerance into the cost-benefit analysis is tricky, and some have tried to put their thumbs on the scale by changing the way we calculate environmental risk. A common thumb on the scale is the "precautionary principle." This notion purports to use the common-sense standard of "better safe than sorry." It argues that avoiding environmental damage is so important we should tip the cost-benefit scales against allowing products or activities that might pose a risk to the environment. The precautionary principle has been established as law in a number of places, and many environmental activists want to enshrine it in the laws of states and at the federal level. Doing so would mean that where any uncertainty existed, public officials would be required to avoid environmental risk, even if it meant increasing other risks to society. There is no reason, however, that certain types of risk should count more than other risks, especially those with a potentially higher impact. This is one reason Professor Sunstein has called the precautionary approach "incoherent." The precautionary principle sets a standard that says do nothing until we are certain of everything.

The precautionary principle imposes risks of its own. Granting a permit to build a factory may pose a risk to air quality, but if it generates tax revenue that funds the cleanup of toxic waste or simply provides government the resources to make the public roads safer, and save lives by reducing traffic accidents, then accepting a small risk to air quality might be worth it. In other circumstances, the situation might be the other way around: building the factory may pose a greater risk to air quality than would be gained from other social benefits. In either case, the best approach is an honest assessment of the impacts, without skewing the results simply because we happen to think preventing potential risk to the environment is always more important than what is lost. In practice, that may not be the reality.

This is not simply an idle consideration. The way we weigh risk can have a dramatic effect on our daily lives and on the types of public policies we support. It has become a particularly heated debate when it comes to climate change.

Defining the level of environmental risk posed by climate change makes all the difference when trying to assess which policies are worth following. For instance, Yale professor William Nordhaus has been modeling the economic impacts of climate change for more than two decades. He estimates the optimal amount of money we should charge to avoid future climate change is about $30 per metric ton of carbon.[2] This amounts to 30 cents per gallon of gasoline. While nobody likes to see gas prices go up, this is certainly less than the amount of the many fluctuations in the market price of gas in recent years.

There are, however, competing viewpoints. The British government funded a study by Nicholas Stern which also looked at the costs of climate change and its potential impact on the environment. Appropriately entitled "The Economics of Climate Change: The Stern Review," the study recommends acceptance of a very low level of risk for impacts that may happen far in the future. It assumes we should take great steps today to avoid a small level of risk in the future – much like the approach called for in the precautionary principle. As a result, "The Stern Review" argues we should be willing to pay $350 per every ton of carbon emissions, or an additional $3.50 per gallon of gas, to avoid potential impacts from climate change. Simply by changing the level of risk tolerance in the calculation, the acceptable cost of large-scale environmental policies increases twelve-fold, seeming to justify a huge expenditure of taxpayer dollars.

Such a policy would have sweeping impacts on economic prosperity and would dedicate a huge amount of our resources to solving this one environmental problem. It would mean not only fewer dollars for all workers, it would mean fewer resources available for parks, toxic cleanups, reforestation, preservation of the oceans and other important environmental priorities. This is why an informative cost-benefit analysis is so important – it tells us what the tradeoffs are. While the way a free economy organizes the creation of goods and services is not very clear sometimes, we must remember that each dollar represents human effort, physical or intellectual, and time taken from other pursuits we would all like to be doing. Increasing the costs of environmental policy beyond what is reasonable and appropriate means we have less of those things we would like, and we have to spend more time exerting effort to achieve that environmental end. That is why Professor Nordhaus argues that spending $350 per ton of carbon, as "The Stern Review" recommends, would actually do more harm than good. Above a cost of about $30 per ton in 2005 dollars, we actually begin making ourselves as a society worse off. The calamities we are trying to avoid become less important than the opportunities lost – not only to people, but to the planet due to the misallocation of resources.

Bjørn Lomborg, known by many as "the skeptical environmentalist," pioneered an approach that attempts to find the best balance of resources to address a whole range of the world's problems, including those related to climate change. Lomborg, a Danish professor of statistics, convened some of the world's best economists, organizing an effort he called the "Copenhagen Consensus" after the location of the group's first meeting. Professor Lomborg compared the cost of preventing climate change with the cost of simply mitigating some of its worst impacts. He found that in some cases we could do more good for people and the environment by spending our scarce resources on reducing impacts rather than trying to prevent them. After calculating the costs, he discovered that if we are concerned about the impact rising sea levels (caused in part by a warming planet) will have on small island countries like the Maldives, we might be better off spending the funds to help them waterproof their country rather than spending trillions to make a relatively small impact on the level of the oceans worldwide. Paying inordinate attention to environmental risks without looking at the consequences of our actions smacks of redoubling our current efforts while losing sight of the ultimate goal. Fundamentally, that is why an honest, cost-benefit analysis is not only good policy, it will also guide us to what is best for the environment.

There are few things more symbolic of environmentalism than opposition to waste. Recycling is central to environmental consciousness because reusing materials is superior to throwing them away. It echoes the praise we give to tribal cultures that use every part of an animal carcass, or to people who find a way to do more with less, or to those who keep their planetary footprint as small as possible. If waste is wrong in principle, why would we be casual about wasting money, which is really just a way of wasting resources? Whether we count a resource as something tangible, like water, trees or fish, or we count resources in more abstract ways, as with money, we need to look after those resources.

Economic analysis, by thoughtfully assessing the best allocation of resources and pushing us to use those resources wisely, and to do more with less, can be a powerful tool. It can help ensure we are really concerned about the right things and are according them the proper value.

This approach goes beyond simple bean counting. Placing a proper value on the environment, resources, habitat and the planet is a critical part of ordering those values in their proper places. It also makes sure we keep an eye on achieving the ultimate goal, by prompting us to follow policies and actions that have a positive impact. Can we truly be moral if we intend to have a positive impact on the environment but our actions have no real effect? Or even worse, if we actually waste resources and move away from the goal we are trying to achieve? We cannot separate the intention from the deed. We are often quick to argue that those who minimize the importance of potential environmental impacts are immoral or greedy. But if we fail to determine honestly whether the actions we are taking really do have a positive impact, are we any more moral?

Simply saying we care does nothing to achieve actual environmental sustainability. In some ways, feel-good environmental policies are actually worse than doing nothing because they use resources to no good end – diverting them from more productive pursuits that would actually advance the goal we claim to care about.

Assigning Resources Their Proper Value

Activists sometimes argue that society doesn't place enough value on the environment – that we under-appreciate its importance and fail to see the fundamental ways it affects our lives. They argue further, and many agree, there is a value to the environment that is separate from its utility. Living with a view of forests and mountains is something we appreciate. Even if we never see a wild panda, most of us believe there is a value to having pandas on the planet as part of the amazing panoply of life. How we calculate these values varies from person to person, but it is critical that we try to find a common value for the things we care about. If we fail to place a more tangible value on the things we care about, then any attempt to choose among different environmental protection strategies is little more than a random effort at picking what strikes our fancy at the moment.

One reason we often fail to assign tangible values to various goals, environmental and otherwise, is that doing so is so difficult. Each person has a slightly different set of priorities. Before discussing ways to overcome those concerns, we need to remember that assigning values is absolutely critical if we hope to make real progress in addressing environmental concerns. Resources are scarce, and making sure that we spend the dollars and time we have to do the most good is a critical part of helping the environment. Simply saying that such things are subjective guarantees we will make decisions based on whims, and we will simply be following the latest trends. We should commit ourselves to slow, steady progress in one direction. Ecologies change over long periods of time, and a commitment to a long-term view will help prevent distractions that undermine progress. Applying financial values to environmental amenities is a controversial area, but the alternative is extremely unattractive because it makes it virtually impossible to measure success or failure. We can disagree about the various valuations, but sound environmental decisions will be possible only if we agree on a basic tenet: adopting an objective foundation of valuation is more likely to lead to positive results than not having such a foundation.

Setting this objective foundation of valuation by using prices is, of course, fraught with problems. There are many ways to set the prices. One way is to ask people about their willingness to pay for environmental attributes, like preserving forestland to protect particular wildlife or clean water. These results will vary with the economic level of prosperity in each region. Poor areas are going to be less willing to spend their limited income to protect wildlife than are parts of the world where income is very high. This is one reason that countries with the cleanest air and water also tend to be the most affluent – they are willing to pay more for those amenities because the relative cost of preventing pollution to them is small. One problem with this approach is that it is sometimes difficult to find practical ways to collect on people's willingness to pay for a clean environment.

Another problem is how to estimate the impact on human lives using standard metrics set by the EPA or other organizations. They assume the value of a statistical life to be around $7 million, meaning that if a policy saves ten lives but costs $1 billion, the regulation costs too much and actually ends up doing more damage than it prevents.

Sometimes it is possible to measure between two choices, comparing the costs of each approach and determining which path is better. In the 1980s, there was concern that chemicals being released into the atmosphere were depleting the ozone layer, leading to increased health and environmental risks. Ozone in the atmosphere filters out certain wavelengths of sunlight that can cause skin cancer. The concern was that chlorofluorocarbons (CFCs) would react with the ozone, creating a hole that would allow more ultraviolent rays to reach the earth's surface, creating significant health problems for people. When determining how to address this risk, the Reagan administration completed a cost-benefit analysis, comparing the cost of phasing out CFCs with the potential costs of ozone depletion and potential harm to health. The results were clear – phasing out CFCs made economic sense. Award-winning science writer Ronald Bailey, who has written about many "eco-myths," summarized the case in 1993, saying:

> "If CFCs were allowed to build up in the atmosphere during the next century, ozone depletion might eventually entail significant costs. More ultraviolet light reaching the surface would require adaptation—switching to new crop varieties, for example—and it might boost the incidence of nonfatal skin cancer. In light of these costs, it makes sense to phase out the use of CFCs."[3]

The Reagan administration came to the same conclusion in 1987 and supported creation of the Montreal Protocol, an international agreement that phased out CFCs. The key to concluding the agreement was a credible cost-benefit analysis that provided the justification for accepting short-term costs to avoid more significant long-term impacts.

As the case of the Montreal Protocol demonstrates, when we are not comparing values, setting clear prices and comparing various policy options becomes much easier. We simply compare the price to achieve the goal, testing various strategies against each other, and choose the least expensive approach. This is why economists argued that a cap-and-trade system, where companies could trade pollution permits, would be more effective and less expensive than rules that required adoption of a particular type of technology to reduce sulfur dioxide and, along with it, acid rain. If a company found a way to reduce its emissions at a price that was less than it would cost to install the technology, they would do so, achieving the same environmental benefit for a lower cost. The company might even continue to reduce its emissions beyond the level required by law and then sell the additional reductions as permits to other companies having difficulty cutting their own emissions. Those permits were sold on a market, with the price being determined by the bidding of various emitters, just like the stock market. This assigned a price to each ton of sulfur dioxide released into the atmosphere, providing a benchmark that each emitter could use to determine the cheapest way to achieve reduction targets. While some companies may be above their allotted emissions and others below the level, the total level of emissions would meet the target. If installing air-scrubbing technology is the least expensive approach, then companies will adopt it. If there are other ways to accomplish clean air more cheaply, those will be chosen. The outcome is the same, but the range of options is greater, leading companies to choose the lowest cost approach that achieves the goal.

Setting the price for sulfur dioxide did two things. First, it provided information about the reasonable cost to reduce emissions. Companies could decide the best way to meet the mandatory goals. Second, it provided an incentive to find better ways to reduce emissions. Anyone with a good idea of how to address the problem would know if they could provide a better alternative, and they would be rewarded for their efforts. With good information and an incentive to take action, progress on a difficult problem was swift, and the result was more positive than had been expected.

This is the idea behind the much-maligned concept of carbon offsets, activities that indirectly reduce the total amount of carbon dioxide released into the atmosphere. As part of the Kyoto Protocol to reduce carbon emissions, negotiators added a mechanism to encourage those not covered by the emissions reductions to find their own ways of reducing carbon emissions or removing carbon from the atmosphere. Every ton of carbon you reduce, either by modifying your behavior or some other action that reduces carbon, can be sold to companies who need to meet reductions targets. Instead of spending a great deal to reduce their own emissions, they pay others to emit less carbon dioxide, offsetting the emissions of the company. The purpose of this system is to encourage creativity, finding ever cheaper ways to reduce carbon emissions and achieving the carbon reductions more quickly and inexpensively. If it costs me $50 to avoid one ton of CO_2 emissions, I can instead pay someone who can do the same thing for $20. If you have an idea for a technology that can reduce a ton of CO_2 emissions for $15, you now have the incentive to create that technology, driving the price down even further.

Assigning a clear price is critical in weighing which policies make the most sense. Without the ability to trade carbon offsets, there would be little incentive to invent new technology. How would you know whether your technology was cost effective? The price sets a benchmark that sends a clear message about the opportunities that exist to innovators and those who need to reduce emissions. As long as the overall carbon-reductions targets are met, society doesn't care how it is done.

In the case of carbon offsets, the problem became too much creativity. Organizations found ways to game the system, using their creativity to use the accounting rules in ways that were not intended, thereby undermining the credibility of the system. The power of clear and transparent price signals were undermined by rules that were far from clear and transparent. Cap-and-trade, which worked to quickly and efficiently to reduce sulfur dioxide, became costly, bureaucratic and ineffective when applied to everyone using and producing energy in an economy.

Ironically, this demonstrates the power of financial incentives and placing a price on pollution. When funding was offered, creative people rushed to find ways to secure that funding, even in ways not intended by the drafters of the Kyoto Protocol. Putting a price on pollution provides incentives and allows policymakers and those of us who want to buy environmental products to judge. If we have to pay a high price for every bit of garbage we throw away, we will find ways to reuse Ziploc bags and aluminum foil. There is a reason people stomp on the garbage – they pay by the trash can and want to fit as much as they can into one bin. The next time you see a neighbor taking his garbage to the curb at 5:00 a.m. so he doesn't miss the weekly trash pickup and incur extra cost by putting out more than his bin will hold next week, you are witnessing the power of putting a price on pollution and of a personal cost-benefit analysis in action. Your neighbor is deciding the cost of being seen in his or her bathrobe is lower than the benefit of not having to pay more for garbage collection.

The Price of Intangibles

Placing a price on pollution does not solve all problems. There are still value judgments about what is important that are central to the final decision. Each of us weighs the importance of receiving short-term versus long-term benefits. We make decisions that pit security against efficiency. For some, it is worth spending a great deal now to feel secure from a variety of risks in the future or to reduce potential risks to the environment. Others argue that the goal should be to spend our resources as efficiently as possible, even if we incur some additional risk along the way, because we will end up more prosperous and secure in the long run.

These tradeoffs play themselves out in real-world decisions about the environment. When it comes to reducing emissions of greenhouse gases, there are two competing approaches that exemplify this very challenge. Many people in the environmental community advocate a mandatory cap-and-trade policy because they want the certainty of a government-enforced cap on emissions. Even if the system is less efficient and creates more economic hardship, the important thing for them is that we have a cap that guarantees actual reductions to meet designated targets. Others, including many environmental economists, argue that placing a flat price on greenhouse gas emissions is better because it is more flexible, allowing families and businesses to pay the price when they can afford it and to find ways to avoid the tax when that makes more sense. That calculation may change from year to year, and allowing people to decide what is best at a particular moment avoids the high costs that come with guaranteed, but inflexible, caps and emissions-reduction targets. There is less certainty about when and how we will meet the targets, but the cost of reduction is tied to the impact of the behavior, so you pay for the impact you cause.

Which of these two approaches you favor – mandatory cap-and-trade or a flexible price on carbon emissions – probably has a great deal to do with your personal sense of risk aversion. Scientists can lay out the risks for emissions at a range of levels. Economists can perform a cost-benefit analysis on a range of options, indicating what approaches are most efficient, least likely to cause costly unintended consequences and be most effective. There is still a role for personal values in decision making. The information from scientists and economists rarely provides the final word on how a decision should be made, and each of us looks into our heart to make the decision, given all the information, we are most comfortable with.

The challenge in avoiding the seductive lure of eco-fads is to make sure we do not automatically do what our hearts say, especially when the science and economics say it is the wrong thing to do. Our values are important and play a role, but when we use personal preference as a trump card over all other considerations, that is when the trouble begins. Everyone is susceptible to this pitfall. We often hear scientists disagree about the data, the level of risk and what to do about it. Economists argue, often boisterously, about the correct approach to solving society's problems. While they may not like to say it, scientists, economists and all of us make decisions in part based on our personal preferences and values. Rigorously applying science and economics to every problem, while leaving our personal comfort behind, is simply not an approach humans can take. Nassim Taleb, a financial trader who has become famous for his work in trying to understand how humans assimilate information, says that even scientists, who are supposed to be less subject to the whims of sensationalism, are not immune. He writes, "If you think that science is an abstract subject free of sensationalism and distortions, I have some sobering news. Empirical researchers have found evidence that scientists too are vulnerable to narratives, emphasizing titles and 'sexy' attention-grabbing punch lines over more substantive matters."[4]

It is simply too hard to set aside emotion in all of our decisions. As humans we do not have the emotional tools to glibly toss aside the things we care about and focus on the purely logical. And even if we could, the real world does not work this way because the information we have is incomplete. Using our values and experiential rules of thumb make sense to help us reach final decisions.

Avoiding eco-fads is not about utter self-denial or rejecting personal values. If we are committed to avoiding feel-good environmentalism, we need to be aware of our motives and why we are making decisions. If we know that we lack full information and are willing to take our best shot with what we know at the time, then so be it – as long as we have an ongoing commitment to seeking good information and a willingness to change our minds as we learn more.

Eco-fads persist, however, because trusting scientific and economic conclusions that run counter to our personal values requires a leap of faith. The details of scientific and economic conclusions are complex. There can be mistakes in the analysis, leading us astray. On the other hand, our values are our own, are familiar and, for us, readily understandable. You do not have to have a Ph.D. in philosophy to know what you believe is right and what is wrong. We may not know much about art or science, but we know what we like. Substituting someone else's scientific or economic conclusions for our personal priorities is difficult and risky. This is especially true when there is a cost to us personally. Rejecting a popular eco-fad may mean giving up benefits in personal prestige, acceptance by a group and a personal sense of satisfaction. All these pressures combine to encourage us to make decisions backwards – find the environmental policy position that best fits our values and search for the science and economics that confirms our decision. Science and economics play a supporting role in confirming our preferences, rather than acting as a guide to real environmental solutions.

In this circumstance, appealing to common sense becomes a way to dodge the uncomfortable information that does not fit the conclusion we have already chosen. Having set up a view of the world that fits our values, information that contradicts our conclusions seems foreign and nonsensical. Pieces of information that do not fit the puzzle don't make sense. They don't meet the test of common sense, in our view, because a puzzle piece that does not fit seems anomalous or simply the wrong piece. That reaction, however, maximizes uncertainty and makes it hard to arrive at good public policy decisions. New scientific information that does not match our expectations doesn't meet the common-sense test of fitting what we already think we know. Economic analysis that is counterintuitive or unclear conflicts with our preconceptions, encouraging us to reject it by moving to the more comfortable ground of common sense. Common sense, however, is in the eye of the beholder, and when subjective common sense become the primary guide in making choices, each person is likely to make very different decisions, even when the same information is available to all.

There will always be intangible elements to our decisions, and our personal values will always play an important role. It is not only appropriate but, in fact, moral to choose options that honor the dignity of individuals and their freedom to make decisions about their own lives, rather than assuming a paternalistic tone that seeks to dictate the kind of life others should lead. The paternalistic approach comes with its own risks, and sometimes the choices made by honoring individuality have costs or incur risks that science might ask us to avoid. To move beyond eco-fads does not mean ignoring our basic moral grounding. It means recognizing the risks we are taking, starting from a foundation of sound science and cogent economics to make choices that fit our value structure that are consistent with objective information. It means rejecting comforting, but illogical, appeals to subjective standards like "common sense."

Imagine how good we can feel about ourselves twenty years from now knowing we have done the best we could for the environment, having been smart enough to do what is right even when it was uncomfortable. What could be more commonsensical?

Chapter 4

Why Politicians Promote Eco-Fads

Former Seattle Mayor Greg Nickels announced the results with obvious glee. "This is a remarkable milestone that shows how cities can lead the way in the fight against global warming," Nickels said. "It is a success that we can all celebrate."

The occasion was the mayor's release of a report showing that, in 2005, the city of Seattle's emission of greenhouse gases was more than 7 percent below the 1990 level and had met the targets set by the Kyoto Protocol for reduction of carbon emissions. Having staked much of his political prestige locally and nationally on being a founder of the U.S. Conference of Mayors' Climate Protection Agreement, the numbers were a vindication of Nickels' efforts. His announcement was designed to contrast the progress being made by cities like his with the refusal of the George W. Bush administration, and like the Clinton administration before it, to sign the Kyoto Protocol and commit the U.S. to reducing greenhouse gases. In a newspaper column following his announcement, Nickels wrote, "The message to lawmakers is clear: Cities are taking action, and we want the federal government to join us."[1]

Four years later, Nickels released another study showing, once again, that Seattle was below the emissions targets of the Kyoto Protocol. In a press release from the mayor's office, he triumphantly announced, "We have shown the world that reducing climate pollution is an economic opportunity and it inspires us to do even more."[2] Environmental groups heralded the results. Alan T. Durning, of the Sightline Institute, one of Washington state's largest environmental advocacy organizations, praised the mayor, telling The Seattle Times, "I'd say the city of Seattle did better than I expected."[3] Even as the mayor was on his way out (he had been defeated in his re-election bid), he continued to highlight his green credentials and defend the success of his policies.

This is, of course, what politicians do. Successful politicians may not be good at science, economics or other disciplines, but they do know one thing: what sells to the public. That is the one skill all successful politicians share. Unfortunately, what sells well is not always aligned with reality.

When Nickels' carbon emissions report is examined more closely, there was less than what was intended to meet the eye – much less. Although the emissions city officials counted were, in fact, 7 percent below the 1990 level, their calculation left much uncounted. Instead of counting all carbon emissions from activities in the city, they counted only those emissions that actually occurred inside the city limits. That means city officials counted the emissions from Seattle's single concrete plant, but did not count emissions from concrete trucked into the city from elsewhere. The problem is that when it comes to climate change, it does not matter if fossil fuels are burned in Seattle, Toronto or Zimbabwe. All carbon emissions go into the atmosphere regardless of the source and thus exert an influence on the world's climate. If a construction project is underway in Seattle, it doesn't matter if the concrete is made in Seattle or in Portland – the energy used, and the associated carbon emissions, are the same in both cases. By drawing a firm line around the city limits, Seattle reaped the economic benefit of regional construction and growth, while placing carbon emissions totals from that economic growth off the city's environmental books. With this accounting trick, Seattle could close its concrete plant, increase its use of imported concrete, and the total level of carbon emissions accounted for by the city would actually decrease even though the true total level of carbon emissions increased. Claiming the world is better off as a result of this brand of manipulated math smacks of Enron accounting.

There were, however, areas where Seattle did achieve real emissions reductions, such as home heating. Those reductions, ironically, occurred in the 1990s, as city residents converted from expensive, carbon-intensive heating oil to cheaper natural gas, which produces far fewer greenhouse gas emissions for each unit of energy produced. This is the same way Great Britain reduced its carbon emissions, and it is a major reason the U.K. is likely to be the only European country to actually achieve the targets set for it in the Kyoto Protocol. In both Seattle and the U.K., however, the reduction largely occurred independently of government regulations or incentives. In its report on meeting the Kyoto targets, Seattle officials admitted, "For economic reasons, natural gas has gained favor over oil for space heating since 1990,"[4] meaning lower home heating prices encouraged homeowners to switch to gas. Most of the emissions reductions trumpeted in his Kyoto report occurred well before Nickels became Seattle's mayor in 2001.

Perhaps the greatest irony was that when the report was updated in 2009, while touting the fact Seattle was still below the Kyoto target, it pointed out that emissions were actually increasing. If the trend did not change, Seattle would be well above the Kyoto target in 2012, the treaty's actual deadline. Whatever temporary achievements may have been realized, Seattle, in the end, probably will not meet the goal promised by the former mayor.

The accounting tricks, the fact his policies had not caused the reduction and the realization that any environmental gains were short-lived did not stop Mayor Nickels from declaring his policy a major achievement. It did not stop local environmental groups from praising his commitment and the policies he was trying to adopt. As far as the mayor was concerned, the effort had been a success. The purpose of the city's Kyoto report was not to honestly assess efforts to reduce carbon emissions, but to get a political bump Nickels could use to promote himself and the policies he supported. An official report showing his strategy was largely ineffective would have undermined that effort, so his administration simply cooked the books. Of course, this practice is not helpful to the environment. The only way to make environmental progress is to be honest about results – positive or negative – and to learn from them in order to choose the best path. For Nickels, however, helping the environment was only a secondary goal. Personal political advancement was the agenda on the front burner.

As the environment has become a more salient political issue, and as more political candidates tout their green credentials, environmental policy has increasingly become a tool to help win the loyalty of special interest groups, raise campaign funds and, of course, win elections. As a result, when politicians choose which environmental policies they support, they select those policies that can best be conveyed to special interest groups and voters. Elected officials, and those who want to be elected, look for policies that sound good, while shying away from policies that may be more effective yet are harder to take credit for.

Sometimes environmental claims provide cover for politicians seeking to please their constituencies. Are your political supporters unhappy about the noise associated with a proposed factory or gravel mine in the area? No worries. Simply oppose it on environmental grounds. Even the best-managed factory will have some environmental impact, allowing lawsuits and legislative action in the name of environmental protection, while the real purpose is to stop the new factory. Increasingly, environmental action has become indistinguishable from the not-in-my-back-yard (NIMBY) efforts of communities who want to fight development. Arguing that a new strip mall, WalMart or factory will have a negative environmental impact is more appealing to voters than simply saying we should not create jobs and permit economic growth because I live here now. Thus, in this view, any new construction and its associated inconveniences should cease.

Of course, not all elected officials are so cynical as to use environmental issues simply as a way to score political points. There are those who truly believe humans need to be good stewards of the planet and who work to advance policies that best achieve that end. Even for sincere politicians, however, eco-fads can be seductive because they offer short-term gain without much political pain. Few elected officials are scientists, making it difficult for them to understand the information they use to craft legislation. Officials rely on the assessment of others, leaning toward those policies that seem to make the most sense, that most closely match their personal level of risk tolerance, and that offer tangible, near-term results. Even the most clear-eyed and environmentally committed politician will factor the opportunity to take political credit for protecting the environment into his or her law-making decisions. Even for politicians with a real desire to help the environment, embracing eco-fads is tempting.

Once politicians make an eco-fad the law of the land, they work hard to highlight their commitment to its application. With their credibility now tied to the validity of the eco-fad, they, like Mayor Nickels, begin the marketing campaign. With press releases, newspaper editorials, Facebook postings and mailings to constituents, they aggressively promote the eco-fad, touting the benefits and downplaying the costs or risk of failure. This aggressive effort can pay off with voters who, inundated by information and unable to research independently every claim made by politicians, want to believe we are making environmental progress for little up-front cost.

In the political arena, eco-fads build a momentum of their own. Once adopted, each politician promotes them, making it difficult to turn back and admit he or she made a mistake. Voters reward politicians for their environmental stands, encouraging elected officials to adopt the next trendy environmental policy, and the cycle continues. Unfortunately, this cycle is a major reason we find ourselves headed down so many destructive environmental paths. Unless politicians are able to break the cycle, foregoing the political points that come with support for these policies, we will continue to fail to meet environmental targets. Failures like Seattle's failed carbon reductions will mount, even as politicians increase their public commitment to those very targets.

Organizing For Eco-Fads

Nobody who has followed politics in the last three decades will be surprised to learn that environmental activists have become a powerful force in national and state politics. Environmental organizations not only promote their causes, they regularly communicate with their members, offering a formidable source of power for elected officials seeking to mobilize supporters in favor of their policies or their re-election. Even politicians who may not share all of these groups' views know that if they vote against the groups' agendas, there will be a political cost. So, elected officials look for ways to harness the power of these groups and to avoid offending them.

The source of the power is a common belief that we need to protect the environment and to support policies to that end. Environmental groups organize their members in advance, allowing them to call out the troops when necessary. In some cases this means making calls or sending emails when favored policies are being discussed in political arenas. Other times it means telling their members which candidates they should support and to turn out their vote on Election Day. This support not only helps to directly build up the number of people supporting environmental policies and candidates, it sends a signal to others in the public about a candidate's level of "greenness." Knowing this, elected officials take steps to earn that support.

In Washington state in 2009, as the governor prepared to sign an executive order mandating a number of steps to implement reductions in carbon emissions, the state's Department of Ecology, the lead agency on the issue, sent a warning about another issue facing the governor. Worried the governor would veto legislation favored by environmental groups, the director of the Department of Ecology sent an email to the governor's office, cautioning "A veto on this would have a very negative impact on our ability to gather an excited crowd for our rollout of the [climate change executive order]."[5] So important was the environmental community's support for the executive order, the governor's administration appeared to trade a veto of legislation in exchange for gaining the public political support of environmental groups for the governor's order. The governor did not veto the legislation in question, and the environmental community came out in support of her executive order.

Securing support for specific policies is not the only reason elected officials try to earn the backing of environmental groups by supporting eco-fads. Environmental groups have become a powerful force in funding political campaigns, encouraging members to donate to candidates and using resources to promote specific agendas. From the Sierra Club to Greenpeace and other environmental groups, a tremendous amount of money is spent to promote environmental policies they support.

In his book, *The Green Wave*, Bonner Cohen notes that at the national level, environmental organizations receive hundreds of millions of dollars every year to promote their causes. While candidates look for direct campaign contributions, the cash from environmental groups can do much more. Cohen notes, "Money can grease the skids, buy advertising, hire staff, print books, fund demonstrations, and finance studies."[6] All of these help create a favorable public atmosphere for eco-fads and the candidates who support them.

Environmental groups are not the only ones encouraging politicians to support eco-fads. Many environmental policies create economic winners and losers, and businesses work hard to ensure they are on the winning side. Policies that mandate a particular type of environmental technology will find a good friend in the company selling that product. Owners of buildable land will be strongly supportive of efforts to limit the ways surrounding land can be used, reducing the total supply of land available for development and driving up the value of the land they own. Forestry companies benefit from policies on climate change that increase the cost of energy-intensive building materials like concrete and steel, making their products cheaper compared to those of competitors. How environmental legislation is written can make a significant difference in the economic fortunes of companies. Business executives are keenly interested in being supportive of elected officials who can put their company in line for market windfalls.

Not every environmental policy is a fad. The United States has made tremendous progress in clean air, clean water and environmental sustainability, and good environmental policies have played a role (though not the only role) in making that happen. The funding and organizational power of environmental groups, businesses and others help coax elected officials into supporting policies they might otherwise oppose or be indifferent about. Once supportive of an eco-fad, however, politicians are likely to defend those decisions vigorously, seeing any criticism of those policies as an attack on their own credibility. The significant campaign funding available from these environmental groups encourages elected officials and candidates to support policies lawmakers believe might fail in the long run.

Sometimes, elected officials will actually support policies that are highly risky and expensive precisely because of the strong political signal their support sends. Imagine looking at a spreadsheet of the costs and benefits of a particular environmental policy, seeing that while there are short-term costs, the eventual benefit will be quite large in just a few years. Really, no particular ideology is needed to support such a public expenditure. As long as the money is available, one need only compare the costs and benefits to the public interest to see whether it makes sense. Making this decision is easy, and politicians receive very little credit for this type of choice. In fact, the real risk comes from not making such a no-brainer decision. To get political credit and take stands that can be called "brave," elected officials need to support policies that have high costs or that are extremely risky. Those are the types of decisions elected officials can use to solidly earn the support of special interest groups and send an unambiguous signal. "I care so much," the politician says, "that I am willing to take a foolish and costly stand in the name of our values." This is the reasoning behind the political support for many of the eco-fads that find their way into our public policy.

When asked what a particular environmental policy will cost, elected officials often respond that protecting the environment is so important, "we can't afford not to do this." Such an answer is an obvious dodge, but it demonstrates that to someone committed to an eco-fad the actual costs are not what are really important. In this view, even if eco-fad advocates get a few policies wrong along the way, the nobility of the ends make it all worthwhile. The Precautionary Principle explicitly prioritizes environmental protection over all other considerations when any doubt exists. Such an approach says that we do not need to know the costs because anyone committed to helping the environment knows that unless the result is obvious, environmental protection must take top priority, even if the potential costs are very high. The more a political candidate is willing to accept risks in support of the environment, the stronger the signal regarding his or her commitment to environmental protection.

One of the most common ways this effect manifests itself is in the race to be first to call for ever-higher levels of environmental protection. Showing "leadership" becomes a way to indicate that you are not merely a follower of environmental policies, you are more committed than others and are actually at the front of the trend.

It seems everyone wants to be seen as on the cutting edge of the latest environmental trend. When the Spanish government committed itself to funding alternative energy production in an effort to create a national green economy, officials found a strong advocate in Al Gore, who congratulated the government for its efforts. Speaking at the Spain-U.S. Business Sustainability Conference in March of 2009, Gore told the audience, "Green infrastructure is the option of choice to solve the climate and economic crisis. ... Spain is one of the leading countries"[7] developing that infrastructure. Demonstrating leadership sends a powerful political message, but it is seldom the basis for sound policymaking. In the case of Spain, government officials found the very policies that earned them international cachet in the fight against climate change were also hurting their economy. With unemployment at more than 20 percent in 2010, a government memo admitted, according to the Spanish business newspaper *La Gaceta de Los Negocios*, "Each green job created costs more than 2.2 traditional jobs."[8]

The costs of eco-fads, however, are not always so stark. Often the most significant cost is the lost opportunity to do something meaningful for the environment with the money that instead was wasted on policies that have little or no impact. Taking such risks, however, is the very reason those actions have such power as a signal. Throwing caution to the wind, they symbolize the type of bold action that inspires followers and tells fellow ideological travelers that only someone truly committed to the cause would demonstrate that kind of courageous leadership.

Heads I Win, Tails You Lose

Even when policies go bad, it is rare that elected officials are held accountable for having supported them. New environmental policies are announced, often with great fanfare. The media pays attention, information is sent to supportive interest groups, and constituents hear about the bright promise of the latest environmental initiative. What is reported, however, is not the actual result of a new policy, only its future promise. Elected officials claim the policy will make a dramatic difference in improving environmental quality and, in many cases, that the benefits of the program are so great that people, wildlife and the environment will be better off in just a short period of time.

Less frequently are the actual results of those policies reported. Sometimes this is because the results are unclear and standard metrics for judging success are not available. Other times the results are not reported because there is no particular news hook to create a news story with. Most important, however, is that for politicians, there are many incentives that discourage them from learning whether or not their policy was successful. Having loudly touted a bold action to promote environmental protection, elected officials are unlikely to point out later that the policy they placed so much hope in never lived up to its promise. The failure of the policy, after all, reflects back on the politician who recommended the idea in the first place.

When a biodiesel company announced it would be building the largest refinery in the United States on the coast of Washington state, it held a major press event, even inviting one of the state's U.S. senators to join via satellite from Washington, D.C. At the press conference, this new alternative fuel was proudly trumpeted as a substitute for imported foreign oil, creating high-paying local jobs that could replace some of the jobs lost when local saw mills were closed by earlier environmental initiatives. Construction permits, which normally take months or years to obtain, were approved in less than three months. The skids had been greased to move this favored policy forward and to allow advocates and politicians to take full political credit for taking quick action. Television stations, news radio and newspapers all covered the event eagerly. Two years later, however, few reporters noticed the actual results of the alternative fuels project. A downturn in the biofuel industry led to economic difficulties for the refinery, causing layoffs and leaving the plant operating at only a fraction of capacity. There was no press conference to announce the frustrating results. No reporters asked the senator attending the original press conference what had gone wrong or whether the failure undermined support for federal biofuel subsidies. There was no announcement of the eventual cost to taxpayers of the subsidies given to create the refinery or the cost to taxpayers per job created.

The failure of the Washington biofuel plant to create the promised jobs or reduce U.S. oil imports is not the only example of such a failure. In King County, the largest county in Washington state, elected officials sought to create a "green" taxi company to reduce carbon emissions. *The Seattle Weekly* reported the county, "which hadn't issued a new taxi license in 17 years, agreed to give away 50 of them to a fledgling, mostly Ethiopian-run company that had agreed to adopt new eco- and labor-friendly policies."[9] The high costs associated with this new proposal ultimately doomed the project. Other cab companies and drivers, seeing the value of their taxi licenses decline with the market entry of a new cab company, sued to stop the new taxi business from getting out of the garage. The new company, known as Green Cab, ultimately opened for business but barely hung on, for a variety of reasons – not the least of which was the high cost of the fleet of Toyota Priuses it had bought. While the lawsuit created media coverage of the problems plaguing the new cab company, the elected official in charge of the program, former King County Executive Ron Sims, was not held accountable for its expensive failures. In fact, Sims ended up with a job in the Obama administration, moving up to the number two position in the Department of Housing and Urban Development. The administration's announcement of his appointment even prominently mentioned his work on the environment as a reason for his selection. An elected official's record is more than the success or failure of one policy, to be sure, but the Green Cab story did little to undermine his image as an environmentally friendly candidate. The strength of his public image was far greater than his failed policy results.

That political image can also be more powerful than science, especially when the costs and benefits are hypothetical, making it difficult for the public to weigh the tradeoff. Recommending policies to mitigate hypothetical environmental threats allows elected officials to burnish their green credentials without causing tangible economic harm. Such amorphous calculations are ready-made for political demagoguery.

From 1995 through 2002, Russ Harding served as the director of Michigan's Department of Environmental Quality. In the 1980s, legislators in Michigan banned direct drilling for oil and natural gas beneath the Great Lakes. The issue was raised again in the late 1990s when the possibility of drilling from land on an angle underneath Lake Michigan and Lake Huron was broached. Before the state considered allowing under-lake drilling, Harding placed the issue before a group of university professors and scientists on the state Environmental Science Board. The board was commissioned to determine whether drilling was safe and what precautions should be taken before drilling was allowed.

After consideration, the scientists determined that drilling could, in fact, be performed safely with appropriate environmental protections. The oil and gas were contained beneath the bedrock that provided the foundation for the Great Lakes and thus prevented the water in the lakes from leaking away. The hard bedrock provided an impenetrable barrier between the oil and water, offering safety for drilling operations. The board even noted that removing the oil and gas could actually be beneficial, removing the risk that a future deep earthquake might crack this barrier and lead to the natural leaking of oil into the waters of the Great Lakes. Earthquakes are quite rare in that region, so this was not a significant consideration, but the finding highlighted the general opinion of scientists that the people of Michigan could benefit from recovering the energy below the lakes if the drilling were done correctly.

Using those conclusions, Harding and the Michigan Department of Environmental Quality drafted regulations that would guide the drilling effort. Those rules, however, were soon blocked by politics.

Some members of the state Legislature were concerned about the risk of oil spills in the Great Lakes, despite the assurances of the scientists who had studied the issue extensively. A proposal to ban all drilling below the water was introduced and moved through the Legislature. Harding recalls a phone call he received from a conservative legislator the night before the vote. "He told me that he knew it was the wrong thing to do, but he was voting for the ban and apologized to me," Harding said. In the Legislature, politics and the value of a "green" image proved more important than the scientific data.

In circumstances like this, elected officials can argue they have prevented significant environmental harm, painting stark images of potential catastrophe like the 2010 oil spill in the Gulf of Mexico or the 1989 grounding of the Exxon

Valdez oil tanker. Judging the chances of such an event actually occurring, however, is very difficult, and the economic benefits are purely hypothetical. Behavioral economists have long recognized that people's fear of loss is far more powerful than future hopes or expectations. People focus more on potential losses than gains, giving politicians who claim to have avoided widespread environmental damage the benefit of the doubt. Few politicians are likely to be held accountable for this type of mistake, even when supporters of allowing the Great Lakes drilling had the science solidly behind them.

Given how rarely elected officials answer for their mistakes, what risk is there in overselling the potential benefits of new environmental policies? The public is likely to remember the promises, but may never hear whether those promises turned out to be true. The message to politicians is to promise big and receive the public recognition for their strong commitment to the environment – because it is unlikely that their claims will be audited and they will be held to account. Special interest groups who do follow up are likely to forgive candidates for overpromising, as long as those failures generally match the policy direction they favor.

Cultivating a green image also sends a strong message to the public about the values of a candidate. Voters simply cannot judge a candidate's position on all the potential issues that a candidate might have to face as an elected official. Further, environmental policies can be very complex, and understanding all the elements involved is beyond the time or ability of most voters who have to choose among competing candidates. So, we look for shortcuts and signals that indicate what a candidate will do when faced with complex issues we cannot anticipate. As a result, rather than outlining their position on every issue, candidates seek to signal voters about the kind of person they are. Expressing concern about the environment and a desire to leave a healthy planet for future generations is a good way to present a caring and sound character. Voters are more comfortable determining if a candidate seems like a good person whose concerns and attitudes match theirs, rather than trying to sort out the difficult details of every significant public policy. Voters want to be proud of the candidates they support. Promoting environmental policies, especially eco-fads that are visible, popular and specifically crafted to appeal to the public, can be an effective way to send a message about the candidate's character. Indeed, eco-fads are more effective at achieving this goal than legitimate environmental policies that are more complex or have results that are more ambiguous. The clarity and promise of eco-fads makes them perfectly suited to yield the public-image benefits that elected officials seek.

Seducing the Sincere

It is no surprise politicians are primarily concerned about getting reelected and that they take steps to ensure they continue in power. Not all elected officials, however, are driven purely by a desire to stay in office, willing to sacrifice their personal values in the name of political expediency. Politicians, for all their other faults, give up a great deal to run for public office. They endure numerous attacks, spend countless hours away from home, often make little or no money and put themselves and their families in what is an often uncomfortable limelight. It is simply not the case that politicians put themselves through all of these things to earn a little notoriety, a small paycheck or some amount of power. Many elected officials, perhaps most, are sincere about their desire to make their community, state or nation a better place, and they generally want to adopt policies that achieve that goal. Even these politicians, however, find numerous reasons for choosing eco-fads over other less popularized policies.

As we have seen, it can be difficult to distinguish good policy information from bad. With so many issues facing elected officials, legislators cannot be expected to research every single one. There isn't enough time in their day to sort through the mountains of information to determine what data is credible and what falls short. Legislators develop shortcuts to help them decide what information is most likely to be correct. In the absence of clear evidence, they learn to rely on a few trusted sources of information – individuals or groups who share their values and seem to provide good information. Rather than trying to decipher the latest science or economic research, they turn to environmental groups or others to determine the best approach.

In other cases, they look for indications about what information is more likely to be correct, such as unusual coalitions of groups that support a single policy. Legislators who see environmental groups, unions and businesses join together behind a particular policy may decide they do not need to know much more about the policy in question. After all, with such a diverse group of interests in favor of a policy, how likely is it that the policy is going to be controversial or wrong?

There are strong incentives for elected officials and policymakers to unquestioningly accept the information they are handed, especially if it happens to contain good news. Elected officials run the gauntlet of political campaigns because they want to find positive solutions to the problems society faces. Finding solutions is the reward for the hard work of running and serving. And, when provided with a clear solution to a problem, policymakers are likely to jump on the opportunity.

Dr. Jerome Groopman, the chair of medicine at Harvard Medical School, sees this behavior in doctors looking for diagnoses in difficult cases. He calls the desire to seize on a solution, even if it is not the correct solution, "satisfaction of search" or "search satisficing." Groopman notes that this is the tendency to "stop searching for a diagnosis once you find something."[10] When a group comes to an elected official with a solution to a difficult problem, politicians, like doctors, can be inclined to believe the solution is real, substituting hope for skepticism and gaining the satisfaction of having fixed the problem. This effect can cloud the judgment of policymakers, however, blinding them to potential weaknesses in the proposed policy. Questioning a proposed policy delays gratification, giving elected officials a strong emotional disincentive to be skeptical of policies offered by groups they want to trust. Elected officials want to be able to say they found a solution. They put doubts about the efficacy of the policy behind them, seizing on to the hope that the policy being offered is sound.

In addition to providing emotional satisfaction, claiming to have found solutions to environmental problems also allows policymakers to look good to their peers, to voters and to the public. In many campaigns, elected officials highlight the number of pieces of legislation they have passed, adding to their desire to find solutions and put them in action in the form of legislation. On the other hand, politicians tend not to get credit for the bad policies they stopped, making it harder to take a stand against policies that may do harm.

The desire to take credit for environmental solutions also impacts the types of policies favored by elected officials.

First, near-term solutions are more attractive than solutions that will show results only in the distant future. Not only do politicians want to demonstrate their effectiveness by highlighting the good votes they cast, but they want to be able to point to practical results. This is ironic given that many of the environmental problems we face today, like climate change, will take decades to address. This does not stop politicians from tallying and announcing the positive results as they come in. Mayor Nickels' reports on the progress Seattle was making toward achieving the carbon-emissions-reduction goals set by the Kyoto Protocol, faulty though these reports were, was part of his effort to tangibly demonstrate the near-term success of his policies and help justify his re-election effort and his plans to implement more carbon-emissions-reduction policies in the future.

A campaign slogan that proclaims, "Be patient: we will reap the rewards of these policies twenty years from now," is not very compelling to voters. Rather than choosing small, consistent, and meaningful changes that add up to significant results over time, even elected officials who are sincere about helping the environment will favor policies that can demonstrate quick results.

There is a practical side of this approach. Politicians understand they are in office only for short periods of time. Parties can lose power, undermining the progress made in previous years. Elected officials can see the legislation they worked hard to craft undone by the stroke of a pen. Understanding the temporary nature of politics, it is understandable that elected officials seek solutions that offer quick returns and are less vulnerable to the shifting winds of politics.

The combination of these forces, however, is not conducive to development of the best environmental policy. In fact, a short-term focus may force elected officials to force dramatic and abrupt policy changes that create large costs and undermine long-term public support for protecting the environment. In those circumstances, an intense but near-term focus becomes self-defeating.

Second, elected officials want to be able to tie those positive results back to the policies they supported. Claiming credit for general innovations is very difficult. What elected official can credibly claim his or her actions created the automobile, the personal computer, the Internet or other breakthrough technologies? Indeed, the few politicians who do make such claims are not taken seriously. While good public policy can pave the way for remarkable innovations, it is understood that the triumphs, failures and credit lies with those in the private sector who developed the technology.

This is also true when people change their behavior to adapt to changes in energy prices or other personal incentives. During the increase in gas prices in 2008 and the subsequent economic downturn, families used less energy, found ways to avoid driving and generally reduced their greenhouse gas emissions. As a result, in the years following, total U.S. emissions of greenhouse gases fell significantly – 7 percent below the 2008 level. This dramatic drop, however, did not occur as a result of any particular public policy. It was the natural reaction of people worried about spending too much and finding ways to reduce the energy they used.

For this reason, politicians favor direct environmental approaches, requiring people to take certain actions, mandating particular technologies or providing government subsidies for selected solutions. General incentives that encourage people to take a wide range of effective but politically invisible actions are less attractive because elected officials cannot point to them and take credit. They themselves do not know whether the new technologies or positive environmental changes occurred as a result of the policies they favored. This leaves them without the satisfaction of knowing whether they did the right thing or whether there is more they could have done.

When the range of favored policy options is narrowed to those that offer short-term results and are directly imposed by policymakers, the chances of achieving lasting protection for the environment are significantly reduced.

This is fertile ground for eco-fads. A trendy approach that promises satisfying and immediate results, and that can be clearly tied to the actions taken by a politician, cannot help but be seductive – even for office holders who otherwise have a sincere interest in promoting long-term environmental sustainability. Focusing their vision on a narrow subset of policy solutions, however, undermines the likelihood of achieving lasting success.

No Going Back

The fundamental problem for advocates who promote eco-fads as political policy is that once enacted, these policies are rarely changed. Policymakers have a strong desire to see the policies they advocated and supported succeed, and a great reluctance to admit they may have been wrong. This desire undermines efforts to change failing environmental policies. Some policymakers go so far as to oppose or rig efforts to measure whether a favored environmental policy is having a positive or negative outcome. Preventing the collection of data makes it difficult to determine the success or failure of the policy, leaving politicians comfortable leeway to assert positive claims about how successful they have been in protecting the environment.

A dramatic example of this approach was the refusal of Sir John Cowperthwaite, who served as Financial Secretary of Hong Kong during the 1960s, to collect economic statistics. Favoring an approach to the economy that discouraged government intervention, Cowperthwaite refused to collect any data he believed would encourage officials to meddle, taking steps to address whatever perceived shortcomings the data demonstrated. Denying officials the use of data denied them the opportunity to use the statistics as a weapon to advocate for their favored policy. How could economic planners make decisions without reliable data?

Once eco-fads are made policy, politicians have a similar incentive. Auditing the results of a policy serves only as a tool to point out the shortcomings of favored environmental approaches. Data that are not collected cannot be used to show whether elected officials made a mistake. Whether politicians are in the group of sincere or the crowd of the insincere in their support of eco-fads, neither set wants to face the fact they chose the wrong policy. Since positive feelings are an important part of the attraction of eco-fads, collecting accurate performance data can only undermine that good feeling.

In 2008, the city of Seattle, as part of its effort to "campaign to combat global warming by encouraging residents to drive their cars 1,000 miles less a year"[11] began a program called "Car-free Days." The program closed certain city streets during summer weekends, opening them up for pedestrians and bicycles. The program was launched with press releases and was a high-profile part of the mayor's effort to burnish his reputation as an aggressive warrior against global warming. At the end of the summer, when asked how successful the program had been, an official in the city's Department of Transportation admitted in an email, "I don't have information on the reduction of miles and reduced carbon output based on the [car-free] events, as they were intended to promote awareness of global warming."[12] The goal of the campaign to reduce driving wasn't actually to reduce vehicle miles, but to "promote awareness." Without data, who could argue the policy had failed?

To some extent, politicians are hoist by their own petard. In their efforts to sell a policy, they often exaggerate its positive benefits. For instance, we heard from politicians that subsidizing biofuels not only reduces emissions of greenhouse gases, the subsidies help family farms, reduce our dependence on foreign oil and sap hostile countries of the oil wealth they use to support terrorists and others we consider a threat. How could anyone oppose that? But when the reality becomes apparent that biofuels not only do not deliver the promised benefit but create problems of their own, that they are not the panacea that was hoped for and claimed, the elaborate edifice collapses of its own weight. The taller the political promises, the farther they fall. By basing support for a policy on a thin tissue of evidence, elected officials work to prevent the collection of facts running counter to these overblown claims.

In addition to refusing to collect data regarding the results of eco-fads, advocates also say these policies have benefits that are difficult, even impossible, to measure. Benefits such as promoting some undefined level of "awareness." The use of subjective measurements virtually guarantees eco-fads cannot be judged objectively. For example, advocates of "green" building standards often claim that such buildings are more comfortable, reduce health costs and even improve test scores of children who attend schools built to these standards. In some cases numbers are provided that seem to back up these claims, but the measures used are often subjective, attempting to tease out results that may actually be entirely unrelated to the green building standards. The claims and data are so amorphous that even when information emerges undermining the promised results, advocates can effectively muddy the waters, discredit the method of data collection, question the number of case studies and raise unrelated issues to deflect the criticism. Such shifting and vague targets end up giving advocates an opportunity to continue believing in their recommended policy by making it difficult to clearly assess results. Without good information, we cannot say if we are helping or harming the environment. Elected officials can, however, continue to claim the policies they have adopted are moving society toward environmental sustainability, particularly when it is not possible to offer evidence to the contrary.

Showing "leadership" is another way to move from judging a policy on its tangible results to justifying it on subjective grounds. A policy may not meet a reasonable test of effectiveness today, but it will set in motion a series of policies that will make us better off in the end, or so supporters claim. You can't make an omelet without breaking a few eggs, and this line of reasoning assures us that it would be unfair to judge a policy idea based on a few cracked shells lying around, even if the promised omelet is never produced. Policies like this should not be judged on their merits, but on the leadership they provide, supporters argue. This reasoning, however, is nonsensical. It can be argued that any policy shows "leadership," even policies that are demonstrably destructive. If policy efforts are judged only by their magnitude and intent, any approach can be justified, making any effort to assess actual outcomes unnecessary.

There are some office holders, however, who want to do what is right, and given data they can trust, will show a willingness to modify policies that have not achieved the promised results. If these elected officials do decide to change course and reverse failed environmental regulation, they should be prepared to face an onslaught from environmental activists. Failing to enact a piece of environmental legislation will certainly draw criticism, but attempting to undo an eco-fad-based policy after the advocates fought hard to get it in place will create a flurry of attacks. People generally fear losing something they had already gained more than they desire gaining something new. This insight was made famous by Nobel Prize winning economist Daniel Kahneman and his colleague Amos Tversky. They noted that people make decisions by observing the status quo, then judge change from that point of reference. If a policy change results in a reduction in perceived environmental protection, even if the new level of protection is still greater than it was previously, the policy change is judged against the current state of affairs, not against what was the reality just a short time ago.

Additionally, Kahneman and Tversky found that people feel losses more than gains. Using psychological experiments, they found "losses and disadvantages have greater impact on preferences than gains and advantages."[13] Loss aversion is so universal that one study found even Capuchin lab monkeys feel it and act in a way that is "indistinguishable from most stock-market investors."[14] Advocates of eco-fads may be disappointed when their policies are not enacted, but the threat of losing a policy they have already enacted inspires far greater resentment and is seen as a more significant threat. This is why it is easier to rally political causes around a common enemy than a common aspiration. Even if the current situation is bad, there is a strong fear that things could get worse, and those who benefit from eco-fads will work hard to ensure there is no backsliding.

Add that to the pain of having to admit you made a mistake, and most elected officials will strongly resist repealing a policy they previously supported – even if it turns out to be more about passing fashion than solid results. Ironically, when politicians find their policies are not living up to their promises, the option that becomes most palatable politically is to actually re-double efforts in the same direction. Supporters of these failed policies argue the reason a strategy is not working is not because the policy is ill-conceived, but because we have not dedicated sufficient resources to it. In a democracy, when elected officials are regularly judged by the success or failure of their policies, there is a strong incentive to do everything possible to turn a failure into at least the appearance of a success.

In their book, *The Logic of Political Survival*,[15] Bruce Bueno de Mesquita and his fellow authors study the various strategies adopted by politicians in democracies in their efforts to remain in office. In countries where politicians are selected by the public at large, elected officials survive primarily by delivering benefits to the general public. Those benefits include economic prosperity, environmental health and other amenities that are good for the society. In contrast, leaders in dictatorships provide private benefits to the handful of people who are potential rivals, buying their loyalty by offering wealth and rewards to placate their ambitions. Staying in power requires that established leaders retain the loyalty of those who chose them. In a democracy this means delivering prosperity and succeeding in their political aims. Elected officials who fail to deliver on their promises face eroding support. Rather than admit defeat, then, democratically elected leaders will call for more time and increase their commitment to failed policies, hoping to avoid the politically costly results of eventual failure.

These same incentives apply to politicians when addressing environmental policy. When environmental policies fail to achieve the expected results, elected officials are likely to decide to increase their commitment to the policy rather than cutting their losses and finding an alternate route.

This is exactly what happened in Seattle, after Greg Nickels left the mayor's office. By 2010, he was no longer running City Hall. The legacy of his environmentally trendy policies, however, still dominated the city. Despite the failure of Seattle's efforts to reduce carbon emissions, city council members announced their intention to go even further and make Seattle "carbon neutral." The councilmembers were committing themselves to more aggressive versions of the very policies that had failed to reduce carbon emissions over the previous five years. The council's announcement made it clear that public perception was more important than effective policy.

When the councilmembers announced the ambitious goal, they neglected to spell out the policies that would be necessary to achieve that result. The details would be left for later. The lack of a plan, however, did not prevent the council from sending press releases and holding a town meeting to begin the process of determining how to achieve the goal. More than a year later, the only step that had actually been taken toward developing an approach to achieve this new, more ambitious, goal was a public contest to develop a logo for "carbon neutral Seattle."[16]

The important message to convey was not that the city had failed in its early efforts – it simply had not committed enough resources to the problem. Put simply, the council members doubled down in the face of failure.

To further justify putting more effort behind an existing policy, elected officials and advocates also claim the threat from environmental problems is greater than ever, so ever-more drastic action is needed.

At the city council meeting announcing Seattle's new carbon neutral goal, there were dire warnings that we are already "beginning to see climate refugees," and despite inspirational rhetoric about creating "sustainable prosperity," there were no clear policy ideas offered. The members of the town-hall audience were, however, reassured that if these unnamed policies were enacted, "We'll all be a little prouder on our death beds."[17]

Such rhetoric is designed to reward politicians for their support of environmental policies, even if those policies have not been identified. It lays the foundation for what is to follow. Having built public momentum for creating a carbon neutral city, the Seattle City Council can argue that whatever policies they recommend are designed to achieve that important goal. Promising to achieve a goal without an idea of how to reach it, however, is clearly more about receiving glowing accolades than actually reaching the target. Such proclamations set the expectation of a solution. Having confidently set the goal, elected officials can hardly declare they are unsure how to achieve it. Such an admission would not only deny them the sense of achievement, but would make them look foolish in the eyes of the public, risk the support of groups they are cultivating and defeat the reason for promoting the carbon-reduction goal in the first place.

The shifting predictions about the timeline for climate change follow this same pattern. Highlighting a report by the International Climate Change Task Force in 2005, the BBC reported, "The world may have little more than a decade to avert catastrophic climate change, politicians and scientists say."[18] Just four years later, Professor James McCarthy told the BBC, "Major policy changes are needed in the President's first term of office or the planet will be in 'huge trouble.'"[19] Environmental activist Bill McKibben went even further in 2008, writing that levels of carbon dioxide are already beyond where they should be, saying, "We're already past the line, out of the safe zone."[20] Each of these groups and individuals argue the contradictory claims are based in science, but it is clear that each advocate also has an incentive to increase the apparent threat posed by climate change.

As time passed and governments failed to adopt their favored legislation, advocates' rhetoric became more heated. While the Kyoto Protocol was hailed as an important step, it was not enough, they argued, and they increased the size of the threat to justify adoption of more drastic measures. If Kyoto or other initiatives have failed, they said, it is only because the policies were not aggressive enough. Indeed, for journalist Paul Greenberg, even Bill McKibben's policy proposals are not enough. Reviewing McKibben's new book, Greenberg wrote in The New York Times Book Review that what we need is "some overarching authority, a kind of ecologically minded Lenin."[21] If the danger from climate change is as serious as McKibben says, according to this view, and we have already passed the tipping point, why not take steps as serious as the problem calls for?

As far as protecting the environment is concerned, the allure and tenacity of political eco-fads is almost certainly damaging. Politically, advocates of eco-fads benefit by making it difficult to come to an honest conclusion about the plusses and minuses of various environmental policies. Correcting bad policy becomes more difficult when politicians have incentives not only to prevent their policies from being undone, but they actually benefit from expanding upon measures they may acknowledge are not producing positive results. Eco-fads build their own momentum, yielding political rewards, demonstrating leadership on an issue important to voters. Hoping to retain that positive feeling, advocates make judging these eco-fad-based policies difficult, resisting efforts at accountability and instead substituting subjective justifications for concrete measurements. And even when the passage of time shows the claims are not holding up, the logic of political survival encourages elected officials to add new, trendy policies to those already adopted. Once an eco-fad takes firm root in public policy, it is difficult to go back, or even admit something's wrong.

Elected Officials' Trendy Green Policies

The support of elected officials and other policymakers plays a significant role in the increasing trend toward eco-fads. When officials look for policies that can supply them with an environmentally conscious image, trendy environmentalism is made-to-order. Eco-fads hold out the promise of gaining support from special interest groups and the resulting positive public image. Unlike environmental policies that would achieve slow but incremental progress, eco-fads promise near-term results elected officials can take credit for. Once adopted, elected officials find themselves tied to these trendy environmental policies, lending their voices and marketing efforts to the credibility of these fads, promoting their supposed advantages to the public.

Fads of any type thrive because there is a sense that "everyone is doing it." When eco-fads are adopted, politicians, government agencies and advocacy groups join together to sell the public on the promised benefits of the new policy. At some point, other elected officials and the public come to believe the claims, especially when evidence to the contrary is either hidden or muddled.

The result is that the potential political benefits become an important guiding force in how we choose environmental policies. With limited information, politicians make decisions using the criteria they best understand: what sells with the public. Some politicians are more sincere than others about their desire to follow good policy, but few of them are entirely insensitive to the public's perception about the decisions they make. Given a choice between a policy with benefits that are opaque today and will be tangible only in the future, and one with near-term benefits that are clear and popular, there is little doubt which approach will be chosen by politicians.

It is unreasonable to expect politicians to ignore those pressures. The problem is those pressures play more of a role in setting environmental policies than alternatives that may be more successful. Even when trendy environmentalism proves to be a failure, elected officials stick with what is popular and increase their commitment to their chosen direction.

Eco-fads, environmental policies that are trendy and seductive, provide the political benefits politicians want, and they can be pointed to as evidence that politicians care about the environment. As we will see later, this is a powerful combination that has served to move much of our environmental decision making into the destructive realm of the eco-fad.

Chapter 5

The Profitable Business of Eco-Fads

These days, there is hardly a business that doesn't hope "going green" will add to its bottom line. From landscaping firms, to car makers and clothing manufacturers, companies hope to reach their customers through green appeals, offering their products with an environmental ethic to boot. The increase in the number of companies making green claims for their products has been dramatic. One study found "73 percent more 'green' products on the market [in 2010] than in 2009."[1] You don't have to look far for examples.

- Audi purchased airtime during the 2010 Super Bowl to promote its "clean diesel" cars. The ad, with the song "Green Police" (a modified version of the Cheap Trick song "Dream Police"), showed drivers being stopped and arrested for environmental crimes. The owner of an Audi, however, was cheerfully waved through a "green police" checkpoint.

- Nissan soon countered with an ad for its new Leaf, a plug-in electric car. After trekking thousands of miles through all sorts of weather and landscapes, a polar bear finishes his journey by gratefully hugging the owner of the zero-emissions car. The ad ends with the tagline "Innovation for the planet. Innovation for all."

- The website for Eco Fabulous offers "stylish, sustainable living"[2] for those who want to look good while saving the planet. In most cases, fashion knockoffs attempt to look like the real thing while hiding the label. In the case of green fashion, the green label is the selling point. The whole purpose of enviro-fashion is to be environmentally flamboyant.

- Whole Foods built its business model on offering organic and other green products. The founder of Whole Foods, John Mackey, writes in his book, *Be the Solution*, that "the best way to maximize profits over the long term is not to make them the primary goal of the business,"[3] so he focused on an environmental ethic. What started out in 1978 as a single store in Austin, Texas, run by him and his girlfriend as "a way for us both to engage in a right livelihood,"[4] became a store with sales of more than $5.6 billion in 2006.

All these businesses, and many more, recognize that consumers often have discretionary income they can use to reward companies who offer the products they want in a way that is consistent with consumers' beliefs. Many shoppers are willing to pay a little more for a tomato that was grown without pesticides. If you doubt this, count the cars in a Whole Foods parking lot. Green is good marketing.

Green is also good economics. Companies that find ways to use fewer resources and less energy, and cut down their impact on the environment, also find they are spending less on materials and putting more profit in their pocket. They might also find they can lower their prices and stay competitive, earning a larger market share. Since 1980, American companies have found a way to produce goods using about half the energy they used thirty years ago. To an accountant, cutting production costs is just smart business. To those in the marketing departments of today's businesses, that is a selling point – less energy means a lower impact on the environment.

Seeing the opportunity to profit from the environmental motives of consumers, and observing the trends in environmental politics, General Electric (GE) made its ecomagination brand a centerpiece of its future growth. In 2009, when *Newsweek* magazine ranked the top 500 "greenest big companies in America," it awarded GE its eighty-second spot, noting how significantly the company was shifting its business model. They noted the change:

> "Old image: a prototypical dirty industrial giant known for dumping toxic chemicals in the Hudson and other rivers. Now known instead for wind turbines, compact fluorescents, low emission locomotives, and high-efficiency appliances. Still designs nuclear plants and supplies technology to coal plants but is tracking towards a future of clean energy."[5]

Although it still had work to do to move up the list, the area in which GE fared best was its reputation, where it ranked second overall. With a strong marketing push to burnish its image as a new, green company, the high ranking should not come as a surprise. A key goal of creating the ecomagination brand was to identify GE in the minds of consumers as a leader in the green economy.

They backed that push up with heavy media exposure, including their "Green is Universal" campaign, run by NBC Universal, in which GE owns a 49 percent share. NBC and other Universal channels heavily promote Earth Week, with each channel taking steps to reduce its carbon footprint and running shows on how to be green. GE's 2009 ecomagination Annual Report bragged, "In November 2009, NBC Universal's 'Make Green Count' campaign encouraged audiences to make one small 'green' change to their daily lives — from turning the lights off to walking to work."[6] Even Jerry Springer got in on the action.[b]

The brand is also intended to set a corporate tone and encourage innovation. GE backed this up with significant investments in energy-efficient products. When it launched the ecomagination effort in 2005, GE pledged it would invest $5 billion in energy-efficiency research. This included investments in improving its line of airplane engines, locomotives and other products, as well as looking to future demand, like more powerful batteries and electric car charging stations.[7]

GE is very clear about its motive. CEO Jeffrey Immelt told an audience in Washington, D.C., when launching ecomagination that "things that are good for the environment are also good for business."[8] That same year Immelt was more blunt in a speech to the George Washington School of Business, telling the audience, "We're launching ecomagination not because it's trendy or moral but because it will accelerate our growth and make us more competitive."[9] Years later, the move certainly has been good for GE. In its 2009 ecomagination report, GE reported that "in the first 5 years, we invested $5 billion in clean tech R&D, and we generated $70 billion in ecomagination revenues."[10]

Indeed, GE's ecomagination line has demonstrated so much promise, and profit, that GE does not want to leave future growth to the whims of the market. It has found a new partner to help ensure there will be a continuing market for their clean energy products – the federal government.

The market can be tough and unforgiving if the products you produce do not meet the needs of the public or competitors are able to out-innovate you. For some companies, it is cheaper to hire lobbyists than scientists. GE understands this. In the introductory letter to the 2008 GE Annual Report, Immelt wrote

---

[b]   I think the guests beat each other with renewable cork furniture that week.

"The interaction between government and business will change forever. In a reset economy, the government will be a regulator; and also an industry policy champion, a financier, and a key partner."[11] Using government power to secure market share, funding and other preferences was now a central part of GE's business strategy. While they accelerated the strategy in 2009, the trend was not new.

Recognizing that new energy regulations would increase demand for ecomagination products, GE has been aggressive in recent years about lobbying in favor of tighter government restrictions that increase the price of energy. Testifying before Congress in 2008, "GE vice chairman John Rice argued that market pricing for carbon emissions, along with government tax credits, will encourage new investments in emerging low-carbon technologies." Pushing up the price of traditional, carbon-emitting energy sources would make GE's energy-efficient products fare better in a cost-benefit analysis, offering savings that cannot be realized under current prices. Throw in a few tax credits, and buying GE's products becomes a no-brainer for potential customers.

Lobbying government in support of costly energy regulation is only the start. GE is an active participant in the U.S. Climate Action Partnership, whose stated purpose is to "call on the federal government to quickly enact strong national legislation to require significant reductions of greenhouse gas emissions."[12] To understand the ultimate goal of the partnership, one need only recall the words of the great economist Adam Smith in 1776, when he wrote in *The Wealth of Nations*, "People of the same trade seldom meet together, even for merriment and diversion, but the conversation ends in a conspiracy against the public, or in some contrivance to raise prices."[13] Higher prices paid by consumers end up in the pockets of those who set the rules.

GE's activities cover a whole range of climate-related legislation, all designed to improve the marketability of their goods. The *Washington Examiner* noted, "Reviewing their lobbying filings, you might think you were looking at Al Gore's agenda. GE's specific lobbying issues included the 'Climate Stewardship Act,' 'Electric Utility Cap and Trade Act,' 'Global Warming Reduction Act,' 'Federal Government Greenhouse Gas Registry Act,' 'Low Carbon Economy Act,' and 'Lieberman-Warner Climate Security Act.'"[14] Each of these pieces of legislation is either a baby step or daddy step toward increasing the cost of energy sources that emit carbon.

Skewing the rules of the game is profitable. With politicians who want to look green as willing partners, GE looks to make government "a key partner" in its business plan, "not because it's trendy," but because it is profitable.

General Electric's business strategy shows both the good and bad of green-oriented business, and the promise and pitfalls of making protecting the environment part of the business strategy.

Businesses have always found ways to use fewer resources, cutting energy costs, using fewer minerals, recycling waste and doing more with less. In the past this was simply called "economizing," today it is called "environmental stewardship." If it reduces our impact on the environment, helping us live more sustainably, then all the better. The push to reduce costs is part of business and goes hand in hand with environmental consciousness. Companies recognize this and they regularly publicize their efforts to reduce resource use, taking advantage of the opportunity to market to consumers willing to spend more to make the planet a little better off.

And good for them. The more powerful the appeal of green, the more companies will cater to those customers. Of course, some companies will overhype their environmental contributions, but such is the case with all products.

The push to go green can turn ugly, however, when companies attempt to use eco-fads to lobby for changes in public policy. The turn to politics tends to shut down the dynamic process of market competition and innovation that can be good for the environment, in favor of government rules that mainly skew the market to the companies' advantage.

When it comes to businesses, eco-fads can be a mixed bag. As with everything else, when it comes to green products and the green government policies promoted by businesses, our motto should be caveat emptor – let the buyer (and taxpayer) beware.

Catering to Green Customers

Often in the debate over how best to protect the environment, America's wealth is portrayed as a bad thing. Americans use, we are told, a disproportionate share of the earth's resources. We consume too much oil, too many trees, too many minerals, too many fish from the sea, and so on. Some of these concerns are real (some wild fish populations are in trouble), while others are exaggerated or simply not true (the amount of forestland in the United States is actually expanding and trees are renewable, while alternative construction materials are not renewable).

There is, however, an environmental benefit to our growing prosperity. It is no accident that air quality in American cities is significantly better than that of poorer countries. We have decided to spend a portion of our wealth on reducing air pollutants, and our air quality today is about the highest it has been in over a century, despite our consuming many more resources. This remarkable environmental progress has been achieved not in spite of our wealth, but because of it.

The same is true of our individual purchasing choices. The more income we have beyond the amount necessary to provide the basics, the more likely we are to spend it on environmental amenities. Who would pay extra for organic fruit during the scarcity of the Great Depression? With food so abundant today, in a richer economy we can afford to have a portion of farming cater to those willing to pay a bit more – whether they are worried about pesticides on their food or want to prevent soil erosion for the good of future generations.

The race for those extra dollars is a powerful market incentive, and there is perhaps no better example of how that race can motivate green business than the dynamic competition reflected in the design of ordinary plastic bottles.

In recent years, plastic bottles have become both ubiquitous and controversial. As people increasingly purchase bottled water as an alternative to soft drinks, there is growing concern about the number of plastic bottles being sent to landfills. Since the 1970s, trash and recycling have been environmental touchstones, and because many plastic bottles do not biodegrade, they are an increasingly frequent target of those with concerns about resource use. Plastic bottles are also made using petroleum products, adding to concerns about the supply and source of our oil.

Several companies see a business opportunity in attempting to address these concerns.

Perhaps most aggressive is water filter company Brita. A television commercial for Brita shows people in their house surrounded by empty water bottles, a swimming pool filled with the bottles, a woman exercising as empty bottles cover the floor, and as people open closets, empty water bottles come pouring out. The end of the commercial asks, in subtle white lettering superimposed over the images, "Ever thought about how many plastic bottles Canadians bought last year?" The final screen says simply, "The Earth needs Brita." The ad says buy a Brita water filter and get clean, filtered water directly from your tap, rather than destroying the planet by wastefully buying so many plastic bottles.

In case the message is too subtle, Brita has taken the next step, joining with an environmental group and promoting reduced use of plastic bottles. As the funding partner for "Filter for Good," Brita and the Surfrider Foundation work "to help ensure that our nation's waterways stay clean and healthy for generations to come."[15] On the group's website you can even get a $5 Brita coupon by pledging to reduce your bottled water waste. The message is: Why spend money on bottled water, especially since those bottles are likely to end up in landfills rather than recycling bins? Buy a Brita water filter and you can save money and the planet.

Perhaps, however, taste is not the reason people choose bottled water over tap water. A taste test run by the comedy team of Penn and Teller indicates people's ability to tell the difference between bottled water and tap water is pretty limited.[16]

If people buy bottled water for the convenience instead of taste, a Brita filter is not a perfect solution. People don't always remember to fill their water bottle before they leave the house. Since convenience is a part of the reason people buy bottled water, companies that sell bottled water are working to soothe your guilty environmental conscience so that you can more comfortably buy their product.

Arrowhead, a bottled water brand owned by Nestle, has made reducing the environmental impact of its water bottles a central selling point. The company created what it calls an "eco-shape" bottle. Nestle says "sometimes making a difference isn't just about what we put into the bottle. Sometimes, it is what we take out."[17] The Arrowhead eco-shape bottle features a slender bottle with a concave indentation around the middle that makes it "easy to carry." The indentation, however, does more than provide a place to hold the bottle. It is an integral part of how Arrowhead reduced the amount of plastic used to make the bottle. Working like an arch in an aqueduct, the water pressure on the inside of the bottle presses out on the indentation, causing the arch to strengthen the entire length of the bottle. This is important, since the bottles need to be strong enough for shipping, and bottles that are too flimsy cannot be piled on top of each other in a delivery truck. In addition, ridges at the base of the bottle add to the strength, as *Wired* magazine reported, "the same way that a fold in a piece of paper allows it to stand up on its own."[18]

Arrowhead also made the lid smaller, using less plastic there as well.

Perhaps you still aren't satisfied. After all, using fewer petroleum products is still using some petroleum, decreasing the supply of worldwide energy and putting carbon emissions in the atmosphere in the process. In that case grab a bottle, or rather PlantBottle, of Daisani water.

Coca-Cola, the owner of Daisani water, launched their new PlantBottle at the 2010 Winter Olympics in Vancouver, British Columbia, using their sponsorship of the event to highlight their new product. Marketing the event as "the greenest games ever," members of the Vancouver Olympic Committee took great strides to show off their environmental consciousness, and Coke's new bottle fit well with their chosen theme.

The new bottle, while still largely made of the same polyethylene terephthalate (PET) as ordinary plastic bottles, uses a sugar-cane based product for 30 percent of its material. The green cap on the top of the bottle signals the consumer that the bottle is created, in part, by using a renewable plant resource rather than oil.

The PlantBottle provides a couple benefits for Coke. First, it helps the soft-drink giant keep pace in the competition for green consumers. Coke executives have a product they can market to those who drink bottled water but who want to minimize their impact on the environment while doing so. This is a big reason they used the Olympics to launch the bottle – a highly visible event with a strong environmental theme.

Second, the plant-based design helps diversify their sources of material for their bottles. Although the bottle costs more to produce initially, Coke hopes to cut those costs as time goes on. It also helps inoculate them against fluctuating oil prices. If traditional sources of polyethylene increase in cost, Coke has another alternative. Coke also believes it has a way to supply the remaining 70 percent of the bottle with renewable materials. Their hope is to eventually develop a bottle made of 100 percent renewable materials.

To go along with the renewable product, Coke stepped up its effort to promote recycling. They intentionally made the PlantBottle similar to current PET bottles to take advantage of the recycling stream that already exists. Of course, no recycling system captures 100 percent of the bottles produced, so some in the environmental community are not convinced by Coke's efforts.

When it comes to plastic bottles, the race to reach environmental consumers has been ferocious, even if no single product satisfies everyone. For consumers who want to reduce the amount of plastic used in water bottles, they can choose Arrowhead's eco-shape bottle. Others, worried about the use of oil resources they believe are disappearing, can turn to Daisani and the PlantBottle. Those looking to get rid of plastic bottles altogether can buy a Brita water filter, filling their own reusable container with purified water. Each choice satisfies a particular environmental ethic, and we can be certain none of these ideas are the last word in the ongoing effort to create bottles that gain a sales advantage in the competition for consumers' discretionary, green income.

Additionally, Nestle and Coke found a way to improve company economics. In the case of Arrowhead, shaving small amounts of plastic from each bottle adds up over the millions of bottles they produce, leading to significant cost savings and allowing them to maintain competitive prices. Although the PlantBottle increases costs for the time being, Coke hopes to bring those costs down with an improved supply chain and by using materials less prone to the fluctuations of petroleum prices. In the end, the goal of each company is to improve its own market position and profitability.

Companies that produce plastic bottles are not the only ones who see the market potential of going green. Coffee companies have also found a way to use the green qualities of their products, like "shade grown" coffee, to earn higher profits per cup of coffee.

Coffee consumers looking for an environmentally friendly way to enjoy their java can purchase "shade-grown" coffee that claims to be more sensitive to the environment because it does not require cutting down trees that serve as habitat for birds. Growing coffee under these trees reduces crop yield, driving up prices, but it also benefits the environment. Less deforestation, more birds, same delicious coffee. Producing less coffee per acre means higher prices, but it also provides environmental benefits some consumers are willing to pay for.

A number of coffee companies offer shade-grown coffee. Starbucks, for instance, charges $11.95 for a pound of their "Organic Shade Grown Mexico" blend. The growers who sell it to Starbucks "are protecting the forest's birds and biodiversity through the use of organic and traditional shade-growing agricultural methods."[19] By way of contrast, Starbucks Latin American House Blend will set you back $9.95 a pound, about 17 percent less. You pay a little more for the organic shade grown coffee, but many Starbucks customers are willing to do so.

Although Starbucks may have an environmental ethic, there is another reason it and other coffee companies offer shade-grown coffee at a premium: price sensitivity. Imagine ordering a morning cup of coffee and, when you ask the price, hearing the barista say, "What's it worth to you?" Most of us would be a bit put off. The reality is, though, that some coffee drinkers would be willing to pay one dollar, while others, either because they are rich or extremely groggy, would be willing to pay three dollars. The first group is very sensitive to changes in the price of a cup, the second group much less so. The challenge for coffee companies is to tell the difference between the two, ensuring they don't leave potential profits on the table.

British economist Tim Harford has an idea about how coffee companies find out who is willing to pay more. Harford argues that very little of the higher price consumers pay to get shade-grown coffee, or other products like "fair-trade" coffee, actually goes to covering the additional costs of that product. In examining the pricing of a cup of fair-trade coffee, Harford found that "The Fair Trade premium [the extra amount we pay for Fair Trade coffee], so important to a struggling grower in Kenya or Ecuador, is typically less than a penny when applied to such a small quantity of coffee."[20] When you pay more than this small, additional cost for the cup, the additional amount goes to the bottom line of the coffee company, and some of it likely ends up as additional profit.

Some people may bristle at the notion that some of the money they are spending ends up as profit for the coffee company instead of going to the grower. But why? You get the coffee you want and help the planet. Growers who grow shade-grown coffee or fair-trade coffee get to stay in business, or even expand. The coffee company has an economic incentive to continue to offer a product that consumers demand. It seems odd that consumers would complain that Starbucks or any other coffee company would receive some benefit. After all, consumers receive a benefit, and it is not like they are making a great sacrifice – they are simply buying a cup of coffee.

If other coffee companies see those who sell shade-grown coffee prospering, it is likely that they will find a way to offer customers the same option or, as we saw in the case of the competition over plastic bottles, new coffee products that expand and improve on those environmental benefits. As people who care about the environment, that is something we should celebrate.

There are circumstances where adding an environmentally friendly element to a product is simply the cost of doing business. For companies selling canned tuna since 1990, having a "dolphin-safe" label may not add money to their pocket – it allows them simply to stay in business.

Public awareness of the impact of tuna fishing on dolphins began to grow in the late 1980s, especially with the release of videos taken secretly on tuna boats showing the high number of dolphins being killed as bycatch. Companies started offering dolphin-safe tuna at a higher price, and fishermen began receiving a price premium of $400 per ton.[21] Soon, however, it became clear that consumers were going to demand dolphin-safe tuna and would not buy any other kind. The major producers of canned tuna agreed to sell only tuna that met the dolphin-safe standard. They publicly pledged to "sell only tuna caught without the use of purse seine nets"[22] that also catch dolphins swimming nearby.

A United States Department of Agriculture (USDA) report in 2000 noted that "the three largest canned tuna producers had an 84-percent share of the market. Action on their part dictated the outcome for the whole market."[23] Dolphin-safe tuna was the price producers had to pay simply to sell in the market. In response to consumers, dolphin-safe is now the industry standard.

Subsequently there have been debates about the various dolphin-safe labels and whether they live up to their promises. The USDA, however, estimates that in the decade following the labeling, the number of dolphin deaths associated with tuna fisheries annually fell from 100,000 to about 5,000, a twenty-fold reduction.[24] The economics of tuna in a dolphin-safe world played an important role in making that happen.

The Products Are Not Always Greener on the Other Side

Whether seeking to expand market share by appealing to consumers with an environmental conscience or simply trying to cut costs by reducing the amount of energy and resources they use, businesses can play a positive role in creating environmental sustainability. Business owners understand this, and the push to use environmental appeals is more robust than ever. While there are many benefits of this new awareness, there are also pitfalls.

As consumers we want to believe we make decisions about the products we buy based on a clear-eyed assessment, but that is not always the case. Eco-fads make it more difficult to sort out the benefits from the trendiness involved in these appeals. Increasingly, business appeals to consumers are not based on the bottom-line environmental impact, but on something else: guilt.

Fashion is a social commodity. Few people wear tuxedos or ball gowns around the house. The value of environmental fads is the same – their real value comes when displayed in public. That leaves consumers open to peer pressure and guilt to conform to common opinion. In his book, *Fostering Sustainable Behavior*, psychologist Doug McKenzie-Mohr discusses how to encourage people to behave in a way that is more environmentally friendly. In an interview in The Wall Street Journal, he rejects the notion that "if we simply provide people with information, they will make changes in their lives," adding, "we know pretty conclusively that's not true."[25] Instead, he and others advocate using peer pressure. The Journal notes that "researchers at Michigan State University found that paying Chinese farmers to adopt environmentally friendly techniques didn't work as well as telling them that their neighbors were already farming that way."[26]

Effective though it may be, the peer pressure approach has real problems. Pressing people to act a particular way treats them as pawns, simply to be steered in one direction or another to achieve an end desired and dictated by others. The question is not whether something is good for people (that has already been decided), but how to make them do it. Another term for peer pressure is "bullying," and when you put the power of business or government behind an approved message, there is a real danger the result is not for the benefit of the individual, or even for the environment, but for those applying the pressure.

In the case of businesses, this can lead executives to emphasize environmental guilt over environmental benefits. Brita's commercials don't lay out the financial benefit of using its product. Brita ads focus strictly on making those who choose to use plastic bottles feel as if they are destroying the planet. Brita certainly benefits from this, but the planet may not. In fact, a recent study found that 95 percent of environmental claims about products fell short in one way or another.[27] As some advocates in the environmental community encourage the use of guilt and peer pressure to change behavior, others warn that such approaches can mask bad business practices.

In the end, however, consumers are all too familiar with the peer-pressure approach to marketing. Guilt is used to sell more than just green products. Watch any commercial targeted at moms and there will be a subtle, or not-so-subtle, message that good moms choose this product over others because they are thinking of their children.

For all of the potential pitfalls, the push by businesses to sell environmental amenities that boost their bottom line is likely to be a net benefit to the environment. "Whiter and brighter" has been replaced with "greener and cleaner." Even if a low-cost eco-shape bottle still uses plastic, it is a clear step forward. Even if some dolphins are still killed by tuna fleets, the number of such deaths has fallen dramatically. Even if some organic foods are grown by agribusinesses (in part because demand has grown), those fruits or vegetables are likely to have fewer pesticides or offer other benefits consumers want.

On the other side, just as some complain that these products do not do enough, some people complain that companies' green products cater to and foster irrational environmental concerns. Fear of tiny amounts of pesticides is often unreasonable, and the benefit to the environment of buying organic products can be small or nonexistent. The impact of plastic bottles on the environment, in terms of resource depletion or filling up landfills, is pretty small. Catering to irrational fears by encouraging belief in false environmental fads should certainly be exposed for what it is.

Eco-fads are the counterpart of what some environmental activists call "greenwashing" – exaggerating or falsifying the environmental benefits of a product. Eco-fads seek to exaggerate the danger of an underlying environmental concern, offering products or policies that reduce this inflated threat to the planet. That combination makes it hard for consumers to make accurate judgments. Not only do they have to determine if the product is environmentally friendly, they have to figure out if the associated environmental threat is even real or is simply the result of the latest eco-fad.

The problem for consumers and taxpayers becomes even more difficult when government and business owners team up to advertise and hype environmental concerns that may not be significant, but offer real political benefits to politicians and big profits to favored businesses.

Rigging the Rules of "Green" Business

Competing in the free market is tough. It is hard enough to get people to find and buy your product. Just when you have it right, competitors find a better way to do it, cutting their prices and giving them a market advantage. This is the process that economist Joseph Schumpeter called "creative destruction" – new innovation and creativity builds and improves on what came before, making existing products seem like relics. While market innovation has led to dramatic improvements in energy efficiency, and reduction in the use of resources has improved the well-being of people across the globe, some businesses would rather join with government to rig the rules, making them immune to competitive pressures.

This is nothing new. More than 150 years ago, Alexis de Tocqueville wrote in *Democracy in America* about the desire of businesses to work with government to rig the game to the detriment of consumers. He noted that those engaged in a "new enterprise" generally believe that "as a general principle the public authority ought not to interfere in private concerns but by an exception to that rule each of them craves for its assistance in the particular concern on which he is engaged and seeks to draw upon the influence of the government for his own benefit though he would restrict it on all other occasions."[28] Each business, believing its unique circumstances require the intervention of politicians and government, seeks rules that favor it over its market opponents or that artificially increase demand for its products by requiring people to buy them.

Promoting environmental fads is a powerful way for politicians to reap the rewards of looking green and a profitable way for businesses to create and corner the market for products they claim are needed to save the planet.

And they are not shy about it.

The vice president of one Seattle-area construction company told an audience at a public meeting unveiling Washington's new "green business" strategy that his products offered "environmental salvation."[29]

In the 1990s, Enron made adoption of the Kyoto Protocol's cap-and-trade system to reduce carbon emissions a key part of its business strategy. Chris Horner, who worked in Enron's Washington, D.C., office at the time, recalls one top advisor to Enron chief Kenneth Lay writing "if implemented, this agreement will do more to promote Enron's business than will almost any other regulatory initiative outside of restructuring of the energy and natural gas industries in Europe and the United States," going on to exclaim that the Kyoto Protocol "is exactly what I have been lobbying for."[30] Enron's business was selling energy, and in a world where energy is increasingly constrained it saw huge profit potential in creating a large and complex system – a system it could dominate.

Energy companies like Enron are not the only ones seeking to cash in on climate legislation. Wall Street also sees big profits.

In the aftermath of the 2008 mortgage crisis and the failure of a number of Wall Street firms, New York's junior U.S. Senator Kirsten Gillibrand got to work finding ways to reinvigorate New York's financial district. She saw the passage of a complex, cap-and-trade system of energy credits and financial instruments as the perfect opportunity.

Writing in The Wall Street Journal, Gillibrand described the complexity of the system not as a drawback, but as an opportunity from which Wall Street could profit. At a time when securitized assets and creative derivatives were being fingered for their part in creating a nationwide housing bubble, she saw an opportunity to use those same instruments in the energy market. In a piece entitled "Cap and Trade Could Be a Boon to New York," she argued that it would require "innovative specialized contracts" due to the complexity of the required energy-trading system. Addressing the complicated accounting of carbon-reduction programs and systems to assess carbon emissions, she argued:

> "We must allow the market to provide the ability to customize products. These customized contracts are essential for firms to adapt to the new regulations, hedge risk, and raise capital. New York's financial industry is already the global leader for existing customized commodity products and would be exceptionally well

positioned to provide the legal and financial expertise necessary for these new products."[31]

The more complex the system, the bigger share of the pie that can be claimed by experts, consultants and lawyers who would be needed to manage the government-imposed system. Even if we set aside comparisons to the hubris of the experts at Enron who believed they could control the energy market without problems, or the mortgage bankers who ignored warning signs in favor of faith in their own expertise, this attitude should raise red flags. Senator Gillibrand argues that she is supporting cap-and-trade not because it would reduce carbon emissions, but because it would funnel money to a politically favored constituency.

None of this push for new regulation creates wealth or even helps achieve the desired environmental goal. Instead it creates complex regulations that financial companies can take advantage of, offering lucrative business opportunities for accountants, lawyers and financial experts to manipulate the system to their advantage. These new costs are paid, ultimately, by customers who use energy to heat their homes or to produce goods. As we have seen with Europe's struggling cap-and-trade system, the proliferation of creative accounting undercuts the goal of emissions reduction itself, encouraging the exploitation of loopholes that allow companies to violate emission targets.

Such regulatory systems do, however, benefit companies and politicians willing to play the game. Politicians enjoy the financial campaign support of Wall Street and the boost to their public image as an environmental crusader. Businesses take advantage of government regulations that reward those who are well connected or who have particular expertise, using the rules to steer business their way at the expense of competitors who can't afford to pay lobbyists and lawyers.

The irony is that critics of cap-and-trade or similar regulatory systems are often accused of being bought off by "big oil" or "big coal." Even when critics have no connection to industry, such accusations are assumed to be true because industry groups have an obvious interest in protecting a system that puts profit in their pocket. We rarely, however, hear the opposite, but equally legitimate, view that companies like GE or Wall Street bankers have an interest in turning the regulatory system to their own benefit. Indeed, environmental groups often trot out companies supportive of new environmental regulations, implying "even these businesses know this is the right thing to do," while ignoring their obvious financial interest in securing passage of rules that will hurt competitors.

In 2010, the Seattle environmental group Climate Solutions put together a group of businesses in the Northwest calling for policies to cut carbon emissions. At the inaugural press conference, Climate Solutions representatives highlighted the many businesses that supported a new cap-and-trade system, citing "a report from the American Businesses for Clean Energy that said more than 6,000 businesses with 2.5 million U.S. workers support energy and climate legislation."[32] Conveniently omitted was how those companies would financially benefit from cap-and-trade rules. Partnering with an environmental group like Climate Solutions is a good way for some businesses to cloak their economic motives in the guise of environmental consciousness.

Climate Solutions has been so effective at finding business owners willing to argue that new energy restrictions will help the economy, the group was named one of the top green "businesses" in Washington in 2009. In adding the nonprofit group to their list, *Seattle Business* magazine noted, "Old-school market capitalists may scoff at the idea of a 'not-for-profit' organization having power over the local economy, but some of these groups have had a major impact on state and regional policy in recent years."[33] Businesses, however, are not scoffing, and they recognize the profit potential of using environmental groups as a lever to move government regulations in their direction.

Climate policies are not the only kind of environmental regulation companies, environmental activists and politicians use to rig the rules for their mutual benefit.

- Across the country, architects push for "green" building standards that add to the cost of designing and engineering public buildings, resulting in higher fees for themselves.

- Farmers and biofuel manufacturers advocate for farm and export subsidies, trade barriers and even requirements that ethanol be mixed with regular fuel to increase demand for their product, while receiving money from taxpayers to help them stay in business.

- Government rules regarding organic fruit and vegetables add significant paperwork and oversight costs, making it hard for small farmers to earn the organic label, even if their farming practices meet the standard. Heather Rogers writes in her book, *Green Gone Wrong*, that small farmers like Morse Pitts "are also critical of the process of earning USDA certification because it's costly and time-consuming. They must keep detailed records on the planting and tending of each individual crop ... something that's clearly inappropriate for a farmer such as Pitts, but highly doable for a large-scale operation."[34]

Even when it is obvious that political games are not in the interest of consumers or the environment, some still advocate more of the same. Ironically, Heather Rogers goes on to call for more, not less, regulation on organic foods, which shows how seductive environmental regulation can be, even by those who should understand its obvious flaws.

From global climate policy to the organic tomato, businesses look to politicians to impose rules that protect them from competition, rigging the rules to ensure innovative, small companies are locked out of the market, while big companies with effective lobbyists receive government favoritism. As de Tocqueville's comment demonstrates, businesses have always looked for ways to rig the system. Business interests often use eco-fads as cover for political favoritism, and this is only the most recent way, but one that is growing rapidly, that politics impacts energy, financial, farming, construction, transportation and many other aspects of our economy and our lives.

The Good and Bad of Business Eco-Fads

Among all the villains targeted by traditional environmentalists, businesses have no equal. Ironically, however, it is when those environmental groups team up with businesses that may actually present the most significant threat to sound environmental policy and behavior.

Businesses are quick to recognize the profit opportunities that eco-fads present, jumping on the bandwagon to offer products that suit the demands of environmentally conscious consumers with money to spend. Businesses lend their voice to efforts to emphasize environmental threats that play to the strengths of their product line, even as they work to discredit concerns about potential harm to the environment caused by other parts of their operations.

When politicians, environmental activists and businesses join forces, the result seldom works in the best interests of the average citizen, or the planet.

Truth be told, the power consumers have over businesses has yielded a range of environmental products that have made a real positive difference for our environment. Dolphins are safer and coffee is grown with less impact, thanks to consumers who demand better products and have income to put behind those desires. Companies are constantly finding ways to economize on their use of resources and are quick to tout each new innovation as a step forward in global sustainability.

When it comes to business, eco-fads are a double-edged sword. Even as environmental trends put pressure on businesses to find ways to do more with less, they offer savvy businesses an opportunity to rig the rules of the game. It can be a dangerous game, and if we are not careful, they will do more harm than good.

Chapter 6

The Media and Eco-Fads

For sixteen years, John Charles ran Oregon's leading environmental advocacy organization, the Oregon Environmental Council. As a native of Pittsburgh whose parents grew up at the height of the steel era, he recalls the air pollution that left a dark layer of soot on many of the buildings in the city. What he saw moved him to become environmentally active. After graduating from the University of Pittsburgh, he began working for Environmental Defense Fund in New York, then to Oregon where he helped earn the state its strong "green" reputation.

In time, however, he became increasingly disillusioned. He grew concerned that many environmentalists he worked with cared only about promoting a particular leftist political ideology, even if it was ineffective or likely to damage the environment, albeit unintentionally. On a range of issues, he saw the leadership of the organization choose an ideologically comfortable and environmentally trendy policy, rejecting market-based alternatives that were more likely to promote real sustainability.

Ultimately he left the movement, ending up running a think tank on the other side of the aisle. Today he runs Portland's Cascade Policy Institute, a free-market-oriented policy center. He has not lost his attachment to the environment – he laughs as he admits he still is an avid recycler although he is now more skeptical of its benefits. He feels the traditional approaches to environmentalism do not live up to their promise. And he thinks news reporters share a big part of the blame for reflexively promoting eco-fads and downplaying proven policies that are more environmentally sustainable and effective.

With experience on both sides of many environmental issues, Charles has seen firsthand how reporters favorably treat members of the traditional environmental community and express skepticism about people outside the movement. In 2003 and 2004, Charles attended the annual Society of Environmental Journalists (SEJ) conference in New Orleans. At the time he was particularly frustrated by the failure of environmental reporters, especially at The (Portland) Oregonian, to cover the findings of Bjørn Lomborg in his book, *The Skeptical Environmentalist.* Using data from the United Nations, Lomborg found that the litany of environmental concerns so often repeated in the media were flawed and exaggerated. Although The Oregonian gave repeated positive coverage to environmentalists proclaiming impending planetary doom, including the repeated (and incorrect) world-ending projections of Paul Ehrlich, no coverage was given to the book that had caused such a stir among scientists studying the true state of the environment.

Heading to the SEJ conference, Charles anticipated what he might find – environmental reporters who, while claiming to be above bias, openly express some very biased ideas about their job. He was not surprised by what he found.

He chronicled his experience in the Oregon political journal "BrainstormNW." Charles noted that one member of the SEJ, attending the conference for the first time, expressed surprise at "how many attendees wore their politics on their sleeves," saying, "These people aren't being objective; they seem like advocates, not journalists."[1] Charles outlined a number of examples of how the environmental journalists, comfortable in what they felt was a friendly environment, expressed views that were consistently slanted in favor of the traditional environmental movement. From the framing of the discussion by the moderators, ("The car will always be the same space-hogging, congestion-causing offender it's always been, and its bulk will cause us to build cities around it to the detriment of human-sized living."[2]) to the standing ovation given to the fire and brimstone message of Robert Kennedy Jr. (Polluters "aren't even making a self-sacrifice like suicide bombers are; they're just doing it for the money."[3]). Even Kennedy, however, recognized the political tone of the environmental journalists in the room, noting, "I think I'm as mainstream as it gets; I'm probably more to the right than many people in this room."[4]

There were some reporters, however, who were disturbed by the biased tone of their colleagues. The dean of environmental reporters, Seth Borenstein, wrote later that the standing ovation given to Kennedy disturbed him, noting "I wanted to sink deep into the padded seats in the auditorium." He complained that "journalists were giving a rousing standing ovation – complete with war whoops" to an obviously partisan speaker. Another journalist observed that one of the panels at the SEJ sounded like "a planning session for the DNC [Democratic National Committee] on Bush's vulnerabilities," adding, "It hardly seemed like you guys were presenting objectivity."[5]

Add to this bias the desire for eye-catching stories, and the result is that sexy and dramatic narratives squeeze out the coverage that is informative but unexciting. This combination, Charles laments, "undoubtedly explains some of the codependency that many journalists have with alarmist advocacy groups." And environmental groups know this.

In 2006, Greenpeace attacked the Bush administration's support for nuclear power and mistakenly rushed out a press release that contained this condemnation: "In the twenty years since the Chernobyl tragedy, the world's worst nuclear accident, there have been nearly [FILL IN ALARMIST AND ARMAGEDDONIST FACTOID HERE]."[6] Although they later claimed the release was a joke, Greenpeace clearly knew its audience.

After two decades working with environmental reporters, Charles knew what to look for at the conference. His personal experience allowed him to recognize the bias, realize what was being left out, and see the questions that weren't asked and the reporters' opinions masked as facts. It is much more difficult for the rest of us. For the general public with lives to lead, looking for reliable information about positive environmental choices and policies is made more difficult by the need to sort through environmental reporting, trying to sort out the sensible from the sensational.

As a result, the media is a powerful force in the promotion of eco-fads. Reporters choose stories that emphasize a particular political angle or simply emphasize trendy stories in an effort to catch readers' attention or ride the wave of popular culture. The growing diversity of information sources may exacerbate this trend, and encourage each small media outlet to become ever-more sensational in an effort to gain a larger audience. With the fragmentation of media readership, the self-imposed restrictions on expressing opinion are loosening.

For the past two decades, I have worked with news reporters on a range of political issues in many different media. There are some truly excellent professional journalists, and too often people reject news stories they consider unfavorable simply by assuming the reporter or newspaper is biased. Coverage of environmental stories can be useful, and there is often a grain of truth even in stories where the slant of the reporter overwhelms objective information. To avoid being railroaded by popular environmental trends promoted by the media, we all need to understand how pervasive the influence of bias and sensationalism actually is. And that influence is far more pervasive than many of us imagine.

Shading the Truth Green

How the public sees the environmental world is filtered through many lenses. The most important lens, perhaps, is the media. In Washington state, say the word "Alar" to an apple grower and you are likely to get either an impassioned lecture about the evils of "60 Minutes," or an apple bounced off your noggin. Or both. After the CBS program ran a high-profile, and what many growers felt exaggerated, story about the pesticide and its health risks, apple sales plummeted.

When presented with an environmental issue, reporters scramble to understand the issue in time to meet their deadline. When I worked at the Department of Natural Resources in Washington state, I would sit with reporters over coffee or lunch to discuss issues before they arose, to help avoid their mad dash to understand a complex issue under a looming deadline. Sometimes I even took reporters into the forest for an Environment 101 tour about the issues they thought were interesting.

Sometimes, after hearing the way they thought about issues, I wanted to leave them out there.

Reporters often claim they can put aside their personal biases and write stories that are balanced and accurately convey all sides. Quite simply, this is not a realistic expectation. It is a truism that writers write what they know, and the ideas they sympathize with are also likely to be those they know best. This effect can have significant impacts on the accuracy of news reporting.

Sitting with a Seattle Post-Intelligencer (P-I) reporter (who later became an officer at the Society of Environmental Journalists) over curry at a Thai restaurant in Seattle, I walked through a number issues facing the state's forests, from preventing forest fire and pest infestations to protecting salmon streams and stopping erosion from timber harvests. Outside the Northwest, it would be hard to find a place in America, if not the world, where the environmental debates about forestry have been more contentious. Well-established groups on all sides of the issue, ranging from a group run by the former head of Earth First to labor unions and family forestland owners, slugged it out in the media and legislature, and the P-I reporter decided to make this ongoing battle a central feature of many of his stories.

Often the challenge is trying to convey how to balance uncertain science in such a highly charged atmosphere – so charged that the genetic research lab at the University of Washington's Center for Urban Horticulture had been firebombed by eco-terrorists just the year before my meeting with the reporter. That event caused many people to reassess the debate about forestry, and polls showed the public turned strongly against environmental groups after the bombing. Apparently, however, pollsters didn't ask the P-I reporter.

Discussing one environmental activist who called himself a scientist, I noted that after the firebombing he actually wrote a letter to the editor of the Seattle P-I in which he lamented the term "eco-terrorists" in the paper's coverage of the event. The activist was a frequent commenter on forestry issues and had been used as an expert witness by one prominent group of environmental lawyers. While claiming to speak based on his scientific credentials, his views of environmental politics were a bit odd and clearly distorted his thinking. Instead of using the term eco-terrorist, he advised the P-I to substitute a different term, arguing "those opposed to such risky business [genetic engineering] are actually eco-patriots." He scolded the paper, saying, "I think your readers deserve a broader perspective on stories such as these, and your reporter should use more care before using inflammatory labels that serve only to distort the truth." One man's eco-terrorist is another man's eco-patriot.

I mentioned this to the reporter over lunch, letting him know that he should be skeptical of the "science" being offered by this individual. The reporter paused a moment and said, "Well, actually I am worried about genetic engineering as well." This was akin to being told about the terrorist attacks on 9/11 and responding, "Well, actually I am worried about our Middle East policy as well." This begs the question of whether firebombing a university is an appropriate response to issues that worry us, or whether the ideas of someone who resorts to firebombing can be treated as reasonable on other moral questions. Those questions didn't enter into the reporter's mind.

Of course, the reporter has continued to claim his stories represented only the objective, and unbiased, reality. Also, of course, that is pure nonsense.

A reporter who has difficulty discerning between legitimate peaceful opposition to policy and violent tactics that are out of bounds, like firebombing, is probably going to have difficulty discerning between real science and empty political rhetoric. Reporters have to make such judgments every day, determining what rings true and what seems out of bounds. A dramatically skewed understanding of that difference will result in news articles that, while claiming to be down the middle, are written and presented in a way that fits that reporter's personal values.

The hidden bias of individual reporters is not the only reason media coverage of environmental issues is so skewed. As eco-fads have gained momentum, the media has recognized that catering to environmental sensibilities is good for business. In the same way talk-radio stations on the right and left cater to a particular audience, news outlets have sought to tilt their environmental coverage to appeal to the upper-middle-class demographic many people in the environmental community come from. As the financial standing of newspapers becomes more precarious, finding ways to appeal to a group with disposable income becomes even more attractive.

The challenge for the environmentally conscious consumer and citizen is that such biases and influences make it difficult to know what information to believe. Few people have the time to follow individual reporters closely enough to learn their particular biases. Rarely do they have the opportunity to catch reporters and editors in unguarded moments, when people in the news business reveal the personal values that play a significant role in choosing what stories to cover and how to frame public debate. Often, stories are written about single environmental issues, raising the danger of a particular risk to wildlife or human health, and are then forgotten. This sort of fire-and-forget approach to news reporting increases the public's anxiety about environmental issues in general, but it leaves little guidance about the nature and scope of the risk or how to solve the problem effectively.

The sad result is the media itself becomes one of the primary sources of eco-fads. When asked if they believe everything they read in the media, readers sensibly answer "no." They understand that reporters are human and have their own set of priorities that invariably shape how they write. Not everything reported in the media, however, is nonsense or unreliable, but sorting the good from the bad is difficult, especially in the case of eco-fads. The very power of fads is that they claim to represent what "everyone" believes. When the media latches on to a popular story, it builds momentum that is hard to combat, even when the scientific facts are at odds with the reporter's chosen storyline.

Understanding how reporters are influenced and the news-business pressures they face offers some hints on how to sort the apples from the Alar.

The Line Between Activism and Journalism

If you want to really annoy a reporter, simply accuse them of being biased. You will be treated to a long and well-practiced speech about their training, their care to ensure all sides are treated fairly and their objective approach to all issues. Some reporters will give you this speech, pledging their dispassionate and unemotional approach to the news, with a raised voice.

Their passion is understandable. Calling a reporter biased is a direct challenge to his or her professionalism. Try calling your family doctor a "quack" just as she gives you a flu shot, and see how well that works. Reporters understand that without objectivity, they are little different than bloggers. Protecting a public image of objectivity and dispassion is central to the distinction they make between themselves and other writers, and is why they argue their work is high-quality and worth paying for. It should not be surprising that threats to the foundation of their credibility will be met with a strong emotional response.

That does not mean, however, reporters are not biased. The expectation that they can meet such a standard reflects more on the unreasonableness of the standard than on the human failings of environmental reporters. There are environmental reporters who consciously set aside ethical boundaries to make their point. There are many, however, who do not seem to recognize the burden their own biases and perspective place on them. The most significant, and often overlooked, way reporters' biases affect environmental coverage is in how they choose stories they think are interesting to readers.

In 2008, the Earth Liberation Front (ELF) firebombed a suburban development outside Seattle. The neighborhood, known as the "Street of Dreams," was a high-end development highlighting a range of "green" building elements, including use of cork floors, energy-efficient appliances and other features designed to improve each home's environmental sustainability. The environmentalist firebombers apparently didn't buy the green image. After destroying the model homes, they drove home the message that they believe suburban development is harmful to the planet by spray painting "McMansions in RCDs r not green." RCDs are rural cluster developments, collections of homes and other services built in rural areas. Some environmentalists see such developments as "sprawl," and they fight new construction like this. Not surprisingly, the public reacted strongly against the firebombing, and the public's positive view of the environmental movement took a hit. Environmental journalists recognized this and worked to defend ELF's position, if not their tactics.

Erica Barnett, of the left-leaning Seattle weekly newspaper The Stranger, wrote, "Obviously, I don't condone burning down houses."[7] Then she added an important "but" sentence: "But the statement that ELF allegedly spray-painted on a sign at the arson scene ... is neither debatable or particularly controversial." In Erica's mind, the political sentiments of the arsonists are not even debatable. She went on to write that "there's no such thing as a sustainable suburban lifestyle." Fundamentally, the story was interesting to Erica not because a serious crime had been committed, but because she agreed with the political views of the firebombers. From time to time we all find people who agree with us on issues whom we wish did not. That distasteful people agree with us is not a reflection on the validity of our views or our worth as a human being.

Barnett's comfort with ELF's message, however, was so significant that she could set aside the firebombing, which was ELF's very reason for existing, with half a sentence. The sting of the story was that ELF's political message was so important and widely supported that it wasn't even controversial. This view might be expected of a reporter at The Stranger, a weekly that is proud of its particular leftist ideological bent. This type of decision making about what stories to cover, however, is not limited to newspapers with an overt bias. For one Seattle Times (the state's largest daily newspaper) reporter, the firebombing served as a "teachable moment,"[8] a chance for the public to learn about ELF's ideas.

In Washington state, the issue of how to manage the growth of communities surrounding Seattle has been one of the most contentious for the past two decades. State-imposed growth management rules are seen by some people as the central tool in reducing the environmental impact of new building on surrounding forests, farmland and the rural way of life, and as a key to reducing carbon emissions. One Seattle Times reporter took the opportunity of the firebombing to address this larger debate. In a front-page, above-the-fold story, the reporter noted that the firebombing "reignited an already smoldering debate in a rapidly growing region struggling to find and keep its Pugetopian [the Puget Sound region] identity." The firebombing became the spark for those who opposed development to debate the issues around growth and what counts as "green."

The problem is ELF's very goal in firebombing the suburban development was to send their particular message about growth management by reigniting that debate. ELF activists don't plan to burn down every house they don't like. Instead they use high-profile attacks to spread their political message. They want to create a "teachable moment" as The Times reporter called it. Defending her coverage of the story, the reporter said the event did just that, giving an opportunity to have that debate in public, almost certainly to the delight of ELF.

Additionally, the ELF story did not hold all environmental building standards or policy approaches up to scrutiny – only those targeted by the firebombers. The reporter covered what she, and ELF, thought was interesting, not the subject in general. Even if we assume the ELF attack was a legitimate opportunity to discuss the topic of suburban development, as the reporter argued, it is more difficult to justify discussing only the topic ELF chose and still claim her coverage did not reward ELF for the act and encourage further, similar crimes.

So, why was the topic chosen by The Stranger and The Times? From the tone of the story and the space devoted, the newspapers felt what was newsworthy wasn't domestic terrorism, but homebuilding in suburbia. So interesting, they were willing to set aside the part of the story that made it newsworthy, local arsonists destroying new homes, in favor of focusing on the part of the issue the reporters felt was relevant. Given the increasingly limited space in newspapers, favoring this kind of coverage means other pressing stories don't get published. By focusing on the political claims made by ELF, other parts of the larger story go unconsidered. Ultimately it does not matter whether a reporter's focus on what is interesting to them is conscious or unconscious. The biases that are inherent in all of us as human beings shape the stories that get covered, and which elements within those stories receive coverage. Those biases meant that the question of whether the news coverage served to reward the firebombers never entered the reporters' minds. They were blinded to the ethical implications of their own journalistic choice.

Picking and choosing in this way has the effect of supporting trendy environmental causes that reflect reporters' personal views. The Street of Dreams fire is not the only example of an environmental story that received coverage once it became trendy.

In the 1990s otherwise healthy forests suffered a huge outbreak of insect infestation. The massive bug attack was caused by a range of past policies, including aggressively fighting forest fires, environmental restrictions on thinning forests crowded with small, fire-prone trees and other man-made issues. A wide range of pests attacked trees weakened by competition for light and starved of nutrients and water by too many nearby trees. Think of what happens to carrots when they are planted too close together. Overstressed trees are simply unable to fight off pests in the same way they can when healthy and well-nourished. Twenty years ago, however, the story of forests under stress was relatively uncovered. The solution, removing some of the trees and thinning the forests, was strongly opposed by environmental groups who argued thinning was merely a way for loggers to harvest timber at a profit.

Fast forward ten years and the number of stories addressing pest infestation in those same forests increased dramatically. Why? The cause of the insect infestations was now claimed to be not government policy, but global climate change. High temperatures in the winter failed to kill off bugs, it was argued, leaving them to attack forests with renewed vengeance in the spring and summer. The problem was the same – pest infestations were killing large areas of forest and harming wildlife habitat. Only when the cause came to be perceived as a trendy environmental concern and changed the policy implications of the story in a direction favored by environmental reporters did it receive significant news coverage.

The same effect occurs with coverage of "green" buildings. Across the country, newspapers proudly highlight the opening of the latest green school, designed to be more energy-efficient and healthier for kids and teachers. They even claim such schools reduce absenteeism and improve student test scores. The opening of this latest generation of modern buildings is frequently news. Less frequently, however, do reporters actually go back and assess the real-world performance of those buildings. Few of the newspapers or reporters who wrote so favorably about the vaunted green benefits of these buildings are interested a few years later, when the true performance of the schools in saving energy, improving student health or raising test scores can actually be measured. The ironic result is that glowing projections are treated more seriously by reporters than actual performance data.

In some cases, environmental reporters go beyond simply covering favored stories uncritically. Sometimes they actually work to kill stories that would run counter to the standard environmental narrative.

With people increasingly willing to pay for environmental amenities and to live more sustainably, a homebuilder in the Seattle area decided to build homes that incorporated natural features and protected green space, preserving nearby forest habitat. This new "green" neighborhood was promoted by the builder as the next step in sustainable living. And the company wasn't shy about telling the world.

A reporter called me to ask about one environmental claim being made by the builder. The homes were built near a forest, a concern for the wildland firefighters I worked with, who too often see fires jump from the burning trees to nearby homes. Wasn't this development violating that important rule, asked the reporter? I said I would check on that point. I quickly found that the builder had actually worked with our state foresters and firefighters, adding a buffer around the homes to create a fire-safe zone. When I called the reporter back, I described this as an example of how responsible homebuilding should be done. There was a long pause on the other end of the line, and then the reporter said, almost under his breath, "I just don't want to do a good story about a corporation."

These are the most egregious kinds of bias. The reporters have a specific agenda in mind and they allocate the limited airtime and column inches to stories that fit their preconceived notions, and work to kill stories that upset the apple cart. It is also a bias that is increasingly difficult to police. As media outlets become more financially unstable and newsroom staff is cut, editors are pressed to do many jobs, making it more difficult for them to look over the shoulder of their writers. Running a newsroom is already a difficult job – second-guessing reporters who can legitimately claim to have spent more time studying the particulars of a story than their editor. At some point an editor simply has to believe in the writers, especially when editors have other work to do.

So journalists are left with a significant amount of freedom and can choose the stories to write and, unless their bias is simply too obvious or obnoxious, choose how to write those stories. Many activist journalists know how to avoid the most obvious pitfalls that would draw unwanted attention from an editor. They know how to step up to, but not over, the line that separates reporting from editorializing. Whether they choose the stories or simply cover the news of the day, activist journalists see stories as an opportunity to advocate for their beliefs.

Forests may be the most potent emblem of environmental concern in the United States. Images of rugged wilderness and virgin forest call to mind the majesty of nature and our relationship to the wilderness. How we care for forests while using their bounty to make our lives better is a constant source of friction that pits the values of undisturbed forest against the demand for wood products. It is exactly the type of issue that is attractive to those who want to use powerful imagery to promote a political agenda. The battle over forest certification provided a perfect opportunity for reporters to use that imagery and advocate for strict restrictions on timber harvesting. In an effort to balance the competing pressures on the world's forests, especially in developing countries, environmental advocates created the Forest Stewardship Council (FSC), a seal of approval for wood products from across the world, letting the buyer know that the wood has been harvested in a way that meets sustainable standards. The system is designed to offer a market premium to those who follow their rules by creating consumer demand for responsible forestry that leaves resources available for future generations. In developing countries, where poverty creates a strong incentive to focus on short-term benefits to well-being, the FSC symbol can help those who manage forests keep their eye on long-term sustainable management.

Activists in the United States, however, quickly saw FSC as a way to push foresters to adopt stricter standards they felt were more sustainable. What began as an economic incentive, however, quickly turned political, with activists changing the rating system to meet political, rather than ecological, goals. And while seeking FSC certification was supposed to be voluntary, activists began threatening companies that sold uncertified wood, hanging banners off the stores, initiating political campaigns against selected big-box outlets and moving the FSC brand from cooperation to coercion.

Recognizing that consumers want to know their wood comes from sustainably managed forests, landowners created an alternative system, known as the Sustainable Forestry Initiative (SFI). Thus began a battle between the two competing certification systems. Confused consumers looked for guidance about the differences between the two and how to choose the best one.

In 2008, The Seattle Times weighed in, with a graphic outlining the ways to determine what is truly "green" when building a house. The graphic told readers, "Especially for exotics, choose Sustainable Forestry Council-certified wood."[9] Only one problem – there is no such thing as the Sustainable Forestry Council. The name confuses the two systems: the Sustainable Forestry Initiative and the Forest Stewardship Council. The story that accompanies the graphic is more clear, saying FSC is better than SFI. Why is it better? The article doesn't explain, other than to say FSC is backed by the environmental community. It is hard to argue The Seattle Times made a conscious and considered decision when the paper can't even keep the names of the organizations straight. The presumption, conscious or not, is that the system preferred by environmentalists must be the right one, whatever it's called.

Despite the lack of real understanding of the system, the graphic is unequivocal in its guidance, telling readers to "choose" one system, especially when the wood being chosen is exotic. The Times substitutes certainty of tone for certainty of knowledge.

This approach has also been used to a great extent in the news coverage about global climate change. One newspaper even ran a story under the headline "The truth about global warming."[10] Coverage of the causes and potential impacts of climate change, the central environmental fight of the last ten years, has received a great deal of attention and each side accuses the other of ignoring key facts and slanting the information. Reporters themselves admit that what they believe affects how they cover the issue. One reporter wrote in the newsletter of the Society of Environmental Journalists, wondering, "Does 'balanced' mean pitting the conclusions of the world's leading scientists about global warming against a well-paid industry spokesperson's conclusion about global warming? … One thing I fear is that the 50 percent of the dialogue from a scientist paid by ExxonMobil under the guise of think tank just might help justify someone's decision to go ahead and buy that Chevy Suburban rather than grow concerned about global warming."[11] As a result, reporters cover what they believe, using a confident tone and careful omission to become advocates for a political agenda, and to make sure people don't buy that planet-destroying Chevy Suburban.

The tone of a reporter's writing sends signals to readers about what environmental positions are socially correct and which are unacceptable. Associated Press reporters covering the 2010 Wisconsin Senate race made clear their opinion about Republican challenger Ron Johnson's position on climate change. Citing the candidate's position on climate change, they wrote, "Johnson's campaign has stumbled on occasion. He drew scorn last month when he said he 'absolutely (does) not believe' in the science of man-caused climate change."[12] Characterizing this as a "stumble," noting that he "drew scorn," although reporters do not say from whom, says more about the reporters' judgment than the public's. There are few candidate positions that do not draw fire from someone, yet not all such statements are identified as political errors. Imagine a reporter writing that a candidate "drew scorn calling for tax cuts." Would anyone doubt the reporter's anti-tax cut position on the issue? Whatever the truth or falsehood of Johnson's views on climate change, the reporters put his comments in a negative context, sending readers the message that expressing doubts about climate change is a mistake, one that only rookies and rubes would make.

The way climate change induced sea-level rise is described is another example of how context makes the difference in reporting. Al Gore made concern about rising oceans popular in his film, "The Inconvenient Truth," showing computer-generated projections indicating large parts of the world would be swamped by rising water. Statistics that call those images to mind frequently find their way into news reports of the issue. The Port of Seattle worried that rising water would affect their container operations during the next hundred years and looked for a solution. Laying out the risk, a reporter in the Seattle Post-Intelligencer noted, "Just a 2-foot rise in sea levels ... would inundate 56 square miles and affect at least 44,429 people, according to a state study that identified the area between Tacoma and Olympia as among the first that would be affected."[13]

The catch? Scientists say a 2-foot rise in sea levels is not only "very unlikely," it is beyond even the high end of the predictions of the Intergovernmental Panel on Climate Change (IPCC), the group that environmentalists most often cite as the authority on climate issues. The reporter actually admitted this is the case later in the same article. Citing the University of Washington's application of the IPCC's science, she noted that the projections are "2 inches beyond the upper bounds of the UW predictions for 2050." Why refer to this as "just" a 2-foot rise when, in fact, that level is beyond the extreme? By framing the discussion using the most extreme numbers and failing to report more likely estimates, the reporter sets the frame of reference for readers, pushing the public and policymakers toward accepting a particular policy solution to the alleged problem.

Choosing how to present numbers to readers is an important part of telling a story. The same numbers can be understood in a variety of ways and, without reference points, reporters can use ambiguity to urge readers toward desired conclusions.

In 2008, a reporter for the Seattle P-I wrote an article on predictions of the rise in sea levels resulting from increasing global temperatures. Since water expands when heated, an increase in atmospheric temperature would also cause ocean levels to rise. These impacts are some of those most frequently mentioned by those advocating aggressive efforts to reduce carbon emissions. It was not the first time this particular reporter had written about the environmental risks of rising water.

In 2005, when the Puget Sound Action Team published a report called "Uncertain Future," she wrote a piece[14] outlining the risks to Puget Sound from climate change. Among the impacts was a greater than 3-foot increase in water levels around Seattle by the year 2100. Her article included a graph showing the potentially dramatic impacts from the rising ocean water.

When she returned to the topic in 2008, the entry on her environmentally oriented blog cited new data from the University of Washington. She said new data for Puget Sound showed that the projected "average increase is 6 inches by 2050, 14 inches by 2100."[15] Putting these numbers in context and ignoring her prior reporting, the reporter added, "The figures seem pretty similar to what's been predicted in the past." That comment was sheer nonsense. Just three years earlier the projections had been more than double the 2008 prediction. Such a significant downgrading of the rate of predicted change would seem to have called for a thoughtful comment, or at least a bare acknowledgement. Admitting the dramatic reduction, however, would have shown her readers how uncertain the science of climate impacts is and might have called into question some of the costly carbon-reduction policies being proposed to address the impacts of supposed sea-level rise. By instead claiming the 2008 numbers were consistent with, rather than half of, what was predicted in the past, the reporter expressed a degree of certainty about the science and risk from climate change that simply didn't exist. The numbers she reported were not the issue – the context in which she placed the numbers made all the difference.

How a reporter presents data and environmental risks has a great deal to do with the particular outlook of the reporter. This personal viewpoint is not always conscious. Our experiences invariably color our perspective on events, and we fit information into the context we are most familiar with. It is hard to criticize reporters for being influenced by what they know and have experienced – we all are. The problem is that some reporters pretend such limits do not exist, even when their presence is obvious. When the Seattle P-I ended its print operation and laid off most of its staff, two of its reporters, including Lisa Stiffler, the reporter who wrote the story on the sea-level data, immediately went to work for an environmental activist group in Seattle. The environmental community already knew she was an ally, even in the years she was a supposedly objective reporter for one of the city's major newspapers. In fact, the environmental group People for Puget Sound had given an award to Stiffler and another P-I reporter, Robert McClure, for their reporting on the environmental threats to Puget Sound. While most newspapers would not allow reporters to accept an award from an organization they are supposed to cover impartially, Stiffler and McClure actually bragged about it on their blog. They were so aggressive about their advocacy, they even went on to note that Washington's governor was about to sign a new piece of legislation on the Puget Sound, claiming they "helped inspire it."[16] The blog entry was actually circulated among the professional staff of The Seattle Times as an example of ethical violations that would not be tolerated there.

The job of a reporter is not to "inspire" legislation or campaign for it. Reporters are not supposed to be activists. The line gets blurred frequently when it comes to environmental reporting, however.

In October of 2006, The New York Times printed an article about a new "green" house in Oregon built to meet the standards of a rating system for assessing the environmental sustainability of buildings. The system, known as Leadership in Energy and Environmental Design (LEED), was growing in popularity, and the article was designed to show the benefits of the system. The reporter, Colleen Kaleda, was a freelance reporter for The Times. She also happened to be the editor of Tidepool, an environmental news aggregator run by a Seattle environmental group, the Sightline Institute. When the article appeared, Sightline highlighted the fact that one of their employees had a story in The New York Times, writing, "The piece profiles a house near Mount Hood that's the first single-family residence in the West to win LEED certification," noting "The article was written by Colleen Kaleda, who's the back-up editor for Tidepool (operated, of course, by Sightline)." How did she find the story? Well, the home's owner was a donor to Sightline. As a result, The Times had published a story written by an environmental activist about a green building owned by a donor to her environmental group. She wrote a glowing, complimentary news story about someone who helped pay her salary.

To their credit, when the conflict was brought to the attention of The Times, editors there added a note to the end of the online version of the story:

> "After the article appeared, a reader alerted The Times that [homeowner] Mr. Kelly had made financial contributions to a nonprofit organization in Seattle for which the writer of The Times

article, a freelancer, had worked. ... The writer did not list her work at Sightline when she filled out a contract that The Times requires of all freelancers. She later told The Times that she had not been aware of Mr. Kelly's connection to Sightline when she quoted him in the article. Had Times editors been aware of her association with Sightline, they would not have given her the assignment."

The Times even went on later to discuss the challenge of using freelance writers on stories, noting the difficulties involved in finding potential financial or philosophical conflicts of interest.

All of this makes it difficult to know whether what we read is being presented accurately and whether reporters approach a story with a particular bias. Some environmental reporters end up on that beat because they care about the issue and offer expertise in the area that is unmatched by reporters without a similar interest. How is an assignment editor to weigh those potentially conflicting influences? Are they supposed to assign reporters based on a long history of environmental writing, even if that professional experience means the reporter will likely approach the job with a strong set of preconceived notions about the issues they cover? Should editors choose reporters without a background in environmental writing or work to avoid those biases, even if it means the quality of the reporting may suffer as a result? It is not an easy question, and it is even more difficult for readers who do not happen to know the reporters personally.

These challenges mean that reporters with a personal agenda are largely free to write stories in a context that fits their viewpoint. Eco-fads find fertile ground in such an environment. Reporters who choose to promote particular policies, like costly Puget Sound cleanup or new green building standards, can not only have their stories published, but they actually receive awards and public acclaim for that writing. If the eco-fads favored by journalists turn out to be more style than substance, however, the reporters who promoted them are unlikely to write about that failure, making it more difficult for readers to rely on news reporting to make objective decisions about the merits of different environmental policies.

Poor journalism is one of the primary reasons so much of our environmental policy has come to be guided by trendy environmentalism rather than carefully presented scientific facts.

Running the Gauntlet to Get It Right

It would be wrong to argue that all environmental reporting is hopelessly biased. I have worked with many good and fair-minded reporters who work to stretch their own boundaries and perspectives in search of good stories. Indeed, many reporters are excited to find stories that refute the conventional wisdom on the environment. Reporters with journalistic curiosity jump at the chance to write a story nobody else has discovered. More than a few times I have offered an unexpected argument and watched a reporter sit forward and take notice, intrigued by information he or she did not expect. Even reporters with a particular ideological bent can be enticed by new ideas, and there are plenty of good stories that go against the grain of traditional environmental reporting.

It is easy, and cheap, to claim a news article we do not like is the result of a reporter's political bias. Sometimes this is true, but not always. The problem is that reporters, whatever their level of ideological bias or, conversely, intellectual curiosity, face a number of pressures when writing about the environment. Reporters who want to get it right must still decide how far out on a limb they want to climb for an argument that is counterintuitive, outside their area of expertise, or takes a position that may come back to bite them later. These factors exert pressure on the best reporters, encouraging them to shade their stories toward eco-fads, nudging them toward the mainstream of environmental thought and discouraging taking risks in their reporting.

The first challenge for all reporters is they can only write what they know. Frequently, however, reporters are put in the position of writing on issues they are unfamiliar with, or they know only what conventional thinking has told them. It does not take long for a good reporter to learn there is a great deal they don't know and to find tricks of the trade to close those knowledge gaps as much as possible. No reporter, however, can close all of those gaps. When they sit down to write or step in front of the camera, they are going to report those aspects of an issue they know best. They don't want to make a silly mistake or report incorrectly. This means reporters will emphasize those messages they are most familiar with and comfortable. This is not only understandable, it is prudent reporting.

When it comes to media bias, that mindset gently nudges reporters to adopt the most agreeable political positions. Reporters, like all of us, are going to be more familiar with the arguments they support. Each of us knows the ins and outs of our political opinions better than we know the positions of those who oppose us. We are more comfortable defending our own opinions than we are with trying to accurately, and fairly, characterize the views of people we think are wrongheaded. Although reporters may strive to present all sides of an issue fairly, when the words are put on paper it is likely the policy position they most agree with will come across as more persuasive and complete. Sometimes this means reporters know how they would respond to criticism but do not know what people on the other side of an issue would say in response. How can reporters report what they don't know?

This does not mean the stories are less biased. It means we too often impute motive to reporters who shade their stories in one direction when it is, at least in part, a function of the limits on their knowledge and experience.

The practical effect is that eco-fads and other bits of conventional environmental wisdom are familiar and comfortable ground for those in the media. Counterintuitive or unfamiliar arguments are more difficult to convey. And, frankly, what reporters want to go out on a limb presenting an unfamiliar argument they may not believe themselves? People in the media sometimes unintentionally promote eco-fads and downplay arguments that run counter to the latest fad because debunking popular beliefs puts reporters in an uncomfortable position.

Those who benefit from eco-fads, like business owners, politicians and environmental activists, know this and they work to increase the pressure on reporters, making it more difficult for them to swim upstream. The easiest way to pressure reporters is to reward them for highlighting potential environmental concerns while punishing them for downplaying risks.

The calculus is quite simple. A reporter writes a story about a potential environmental concern – like global warming, dangerous chemicals, habitat destruction, etc. – saying it could be the next great ecological calamity. Two years later the threat has not materialized. What will people say about the original news report? A few people might say the reporter was wrong and can't be relied upon in the future. More likely, defenders will offer the phrase "better safe than sorry" as a justification for raising concerns about an environmental danger that was probably overhyped. More brazen reporters will claim it was their clarion call that prevented the predicted danger from arising. Their editors, eager to show the power of the media, will agree, saying that without their own diligent news coverage, the environment would have been that much worse off. And if you want to stay informed about the next potential threat, buy a newspaper.

Take the opposite case – a reporter downplays an environmental threat or ignores it altogether. Independent of the environmental outcome, environmental groups and others who gain by hyping environmental concerns, for fun or profit, will fill the reporter's inbox with unpleasant email. Enough of these negative messages can make an editor nervous, requiring the reporter to justify his or her stance on the issue. Who wants to go through that?

Worse, what happens if the environmental threat turns out to be more serious than the reporter expected? The potential landslide that was downplayed ends up washing out a road or a house. The animal species that was years from the endangered species list suddenly sees a serious decline in population. Whatever the issue, the reporter will have to explain why he felt the concern did not merit more coverage. The sequel will almost certainly require a follow-up story involving some kind of media mea culpa. Who wants to go through that?

No apologies are necessary when a potential threat does not materialize. No apology is enough when a downplayed threat does more environmental damage than expected. It is simply safer to exaggerate environmental threats than it is to debunk them. It is difficult to take credit for preventing the needless costs that were avoided by correctly assessing the significance of various environmental risks. It is easy to get blamed for not appreciating the risk from an event that, although extremely unlikely, actually happened. Hindsight is 20/20, but reporters are expected to see the future and are held accountable for their coverage of it.

A certain number of unlikely events will occur no matter what the odds. If there is a 1 percent chance a bad event will occur, at some point, that risk, or one like it, will become reality. Reporters can note that the risk a bad event will actually occur is extremely low, but that is cold comfort when something bad actually happens.

Anyone who invests money is familiar with this effect. Every mutual fund, a collection of stocks chosen by an "expert," claims it can beat the market. Research shows, however, that the simple S&P 500 index outperforms up to 90 percent of those expertly chosen funds. But anyone who beats the S&P 500 gets to claim it was their genius, even if it was only for one year. It is reasonable, however, to ask whether a fund's superior investment performance was the result of brilliance or luck. A certain number of fund managers are going to get lucky and pick a hot stock. Others can make wise judgments and still get shellacked. In either case, however, people attempt to ascribe the intelligence, or lack thereof, of their sources for the losses. The simple fact is, we do the best we can to judge risk based on what we know at the time, and we move our game pieces accordingly.

Reporters are the same. The safest move for them, as a result, is to claim everything is a potential environmental risk. That way if a low-probability event comes to pass, they can claim clairvoyance. That looks pretty good on a resume.

Opinion writers can compound the problem. After a newspaper runs a story on an environmental threat, editorial writers are unlikely to contradict their own reporter by pointing to flaws in the story. More likely, they will use the news article as a cue, picking up on the reporter's theme and expanding on it, demanding policy changes to address the environmental concern raised by their own paper's good work.

If we try to make real-life decisions this way, we end up chasing the latest environmental fad, wasting money, time and effort chasing will-o-the-wisps. In the end, failing to put our time and resources where we can do the most good is a waste and destroys our ability to dedicate those resources where they can do what's right for the environment. When environmental reporting offers an unprioritized litany of the latest potential environmental threats, it fans an undirected popular green passion, encouraging a haphazard approach to addressing environmental policy.

Catering to a Green Audience

Although newspapers and other media outlets frequently portray themselves as a source of unbiased information and news, they are also businesses. This fact is only becoming more significant as the business model of media outlets is being tested and newspapers find circulation and profitability falling. The media need to appeal to a target audience, and offering the public information about being "green" is a growing trend.

From green sections of local newspapers to the Discovery Channel cable offshoot "Planet Green," green consumers are an attractive audience. Consumers with green sensibilities tend to be more prosperous and have greater disposable income, exactly the audience marketers want to reach. The Discovery Channel's advertising section for Planet Green even brags, "60% will pay more for a green product."[17] Discovery Channel marketers are saying, "Want to reach those consumers? Then advertise with us!" Sending the right political message helps media outlets like Planet Green reach that audience and sell advertising.

The media have become very aggressive about reaching cash-ready "green" buyers. NBC and its networks are part of "Green is Universal," scheduling green programming around Earth Day in April. My local newspaper even has a "Go Green" section with tips on how to live an environmentally friendly lifestyle.

Situated in a community with a strong environmental ethic, The Seattle Times has taken great steps to sell itself as a source of environmental news, committing the paper to environmentally friendly practices, highlighting environmental activism and offering a regular column on how to be an earth-friendly consumer.

In 2007, The Times launched its "Climate Challenge" feature, a series of stories about people trying to reduce their carbon emissions by 15 percent. The Times argued that, "If the Puget Sound region reduced greenhouse gas emissions by 15 percent, that could keep 15.5 billion pounds of carbon dioxide from the atmosphere each year, based on 2000 emission figures. That's like taking 1.3 million cars off the road."[18] The Times was not simply going to tell others to sacrifice and not do something itself, however. Under the heading "What is The Seattle Times doing to address this problem?" the paper's managers noted:

> "The Seattle Times Company practices recycling. All newspaper waste is reused, and ink, office paper, cardboard, printing plates, silver film and oil from presses and delivery trucks are recycled. About 70 percent of the newsprint the company uses contains material from recycled newspapers. The rest is made of pulp from sawmill chips. No trees are harvested to make the newsprint."[19]

It seems strange to say that "no trees are harvested" when the pulp for the newsprint comes from trees, even if some of the newsprint they use "contains" recycled material. How can they make this claim? When asked, one manager explained to me that trees being used to make newsprint were harvested for other reasons and that the newsprint was a secondary product. This is like saying no pigs were killed to make the bacon because the animal was killed first for pork chops, ham and ribs. We can only imagine what The Times would say if an elected official made a similar, silly claim. Since pulp is an integral part of the profitability of forestry companies, claiming no trees are harmed by the publication of The Seattle Times is misleading. If The Times editors are encouraging others to live the lifestyle, however, they figure they need to show a little something themselves, even if it stretches credulity.

The effort to reach green consumers did not end with the Climate Challenge. Twice a month, The Times publishes an "EcoConsumer" column, written by a government employee, providing readers advice on how to buy green goods and services and lead a green life. The columns walk a fine line between information and editorial and ends up promoting a number of eco-fads. Columns touting efforts to reduce "food-miles," praising trade restrictions and condemning free trade, and claims that "old growth" forests are used to make toilet paper have all been featured as topics.[c] Newspapers are always a mix of news and opinion and articles covering sports, fashion, food and other topics that are understood to contain the opinions of the author. When it comes to coverage of political

---

[c] We will see later that each of these claims is based on faulty data and the policies actually do more damage to the environment.

choices, like buying green and related public policy, media outlets should be more careful to maintain an image of impartiality, presenting facts and letting readers determine how to use the information. The Times, however, is comfortable stepping over the line when it comes to appealing to a coveted consumer demographic. Green consumers have money to spend, and if advertisers want to reach them, what better way than to advertise next to a column that attracts readers who want to live green?

The mixing of the business side and news side of media makes it more difficult to sort fact from opinion in what we read, see and hear. As business pressures mount, it is understandable that newspapers are more focused on reaching potential readers and improving their bottom line. The problem is the business model can interfere with the traditional role of news outlets as unbiased deliverers of information. How likely is it that a newspaper, having sold itself as environmentally conscious, will report stories that run counter to that ethic? Are reporters comfortable writing that using "food-miles" as a metric to determine one's carbon footprint is extremely inaccurate, when the paper runs a regular column that promotes the opposite view? Newspapers will certainly argue that such columns do not bind their reporters to a particular approach. It would be hard to argue, however, that when news organizations make loud proclamations about their commitment to a particular set of values reporters don't take note.

A Powerful Force for Eco-Fads

Although the Internet has provided a new source of information about a range of topics, newspapers and electronic media are still an important source of information about political issues and news. The public aren't fools, of course. They understand that news is shaped by the views of the reporters and can discern which media outlets have political biases. The difficultly lies in determining which information sources can be trusted and which are unreliable. Even if we are skeptical of information offered in newspapers or by television anchors, we know it isn't *all* nonsense. Trying to sort the wheat from the chaff is difficult, and when trends take hold, readers have a hard time deciding whether something is popular because it is accepted wisdom or simply because it is the latest bit of commonly accepted, though erroneous, wisdom.

When it comes to environmental news, the problem of whom to trust is even more difficult. Environmental reporters are often chosen because they are themselves environmentalists. Reporters who want to present information in an unbiased way know it is safer to raise many red flags, even if those fears don't materialize, than to downplay threats that may someday occur and have to explain later why they didn't take the risk more seriously. Managers of news outlets, knowing green is big business, encourage this approach in an effort to give their readers what they want, even if this stifles stories that question the rush to be green. And with media budgets and staffs shrinking, reporters are required to be experts in more areas. This makes it difficult for them to make sure they don't also get caught up in the latest environmental trend, simply regurgitating popular views they don't have time to examine.

Given all the pressures that shape environmental reporting, and the obvious and shameful ethical lapses and political biases, some observers attack all reporting on environmental issues as biased and unreliable. I think this is foolish. I have worked with several excellent environmental reporters who provide interesting and challenging information for the public and policymakers to consider. Other reporters, however, fall far short of this standard. They see their role as little different from being a political activist, and they shift seamlessly from one role to the other.

Fortunately we now have access to an unparalleled amount of information and viewpoints on virtually every environmental policy, consumer choice and issue. Media reports provide us with the tips we need to do further research about the choices we are making. When writing news stories, reporters don't rely on only one source. We shouldn't either. Of course, not every decision we make requires painstaking research involving the latest scientific and economic journals. We are bound to make some mistakes. But the information needed to make wise decisions does exist and can help us overcome the pitfalls of modern environmental reporting.

Understanding the need to double-check the facts and put news reports about the environment in context with other policy priorities helps us better understand the information we are being offered.

Sadly, the news media doesn't make it easy. If anyone deserves a lion's share of the blame for the current mania for eco-fads, media outlets have made a strong case for that dubious honor.

Chapter 7

The Difference Between Science and Sex Appeal

"Thank you for bringing scientists back to the White House."[1] With those words, Whitman College, a small private college in Washington state, sociology professor Kari Norgaard encouraged newly inaugurated President Obama to take aggressive action to prevent climate change. The professor, whose open letter to the President appeared in the Whitman College alumni magazine, encouraged him to heed the dark warnings of a particular group of climate scientists. "At this juncture, we need science more than ever," she exhorted.

Her advice to the president was to listen to outspoken climate scientist James Hansen of NASA, noting that he is "probably the best known" scientist on the issue of climate change. Indeed, she is correct about his notoriety. Hansen has been a ubiquitous presence in the climate debate since he testified before Congress about the danger of global warming in 1988. The source of his notoriety is clear – he has been quoted thousands of times in the media and actively seeks media attention. He is frequently seen taking part in political protests, including his arrest at a coal mine in West Virginia with actress Darryl Hannah in 2009.

The problem with all of this is that being "best known" is not a scientific credential. Being best known is a measure of skill at getting media attention, not of scientific competence. He routinely makes claims that capture the popular imagination, even if they do not represent the mainstream of scientific thought. With hints that climate change could cause sea levels to rise dozens of feet, he frequently discards the careful language common to scientific professions. In his book, *Storms of My Grandchildren*, he sees those who disagree with him as being under the spell of "intentional misinformation spawned by special interests."[2]

His popularity relies less on his scientific rigor than on the convenience of his political positions. Professor Norgaard emphasized his global warming claims not because Dr. Hansen is in the mainstream of scientists but precisely because he is outside it, and his conclusions are useful in advocating the policies she thinks most appropriate.

This is not an uncommon occurrence. People often have a clearer idea about their values than about the validity of competing scientific claims. We tend to be comfortable making decisions based on what is most comfortable (our personal values) as opposed to what is least comfortable (complex scientific analysis). This is the reverse of the decision making path most people claim to travel. When justifying positions, we like to claim to have derived conclusions from objective supporting science because of the rhetorical power that argument offers.

Science derives that power from a logical approach free of external social or political influences. In his excellent book on the interplay of science and politics, *The Honest Broker*, Dr. Roger Pielke Jr. notes that,

> "... no scientist wants to see his/her work described as 'emotional' or 'selective.' But 'comprehensive,' 'logical,' and 'rational' are positive attributes whether the information being described is scientific or not. This is one reason why advocates of different political views agree on the need for policy to be based on 'sound science' or 'scientific integrity.'"[3]

Discovering what represents "sound science" is the tough part. Judging sound science is difficult even for experts, which is why making accurate scientific judgments is particularly difficult for lay people and policymakers.

Compounding the problem, "science" rarely points in only one direction. There may be a myriad of policy options that rely on the same scientific information. Science itself does not always tell us which approach is best. Policy proposals like cap and trade, increased regulation or imposing a tax on carbon can all be justified by the same level of risk identified by climate science.

And, scientists may have opinions about these issues, injecting their own personal values. When they express those views, they often do so as "scientists," claiming that their conclusions are based on their logical, scientific approach, not simply their own preferences about policy direction. By conflating the two, they attempt to give their recommendation more authority than it deserves.

It is not surprising that scientists want to be involved in deciding how their research is used. Hansen says explicitly that "science and policy cannot be divorced."[4] The problem arises when scientists' value-influenced policy recommendations are conveyed as objective science. Doing so not only allows scientists to participate in political debates from ground that appears more authoritative but is also welcomed and encouraged by those who agree with their policy conclusions. Policy advocates who agree are quick to claim they are not engaging in politics, but simply "following the science." Doing so is much easier than going over the well-worn, and often inconclusive, debate over value judgments underlying various policy options.

It may seem odd that science has become such a powerful tool for promoting environmental fad and fashion. Indeed, the power of true science is that it is immune to the pressures of emotion, which would at first seem to undermine policies that are more about style than substance. Increasingly, however, scientists stand side by side with sex symbols to promote particular environmental policies, cloaking the latest eco-fad in the reassuring language of the scientific.

Separating the two requires an understanding of the line between values and science, the limits of science with regard to policy, the role of uncertainty in science and how we can recognize when the line is being crossed. Understanding the role activist scientists play in promoting eco-fads can help us understand whether the White House truly brought scientists back or simply introduced environmental politics in another guise.

Good science is crucial to making good environmental policy and decisions. Scientists play an important role in preserving a healthy environment for wildlife and for future generations. Becoming good users of science and understanding its limits will help us distinguish good science from bad, and to use good science correctly.

Solving Big Problems With Little Solutions

Who could argue with the call to "follow the science" when it comes to addressing environmental problems? Policymakers cannot ignore the basic facts of physics, biology or geography and expect to be successful. Scientists can provide useful data and an understanding of how natural forces interact that are critical to making good policy decisions. Even when these realities are inconvenient, they are factors that must be considered if policymakers hope to have any chance of success in promoting environmental sustainability.

Relating science to policy, however, presents a number of problems, and scientists are not always good, or supposed to be good, at synchronizing the two. Part of this problem arises because scientists' perspectives are naturally limited by their area of expertise.

Success in science often relies on specializing in a particular discipline. Few scientists can simply be biologists. Biologists must specialize in sea birds or anadromous fish or similar fields. That narrow focus provides an increasingly specific understanding of their scientific field. This is the process of science – researchers work progressively from general phenomena to an understanding of minute details.

Problems arise, however, when scientists concentrate on a narrow range of scientific inquiry. In such a circumstance, scientists often commit themselves to a particular narrative about how the world works. Once committed to a particular framework, they fit new information into that system even when it is difficult to achieve a good match. To a hammer every problem looks like a nail, and to a scientist every problem can be fit into their preferred context. This makes it difficult to assimilate new and contradictory data. As a result, specialized explanations are incomplete and can actually lead to the suppression, intentional or not, of new scientific concepts.

The great philosopher of science, Thomas Kuhn, explained this process in *The Structure of Scientific Revolutions*. Kuhn argued that scientists become committed to particular explanatory paradigms within a scientific specialty. Occasionally new information comes to light that challenges that model. Instead of modifying the paradigm, however, Kuhn notes that scientists will attempt to explain away those conflicts, and "devise numerous articulations and ad hoc modifications of their theory in order to eliminate any apparent conflict."[5] When challenged with conflicting information, scientists remain committed to their paradigm and the worldview that goes with it. This can have an impact on the process of scientific understanding.

The paradigm not only defines how scientists explain the data they are receiving, it also determines what is important to them and what is not. Climate scientist Pat Michaels argues that just such a process has impacted the type of climate-change articles editors select for publication in respected scientific journals.[6] If the editors are committed to a certain understanding of the climate, alternative views will often be rejected because they do not appear to further the understanding of the discipline.

Sometimes this is not even a conscious decision. Editors will view alternative explanations as malformed puzzle pieces that simply have no place in filling in the particular picture they believe exists. American scientist Stephen Jay

Gould explained this process by saying, "Prejudices arising from hope, cultural expectation, or the definitions of a particular theory dictate that only certain kinds of data will be viewed as worthy of publication, or even documentation at all."[7] This important insight demonstrates that even scientists who sincerely want to expand the bounds of knowledge can be misled by their own sense of what is important and what is not. The way scientists shift the information they receive is as important as their commitment to impartiality. Ignoring information simply because it does not fit their scientific paradigm means suppressing data that could be useful to advancing scientific knowledge.

The process of filtering out unwanted information can, unfortunately, involve a more sinister intent. When internal personal emails from the University of East Anglia's Climate Research Unit found their way into the public domain, it became clear some climate scientists were knowingly suppressing contrary information about climate change. Michael Mann of Pennsylvania State University, concerned that a respected scientific journal began publishing contrary science, accused "climate skeptics" of staging a "coup" of the journal. His solution? Mann encouraged his friends in the scientific community to no longer consider that journal as "a legitimate peer-reviewed journal."[8] Mann and his colleagues saw publication as a sort of combat, justifying a range of tactics to suppress alternative viewpoints.

Even absent such contentious disagreements among scientists, a narrow focus on a particular area of science creates difficulties if scientists attempt to put the conclusions of their specialty into a larger social context.

Daniel Sarewitz's work at Arizona State University focuses on science and policy. He notes that the particular worldview of a scientist is significantly influenced by his scientific discipline. In a piece titled "How science makes environmental controversies worse," Sarewitz writes, "Even the most apparently apolitical, disinterested scientist may, by virtue of disciplinary orientation, view the world in a way that is more amenable to some value systems than others. That is, disciplinary perspective itself can be viewed as a sort of conflict of interest that can never be evaded."[9]

The way a scientist thinks about environmental issues cannot help being influenced by his or her area of expertise. When considering the issue of clean water, a fish biologist is likely to have a different perspective than someone whose primary concern is drinking water. As a result, a fish biologist will be prone to suggest policies that address aspects of water quality that affect fish, like temperature, that have no impact on the drinkability of the water coming from your faucet.

This does not mean the science is faulty. Nor does it mean it should not be used by policymakers. It simply means scientific perspective can influence the particular policy solutions scientists recommend.

Add to this the fact that scientists often become very risk-averse in their particular area of focus. It should not be surprising that scientists come to identify strongly with their area of work. That identification can lead to a level of risk aversion that might seem extreme to outsiders. Stanford University professor Deborah Gordon, an entomologist specializing in ant behavior, admitted in an interview that she does not like to kill ants and, when her research requires it, she will often ask research assistants to do the job.[10] This is not a critique of her attitude, but if she were asked to provide policy guidance relating to ant populations, it is likely that she would treat threats to ants much more seriously than would many of us whose relationship to individual ants has often come at the delivery end of a magnifying glass.

Of course we all have such biases. The problem arises when scientists claim that they are immune to having their perspective colored by these personal biases.

In 2008, a fish biologist working with the Tulalip Indian Tribe in Washington state wrote a letter to the editor of the Seattle Times that is emblematic of this phenomenon. In his letter, the biologist complained the tribe was using revenue from the tribal casino to expand nearby development: "I find it very discouraging to see use of these funds for the sole purpose of supporting the economic industry that is destroying the environment. In the years that I have been involved in efforts to restore and protect fish and wildlife habitat, the tribal biologists have been some of the strongest advocates for salmon recovery efforts." How, he wondered, could scientists support economic development when it damaged the environment?

He simply assumed the tribe's biologists shared his set of priorities. Given a choice between economic development and risking salmon habitat, he could not understand how the tribe could choose economic development. His perspective as a fish biologist colored his values, leading him to oppose virtually any change that might pose a risk to salmon. When asked to translate his scientific perspective into public policy, he erred on the side of protecting salmon, justifying high costs even when the amount of habitat saved was very small. So when he goes on to write, "In many cases where development is threatening the environment, the tribes have used their influence and treaty rights to protect the environment," he does not consider alternative motivations that he may not share. The tribe's previous use of treaty rights may have been as much about limiting economic competition as protecting the environment.

Instead, he focused only on potential environmental impact, making it difficult for him to realize that others may not share his priorities.

While some scientists fail to see the role that their biases play, in other circumstances, such biases are actively used to achieve political ends.

In 2001, the Washington State Department of Natural Resources was considering whether to seek certification of its forestry practices from the Forest Stewardship Council. The agency received a report outlining the requirements to meet the standards. Among the requirements was the need for the agency to hire more biologists. The certifiers realized that biologists' judgments are influenced by a set of values that is more likely to lead them to oppose activities that put at risk the animals they have spent their career studying.

Requiring the agency to hire more biologists was an intentional effort by the Forest Stewardship Council to institutionalize risk aversion within the Department of Natural Resources and shift the tone of day-to-day discussions about forestry practices within the agency. This approach, they hoped, would lead to fewer timber harvests and more restrictive rules – rules that did not have to work their way through the legislature but would simply be imposed from within.

When it comes to using science to set policy, the ironic result is that the more expertise scientists have in a particular discipline, the more subject they are to narrowness of perspective. When policymakers look to top experts in order to receive the best scientific information, they may also find it particularly difficult to apply that knowledge to the larger policy challenges they face.

Which Science to Follow?

Imagine, then, trying to make a decision when faced with scientists whose conclusions are colored by their personal perspective as well as their research. How do we choose between the science offered by experts in different disciplines, each of which is correct in its own way but in conflict with each other? This is exactly the problem faced by many of us who regularly look to science for guidance.

Imagine, for instance, the process for determining how to deal with the marbled murrelet, a sea bird that lives along the West Coast. For policymakers, turning to scientists can be very frustrating.

Asked how to protect the habitat of the bird, biologists are likely to advocate placing buffers around areas where the birds live, ensuring that no timber harvests occur near their nests. Foresters, on the other hand, would argue that sustainable forest management ought to replicate the natural pattern of disturbance from forest fire, leaving a wide range of forest types across the landscape – from clearings to young trees to old growth. One approach favors ending timber harvest in particular areas, while the other argues that such a policy is counterproductive. Who is right?

The frustrating conclusion is that both are right. Both biologists and foresters are presenting the best science in their respective fields. Biologists are going to recommend extra steps to protect the birds they study, and foresters fear the risk of mismanaging forests and harming birds and other wildlife. Biologists trust their own ability to design strategies that protect wildlife populations. Foresters trust their ability to be good stewards of forestland and to maintain the wide range of forest types that benefit wildlife.

For those looking for the best policy solution, "following the science" leads to either route. Whichever choice is made, however, can also lead a policymaker to being accused of ignoring the science. If the decision is made not to create no-harvest buffer areas, biologists can correctly say their scientific conclusions were ignored. If more no-cut forest areas are set aside, foresters can rightly say such rules make it more difficult to keep forest habitat in balance, and that may lead to unnatural events, like catastrophic wildfires and serious consequences for other wildlife.

When we choose between these two options, we are not choosing to accept or ignore the best science. We are relying on our own personal sense of what risks are acceptable. If someone asked why we chose one route over the other, the answer might be that we found one approach had less uncertainty, was more rigorous, or express another explanation that attempted to find a rational justification that applied to the question at hand. In reality, the simple fact might be that we were more concerned about birds than the impact of wildfire, because we like to feed birds but had never even seen a wildfire. Who wants to admit that, though? Such an admission would be ridiculed, even though it is not only the reality of how decisions are made when faced with conflicting science, it is as justifiable as many other approaches.

Such conflicts within science allow those who work backwards, people who make up their mind first and then seek data to justify their conclusion, to find plenty of science that validates their predetermined position. They can then claim their decision was based on science all along.

Activist Scientists

This ambiguity not only plays into the hands of policymakers who want to justify their own decisions, it also creates opportunities for scientists who feel strongly about particular policies to use their credentials as a cover for the promotion of their own values. When the science can be interpreted in more than one way, it allows scientist activists to mask their political opinions by presenting them as the result of careful scientific consideration.

When scientists step in front of the public to discuss an issue, they bring credibility born of the majesty of scientific progress. Scientists, echoing Newton, claim to see farther because they stand on the shoulders of the scientific giants who have come before. Rejecting their environmental policy recommendations is viewed as tantamount to rejecting the scientific legacy they represent. Challenges to their policy conclusions are not seen to just question a particular scientist, they are seen questioning the validity of Einstein, Galileo and other great minds of science.

For scientists who cannot resist the heady lure of politics, arguing from such a prestigious position is extremely seductive. They see themselves as not simply expressing one of several competing opinions – they present themselves as giving you unquestioned scientific facts.

Former Washington state climatologist Phil Mote could not resist that lure. Testifying before a Washington State Senate committee, Mote expressed his views on a recent rainstorm that caused major flooding across Western Washington, triggering landslides on the forested slopes of the Cascade Mountains. At issue was what had caused the landslides. Mote said excessive timber harvests had created the conditions for the slides, and he said he had evidence to prove it. At the end of his presentation, he showed a slide indicating that research in Oregon demonstrated landslides increased with the prevalence of active forestry. Forestry was not his area of expertise, but he did not hesitate to share the data he found.

There was a problem, however. Without experience in forestry, Mote didn't realize that the data he had found related to the impact of forest roads on landslides. It is well known that forest roads can create landslides when, built out from the sides of hills, they are undermined by heavy rains and collapse. This is the reason Washington state requires forest roads to be removed after a timber harvest is complete. The data Mote presented to the committee simply did not apply to Washington state, and it bore little, if any, relationship to the situation he was addressing, purportedly as a scientist. At no point did he tell the committee he was speaking as a layperson on an issue he was not an expert on. He was introduced as the state's climatologist and allowed his testimony to carry the weight of his scientific credential, even when speaking on an issue outside of his own scientific discipline.

In such a situation, the appropriate step would have been for him to make clear that his statements were based on personal opinion, influenced by his personal values and feelings about wanting to reduce timber harvesting. Doing so, however, would have made him little different from any other citizen taking the microphone. He knew his words would be taken more seriously, and have more impact on policy, if he claimed to be speaking from the lofty perch of scientific integrity.

Scientists seem increasingly willing to convey personal views as objective scientific judgment. When he wrote *The Structure of Scientific Revolutions* fifty years ago, Thomas Kuhn noted, "One of the strongest, if still unwritten, rules of scientific life is the prohibition of appeals to heads of state or to the populace at large in matters scientific."[11] This is still true for many scientists. They chose their field of expertise because they are driven by a desire to understand the world more completely. In many cases, scientists are as inspired by revelations that do not fit their hypotheses as phenomena that do. What inspires them is not the political implications of their research, but the desire to acquire knowledge itself. The great Russian physicist Andrei Sakharov turned from applied physics to theoretical physics because he wanted to separate the work he loved from the Soviet politicians who used his science in ways he disapproved of.

This leaves the political field open to scientists who are not so reticent about crossing that line. Scientists who are willing to inject their personal values into scientific debates tend to become dominant in public debates. That dominance is not earned by the quality of their science but by their simple willingness to ignore an unwritten rule of their profession. Becoming the "best known" expert in the field is easier when many of your colleagues prefer anonymity.

Public debates about policy can become contests between individuals offering their opinions, claiming that their conclusions are drawn from scientific rigor, not simply personal preference. It then becomes very difficult to determine which viewpoint is the correct one, because the challenge is not simply choosing between alternative perspectives. The correct answer may be an idea that is not even being conveyed to the public. Imagine being asked to choose which door the correct answer is behind without even knowing how many doors there are.

All of these influences combine to make choosing the best science for the problem at hand quite a chore. We can be presented with good, but conflicting, science. Scientific conclusions can be limited in their applicability to policy by the narrowness of their perspective. And politically-motivated scientists, seeing an opportunity to engage when the scientific facts are confusing, may become advocates of a particular policy direction, masking value-based conclusions as scientific judgment. What then can those who have an honest interest in using science to promote environmental sustainability do? How can we judge what scientific conclusions to use and which to ignore?

Logical but False

The argument goes like this. The world is a finite place with a limited amount of oil, land, minerals and other natural resources. As population expands, we consume these resources at a growing rate, rushing onward to the day when one or more of them will be exhausted. When that happens, the world will face serious consequences, including famine, wars over remaining resources and even the collapse of the global economy. It is a logic that is undeniable in its simplicity.

And it is wrong.

Such claims have been made for many decades, and some have even attached timelines to the impending disaster. Each time the deadline passes, however, the underlying logic is not questioned; instead, the timeline is simply shifted to another date in the future. Given the apparent strength of the logic, it is difficult to discard, even when actual events seem to undermine it.

The problem with this type of logic is not a lack of internal consistency. The argument is consistent and, indeed, logical. The problem is that it leaves out key factors that overwhelm the basic logic of the argument. In this case the argument assumes that resources which are in high demand today always will be in demand in the future, meaning that as demand increases the supply of limited resources will fall. What is missing is the reality that resources in heavy demand at one point in time, like silver for photographic film in the 1980s, are unneeded when technology, like digital cameras, change what resources are in demand.

Identifying the information left out of such arguments can be extremely difficult and is a common source of confusion in trying to understand scientific processes.

Seemingly simple scientific arguments have a great deal of appeal. Many people are familiar with Occam's Razor, the principle which states that the simplest solution is often the best. Galileo used this approach when arguing that a sun-centered solar system is the best way to understand the observed movements of the planets. His theory presented the simplest explanation of the known facts, and it had the further benefit of being correct.

Karl Popper expanded on this idea when he created the standard of falsifiability in defining what ideas qualify as "scientific." In *The Logic of Scientific Discovery*, Popper argues that the best scientific hypotheses are those which can be tested and falsified. If there is no way to demonstrate whether a concept is false, how can we know if it is true? Additionally, he argued that the fewer caveats a theory had, the more robust it was. Hypotheses that are simple, broad and can be proven incorrect are the most robust and come nearest to the scientific ideal.

This gives scientists and users of scientific findings the ability to judge the quality of the information they receive. Is a theory simple and direct, or does it contain numerous exceptions to the rule? Does other information show all or part of the concept to be false? This assumes, however, that the public, and scientists themselves, have all of the relevant information at hand to make such a judgment. Uncertainty makes judging scientific theories difficult.

Science is never complete, and the picture presented by experts frequently includes caveats. Often there are questions about how much is known and unknown. When science is particularly complex, much of the debate can revolve around this very question.

For example, the United Nations' climate change organization, the Intergovernmental Panel on Climate Change (IPCC), has attempted to estimate the certainty of its various claims, creating "quantitatively calibrated levels of confidence."[12] Claims that have a nine-in-ten chance of being correct are said to have a "very high" level of confidence, but those with a five-in-ten chance of being correct are only "medium confidence." This, however, has not solved the problem, and there are frequent accusations that the IPCC claims greater certainty for its conclusions than it should.

Compounding this problem is that scientists rarely become renowned for saying "I don't know." Scientists can be enticed into ascribing more confidence to their predictions than is proper. This is not unique to scientists. Studies have demonstrated that experts in many fields believe they know more than they really do, leading to misplaced optimism about their ability to make predictions.

Yale Law Professor Ian Ayres notes that not only are people, experts included, too optimistic about their ability to predict correctly, they are slow to adjust their views when they are proven wrong. In his excellent book, *Supercrunchers*, Ayres notes that when presented with new information "we're likely to discount disconfirming evidence and focus instead on evidence that supports our preexisting beliefs."[13] Once an expert believes she understands the way things work, she fits the information into her current understanding, increasing her level of confidence in predicting the future. As a result, experts can actually handicap themselves when understanding the real world. Ayres notes that very simple statistical models are often better at predicting accurately than experts are because "unlike self-involved experts, statistical regressions don't have egos or feelings,"[14] and experts end up "systematically overconfident in describing their accuracy."[15]

Faced with scientists who convey certainty about an argument that is apparently logical, who wouldn't be reluctant to argue the alternative view? People without a scientific credential would be particularly reluctant to voice dissent. That is one reason many people tenaciously defend eco-fads by using compelling, but ultimately flawed, pseudo-science.

This false certainty can have an extremely high cost to society and to the planet.

The voices predicting resource depletion and the collapse of civilization began to become truly strident in the late 1960s. The most notable name among those forecasting catastrophe was Paul Ehrlich, whose book, *The Population Bomb*, predicted the earth simply could not keep up with the rate of population increase. He wasn't shy about making some bold predictions based on what he thought he knew. The 1980s were to be a time of poverty, famine and world war, as the carrying capacity of the earth collapsed. In 1976, Ehrlich confidently claimed, "Before 1985, mankind will enter a genuine age of scarcity … in which the accessible supplies of many key minerals will be facing depletion."

Of course these predictions were wildly off the mark. According to the United Nations, the number of people living in extreme poverty worldwide fell from 42 percent in 1990 to 25 percent in 2005, perhaps the most dramatic reduction in poverty in human history.

Ehrlich, and the others who echoed his predictions of catastrophe, dramatically overestimated their own knowledge and underestimated their uncertainty. Believing they had an accurate estimate of the world's resources, they confidently made claims about the future. But they didn't have the right information. The simplicity of the logic, however, was irresistibly seductive. Indeed, despite repeated failures, Ehrlich and others continue to apply the same logic, simply applying a different timeline. In an interview in 2008, Ehrlich told a Portland radio station that his predictions were still accurate but the timeline was simply different, arguing that "these things work on a decadal time schedule."[16] Indeed, he argued, *The Population Bomb* was too optimistic and that in many ways, the situation is far worse today than he could have imagined when he wrote the book in 1968."

One of Ehrlich's kindred spirits, Jared Diamond, even titled his book *Collapse*, predicting that modern civilization was likely to go the way of depopulated Easter Island unless we changed our ways.

While supporters of this mindset argue that such warnings are important to keep in mind when making public policy, it demonstrates how difficult and risky it is to ignore the uncertainty that exists in science. Had policymakers acted on the "science" offered by Ehrlich and others in the 1970s, the social costs would have been extreme. Population control, food and energy rationing, as well as other artificial restraints on economic prosperity would have been imposed by force. Millions, perhaps billions, of people would have been condemned to poverty as a preventative measure to avoid a future that was supposed to be even worse. Millions of people would never have known the joy of starting a family. Stagnation, imposed by heavy-handed government regulating every part of people's lives in order to meet artificial resource-reduction targets, would have been the norm.

Fortunately, policymakers did not listen to Paul Ehrlich and the worst did not happen. But there could hardly be a clearer cautionary tale of what can happen when those claiming the mantle of science are arrogant about the limits of their knowledge and glib about the human cost of their claims. The level of uncertainty involved in these predictions is so large it is difficult to characterize them as science, as opposed to personal opinion.

It is not always clear, though, how much scientists really know, and often they do not provide much help in figuring that out. Certainty conveys credibility. Being wishy-washy did not do much for Charlie Brown, and it does not do much for scientists who are trying to persuade the public.

Policymakers, presented with a scientific argument that warns of some threat to human health are put in the position of trying to figure out how certain, or uncertain, the data they are seeing really is. If we do not act, how likely are these threats to appear and how damaging will they be? If we do act, what are the costs and how much can we reduce the risk of truly serious impacts? Answering such questions is not simply like solving an equation where some of the numbers are missing. It is like solving an equation with missing numbers and being unsure whether some of the numbers you do have are trustworthy.

If there is one scientific maxim that is certain, it is that nature abhors a vacuum. The gaps left by scientific uncertainty are filled by the risk tolerance of each individual policymaker. What else can they do? How else can they decide whether to enact a policy that has certain, but hopefully small, costs, or do nothing and risk uncertain, but potentially expensive, impacts?

It is hard to be critical of policymakers who, in hindsight, make the wrong decisions given incomplete science. This means, however, that we should be extremely critical of scientists who give policymakers a false level of certainty. Humility before the data should be a tenet of scientific inquiry, and those who violate that tenet should be called to account.

Politicians who vilify critics who highlight scientific uncertainty should also come in for a serious thrashing. Blindly attacking critics substitutes political intimidation for thoughtful consideration. It is precisely why most scientists avoid the political arena. It also makes it more difficult for policymakers to engage scientists whose judgment is sound but who might lack the political skills to defend their position. Good science is sorely needed, and we need to make the field of policy discussion welcoming.

That is the paradox. We need scientists to feel they can express uncertainty, even if doing so makes it more difficult to make policy decisions. It is better to understand the real risks than to blunder forward with false confidence.

What are we trying to do again?

That does not mean decisions made in an atmosphere of uncertainty will be flawed. It is a fallacy to believe that with perfect science we can make perfect decisions and that we are lost without it. Science informs us, but it does not make decisions for us. The values of society, our priorities and goals set the right direction. Good science certainly helps us reach those goals more effectively, but it is not a substitute for them.

Indeed, a major problem in making good policy is that we can lose track of the goal, or the goal itself can change over time.

Protecting forest habitat has long been a central goal of the environmental movement, a goal symbolized in the 1990s by the spotted owl. Helping the spotted owl meant reducing demand for old growth timber. Soon, however, opposing timber harvests became a goal in itself. The ironic outcome is that some efforts to protect trees end up harming the wider environment.

To save trees, people chose plastic over paper at the grocery store. Lawmakers opposed timber harvests near their community, creating the need to ship wood long distances, which uses more energy, from countries where forestry standards are low or nonexistent. In the case of one construction project in Seattle, the builder bragged that substituting concrete and steel "saved 1,609 trees," despite the fact that the substitution increased the use of energy and greenhouse gas emissions and that concrete and steel are not renewable resources.

Policymakers need to understand that their role is to synchronize societal goals with the available science. Science can be a tremendous tool for achieving good policy, but only if the goals of the policy are clear. Good science cannot make up for the wrong goals. Good policy can take uncertain science into account, providing the ability to adjust to changing information, keeping sight of the goal.

Science and Eco-Fads

Securing the public support of scientists and of science is often seen to be the holy grail of environmental policymaking. The combination of the scientific authority conveyed by NASA scientist James Hansen and the popular appeal of movie star Darryl Hannah's allure is undeniably powerful. With eco-fads, though, there is not much difference between the two types of appeal. The judgment of scientists like Hansen is impaired by a narrowness of view that comes with his area of study, and by a misapprehension of the certainty of his conclusions, and by an undisclosed injection of his own personal values into his conclusions. There is little difference between the appeal of Hansen's seductive, but flawed, science and Hannah's seductive, but unscientific, celebrity. For supporters of the dramatic policy changes Hansen advocates, he symbolizes scientific approval, giving them a basis to support those policies. In this context, science is not an unemotional assessment of the facts. It is an emotional crutch that gives advocates of a particular policy a sense of intellectual superiority and a feeling of emotional security. Few people could be comfortable advocating for costly public policies simply because it makes them feel good. Claiming the science is on their side, however, lets policymakers and advocates feel better about their decision to push for a particular environmental policy. Providing a cloak for the emotional foundation of people's policy positions is what makes eco-fads so powerful.

Ironically, an artificial commitment to the science can actually be used to support trendy eco-fads. In such a situation, the pretense of "bringing science back" to the White House or environmental decision making is more about appearance than reality. Science is a powerful tool when used correctly, but personal bias and other influences can make "scientific" claims indistinguishable from day-to-day politics and cultural fads.

With all of these challenges, scientists are rarely in the position, or have the incentive, to identify the weaknesses in their research conclusions and to help policymakers and the public use science effectively. The burden is on the rest of us to judge the quality and limitations of the science we receive and to use it to adopt policies that promote true environmental sustainability.

Recognizing that environmental policy decisions are about more than just "following the science" is an important first step. Science, for all its deserved respect, is still a human endeavor, and it is subject to outside influences. As users of science, we need to understand that uncertainty is part of science. This is not an indictment of scientific methods. It is an indictment of those who attempt to use incomplete science as a trump card to defeat political opponents, ignoring the limitations. Identifying where science ends and personal values begin can be difficult, but it is critical if we are to make good policy decisions while using the best science available.

In some cases scientists themselves disagree about the proper policy approach, even when they offer policymakers high-quality research conclusions. The conflict comes not from the flaws in the science, but from a policy disagreement about the goal of the science. Should we place priority on thinning forests to prevent forest fires or let forests grow naturally for wildlife habitat? Science can be used to support either course, and so it should be used as a tool rather than a straightjacket. In these situations, rather than rigidly "following the science," the science is rightly used to implement policy priorities set by the public. Consumers or policymakers, looking for sound policy solutions, turn to science, hoping it will provide a clear answer to an environmental problem. But the reality is often the other way round – our values guide us to the science that helps us best achieve those goals. Our value decisions should not be at odds with scientific knowledge, but we should not be afraid of the role our principles play in guiding our decisions.

Scientific research should not be influenced by the personal values of the researchers, but good science can guide us to the ends our values support. We may not be scientists, but we can recognize good science by asking the right questions and understanding its strengths and limitations. Science is a powerful and important tool and, if we use it in the right way, we can ensure that science is used to expose eco-fads rather than support them. Then we can tell the difference between science and sex appeal.

Introduction to Part Two

It is clear that many groups have strong incentives to favor trendy environmentalism over less visible, but more environmentally friendly, approaches. Profit, political benefits and the acceptance of our peers all influence our thinking. As a result, the way politicians, business leaders, individuals and even scientists make environmental decisions has suffered, leading to policies that may actually do more environmental harm than good.

Understanding how those influences actually manifest themselves in real life can help to further illustrate the damage eco-fads have created. In the following chapters, we look at how the influences addressed in the first part of the book play out when actually applied to the environmental challenges we face. For instance:

- Claims that "old growth" forests are being destroyed to make toilet paper are false and ignore the economics of timber harvests.

- Despite their popularity as an environmental symbol, solar panels are extremely inefficient and take money away from projects that could do much more to help the environment.

- Buying food locally can be more environmentally damaging and use more energy and resources than buying food produced thousands of miles away.

- The campaign against plastic grocery bags ignores the fact that they are extremely energy-efficient and is based on exaggerated claims about their impact on the planet.

- "Green" buildings often use more energy than their nongreen counterparts.

These conclusions will come as a surprise to many, precisely because we have been repeatedly told the opposite by politicians, the media and those looking to profit from promoting the eco-fads behind these claims.

By examining forestry, climate, energy and green-living eco-fads, we can receive a more tangible understanding of the role eco-fads now play in environmental policy and purchasing. These discussions are not designed to be comprehensive on each topic. The mere fact, however, that few people have heard the objections laid out here indicates the environmental policies examined here have not been given thorough scrutiny and have benefitted from their fashionable status, which protects them from serious consideration.

There will be those who disagree with my conclusions on some of these policies. Some will make good arguments. Others' arguments, however, will be more about defending emotionally comfortable beliefs. At its heart, that is the challenge of confronting eco-fads – discerning between science and emotion. It is an ongoing process for each of us, and the assessments of environmental policies in the next chapters certainly won't be the last word.

Chapter 8

Forestry Eco-Fads

Some years ago the head of Washington state's largest environmental group sat down across the table from Washington state's Commissioner of Public Lands and me, with the group's primary activist on forestry issues in tow. They had come to discuss the state's proposed new forestry strategy.

Every ten years, Washington officials recalculate the total amount of timber that can be harvested in state-owned forests. The revenue from those harvests helps to fund public school construction. In the policy process, groups attempt to influence how restrictive harvest rules will be – how large stream buffers are, how many habitat trees are left standing, the maximum size of the area harvested and at what age trees will be harvested. Ultimately, a state board chaired by the Lands Commissioner makes the final decision.

Environmental activists asked the Lands Commissioner to leave more trees standing after every harvest, increase the size of buffers around forest streams and not harvest trees until they were an average of 80 years old. The combination of these changes, they argued, would result in a more sustainable forest over the long run, creating more wildlife habitat for spotted owls, cooler streams for salmon and more, old forests.

Making these changes would have a significant impact over the decade the plan would be in place. At stake in the decision was the amount of wildlife habitat, the revenue available for schools, jobs in timber communities and a range of other benefits. Balancing them out is a difficult process.

That balance is guided by Washington's Habitat Conservation Plan (the HCP), a blueprint that describes how much habitat for each type of wildlife should be left in each watershed. Forest ecosystems rely on a wide range of habitat to provide the full range of animals places to sleep, forage and travel. For a functioning ecosystem, forests need everything from open clearings to towering old growth forest, and everything in between. The percentages of each type of habitat are guided by the HCP, set by scientific research and agreed upon by foresters, biologists and other specialists.

Changes in forestry rules have an impact on the resulting balance of habitat types, creating more of one type and less of another. In some places more old growth is needed for creatures that require that type of forest, like spotted owls. Other places, where deer and elk benefit, need more clearings. Other animals like the lynx need all types of habitat – older forests in which to build dens and young forests where they can hunt the snowshoe hares that make up most of their diet.

The goal is to create a mosaic of habitat types across a landscape – diversity that was typical of forests before human settlement. Prior to humans arriving, forest fires and other disturbances created openings in some areas, leaving large fire-resistant trees in other places. Foresters, using an HCP and other science, attempt to replicate that pattern using planned timber harvests in place of random forest fires. The habitat targets in that plan were set with this historical pattern in mind.

After listening to the appeal of the environmental activists sitting across from us, we asked if they agreed with the habitat targets set in the current HCP. Their answer was telling. They told us that had never thought about it and did not have an opinion. This is akin to telling a driver to turn right, and then turn left, without actually knowing where you want to go. The very purpose of a habitat conservation plan is to apply the science of sustainable forestry to managing forests. Changing the rules without considering the impact on the balance of forest habitat is simply an exercise in making the rules up as we go along, based not on what is good for wildlife habitat as a whole, but what feels good at the moment.

Those emotions are inspired by the power of lush, green forests as a potent symbol of environmental stewardship.

Few things symbolize environmental protection as much as images of majestic forests. President Teddy Roosevelt is remembered in large part for his efforts to protect vast areas of forest in the western United States.

Similarly, few things are as emblematic of environmental destruction as the image of a clear-cut. The Sierra Club has even argued explicitly that if something looks bad, it is bad. The Sierra Club's spokesman on forestry issues once claimed, "Anyone can identify destructive forestry practices. You don't have to be a professional forester to recognize bad forestry any more than you have to be a doctor to recognize ill health. If logging looks bad, it is bad."[1] Indeed, in 2004, the Sierra Club in Washington state handed out packs of playing cards attacking the Republican Commissioner of Public Lands, showing pictures of the "ugliest" timber harvests in Washington as a way to accuse him of mismanagement of the forests.

One of the founders of Greenpeace, Dr. Patrick Moore, who grew up on heavily forested Vancouver Island and knows something about forests and forestry, calls the notion that looks alone indicate good or bad forest management "simplistic."[2] Moore cites another icon of environmental policy, Garrett Hardin, whose famous essay, "The Tragedy of the Commons," helped identify some of the causes of overuse of resources and environmental degradation. Hardin said, "The morality of an act cannot be determined from a photograph."[3] As tempting as it is to draw conclusions from visceral reactions to the aesthetics of timber harvests, Hardin adds, "the guts of an argument can't be photographed: they must be presented rationally – in words."

Stark images carry weight with the public, and environmental activists often use them as a substitute for rational discussion.

Finding the right balance between harvesting timber and preserving habitat is complicated. The debate often centers on the tradeoff between protecting wildlife habitat and creating jobs. That is only part of the story. Ironically, failing to balance responsible harvesting with areas where no harvests can occur can also have environmental consequences.

One problem is what happens when we prevent forest fires from playing their natural role and then fail to implement responsible thinning to create healthy forests. Fighting wildfires is the right policy. Letting them burn puts neighboring communities at risk and endangers needed wildlife habitat.

The other problem is wood is an excellent and environmentally responsible building material. Research by scientists at the University of Washington shows that substituting steel or concrete for wood in homebuilding significantly increases the amount of energy and resources used in construction. When comparing three homes, one each built with wood, concrete and steel, the research showed "wood outperformed steel in terms of greenhouse gases, energy use, air and water emissions. The wood wall outperformed concrete in all measures except water pollution, which showed no difference."[4] If reductions in timber harvest lead to increased use of concrete and steel, fewer trees may be cut, but the overall result is actually negative for the environment. The research went even further to argue in favor of harvesting timber at younger ages, stressing the fact that "intensive forest management that can grow more wood on shorter rotations rather than longer intervals between harvesting can sequester more total carbon over time." Instead of harvesting trees every 80 years, as some environmental activists want, harvesting on 40-year rotations removes more carbon from the atmosphere, reducing the risk of climate change.

Some environmentalists are beginning to recognize this science. Others, however, put their hopes in trying to slow economic growth, reducing demand for all types of construction materials. This is not likely to be a successful strategy, as shown by the fact that during economic downturns the percentage of people willing to sacrifice income for environmental protection declines significantly.

Managing all of these competing forces is difficult. At what point do we risk wildlife habitat to ensure we have enough wood for home construction? Is the simple beauty of the forest important enough to sacrifice other potential benefits – both economic and environmental?

As the science of forest management becomes more sophisticated, some of the old rules are no longer true. Policies that seemed obvious in the past are now recognized as counterproductive.

One simple truth is still true – looks can be deceiving. Responsible and sustainable forestry requires that we forget some of the well-worn slogans of the past, laying out a scientific roadmap that guides us as we work to be good stewards of the forest. This is a difficult change for some people, like the environmental activists who offered their disjointed set of recommendations for forest management. Caring for the forests that are such a precious environmental symbol requires us to take that first step to change our thinking.

Certifiably Inconsistent

So, if you can't trust your eyes, what can you trust? That is a tough question, especially when it comes to buying products that fit your values. How do we know the paper or wood products we buy have been harvested responsibly, leaving enough trees behind for wildlife, planting the next generation of trees and allowing trees to shade streams so the water remains cool for fish? Some states, like Washington, have very high standards of forestry. Other places, especially overseas, have few standards, and those that do exist can be ignored for the right price.

Further, what is the incentive to do forestry the right way? If leaving some trees standing means lost profit, how can we trust harvesters, especially those trying to scratch out a meager living in Brazil, Russia or other developing countries?

To address this problem, a group of environmentalists created a system to reward responsible foresters by certifying their practices and then allowing them to label their lumber products as "green certified." As mentioned earlier, initially the system was focused on developing countries to provide a financial incentive to raise their environmental standards to those of the developed world. Buyers would be assured the timber they bought did not contribute to deforestation or cause environmental damage, while knowing their purchases helped improve the lives of those in other countries – at a competitive price, no less. Thus was created the Forest Stewardship Council, known as FSC.

The focus of FSC, however, didn't stay on developing countries. Environmental groups in the West used FSC to pressure Home Depot stores to buy only wood that met their standards. The Rainforest Action Network (RAN) used a variety of tactics to force the company to use only FSC certified wood:

> "RAN had actively campaigned against Home Depot for more than two years, orchestrating more than 700 demonstrations against the company's purchasing policies. RAN had organized activists dressed in bear costumes and using megaphones in the rafters of Home Depot stores; it had draped the Home Depot headquarters building with 5-story banners, and it had filled billboards across the street from shareholder meetings with images of forest clear-cutting allegedly linked to Home Depot's wood purchases."[5]

Initially, the pressure paid off and Home Depot promised to transition to buying only FSC-approved products. Ultimately, however, Home Depot realized that was impractical and began offering timber from other certification systems as well.

FSC's advocates continued to move away from the voluntary, economic incentives they originally championed, favoring political mandates over voluntary agreements.

For instance, the most common "green" building standard, known as LEED, awards points only for designs that use timber harvested to the FSC standard. Federal and state agencies often explicitly prefer the use of FSC for wood and paper. Politicians are encouraged to mandate the use of FSC certified products not only over noncertified products, but over products certified under other systems.

Recognizing that the public is willing to spend more to buy environmentally certified products, other groups created competing certification systems. The Sustainable Forestry Initiative, called SFI, is the most popular alternative to FSC and actually has greater participation from forestry companies. In the United States, there are more than 163 million acres certified under the SFI system, compared to less than twenty-nine million acres that meet FSC standards. Created by timber companies, SFI's principles require certified foresters:

> "To practice sustainable forestry to meet the needs of the present without compromising the ability of future generations to meet their own needs by practicing a land stewardship ethic that integrates reforestation and the managing, growing, nurturing, and harvesting of trees for useful products with the conservation of soil, air and water quality, biological diversity, wildlife and aquatic habitat, recreation, and aesthetics."[6]

Of course there is a big difference between principles and how forestry actually occurs on the ground. The environmental community claims the system is not reliable if for no other reason than it was created by the companies who profit from timber harvests. Others argue that in many ways SFI and FSC are very similar, and in some areas SFI actually surpasses FSC, limiting the size of clear-cuts in some places where FSC does not.

Family-forest landowners have also created a rating system that fits their unique circumstances. While large companies can often set aside large contiguous areas of forest for habitat, small landowners simply don't have that flexibility. The American Tree Farm System is created for those small landowners who want to reassure potential customers that they are responsible foresters but need a system that takes account of their unique situation.

It is important to understand that family-owned forests are an important part of the mix. Despite the perception that large companies like Weyerhaeuser own most of the land, in Washington state about half of the total private forest land is owned by small landowners.

The first thing that stands out about FSC rules is that they are inconsistent. FSC sets its standards regionally. Nominally this is supposed to recognize the needs of different climates and forest types. However, regional politics play a greater role in the difference than regional environmental differences.

For instance, FSC calls for a maximum clear-cut size of sixty to eighty acres in the Pacific Coast region, but puts no limit on clear-cut size in natural forests in neighboring British Columbia or in Idaho. SFI allows an average size of 120 acres in all areas, making it more restrictive than FSC in some places, but not in others.

Additionally, future harvests can't occur adjacent to clear-cuts until that forest has regrown to seven feet in the Pacific Coast FSC region. No such rule exists in any of the other FSC regions in the U.S. except the Southeast, where it applies only to fast-growing hardwood plantations.

Finally, while the FSC rules require a 150-foot buffer along fish-bearing streams in the Pacific Coast region, the buffer is only fifty feet in the Rocky Mountain region, and FSC includes no such rule in the Lake States or Northeast regions.

To some extent, these rules reflect the different types of forest in each region. But, there is a large difference in the rules for neighboring states and provinces with similar forests. It is more likely that the FSC rules adapt as much to the political differences in each region as to local ecosystems. FSC does not represent a consistent standard that guarantees a specific level of environmental quality for all wood products. Instead, FSC makes it hard for consumers to know what they are getting because lumber that meets the FSC standard in one region might not in another.

Problems crop up when trying to compare certified wood to wood grown locally but not to FSC standards. For instance, Washington state law requires buffers of about a hundred feet around fish-bearing streams. The FSC Rocky Mountain standard requires only a fifty-foot buffer. Consumers who wish to help protect streams might pass over uncertified timber harvested in Washington state to buy FSC-certified wood from Idaho without realizing they are actually buying from a region where FSC provides less protection for streams.

The very purpose of having a system of certification and a consumer label is to make complex buying decisions easier. A labeling system that is contradictory, inconsistent and convoluted makes things worse for consumers by offering the appearance of clarity when, in fact, what that label actually means on the ground, for forests and wildlife, is anything but clear.

As a result of those inconsistencies, FSC's true effect is its utility as a political tool to mandate a particular set of environmental policies.

Its value certainly is not as economically oriented as was originally intended. FSC-certified forests represent a tiny portion of overall forestry in North America. The FSC system has, quite simply, failed to create enough impact on the market that would make it effective. The returns to foresters who use the FSC label are small or nonexistent. Although the system began with the recognition that providing a financial incentive to improve forest practices could be effective, the actual effort needed to accomplish that goal has been halfhearted.

Instead, environmental activists have turned to politics, offering political benefits to politicians who impose FSC mandates on jurisdictions by setting buying practices, imposing building standards that reward those using FSC lumber or the like. The political benefits of FSC outweigh the once-promised economic benefits. The blanket statement that buying FSC-certified wood or paper makes you a better consumer, with the associated emotional benefits, hides the inconsistencies of the system that make it difficult to determine whether that purchase truly is better for forests, wildlife and fish.

The politics of environmental labels come with a cost, and often it is the small foresters who have the hardest time paying them.

Sherry Fox's forestland is in the foothills of the Cascade Mountains in Western Washington. A small-forest landowner, she and her husband not only manage their own trees but offer their services to other family foresters who may not have the knowledge or experience to care for their land, but who love continuing the tradition of family forestry and the benefits it provides.

Her commitment to her land and stewardship of her forest earned her and her husband, Tom, recognition as the 2005 National Outstanding Tree Farmer of the Year. She worries that FSC only makes life more difficult for family foresters like her. The problem, she explains, is that strict rules requiring large set-asides leave little left for her to harvest. By locking up the economic value of the forest, FSC ends up doing the opposite of what was intended. Instead of increasing the value of forests managed to FSC standards, FSC certification may significantly decrease land values.

Traveling around the country to speak with other family foresters after she won the award, what Fox saw was consistent. "FSC certification is pretty expensive," she says. "And there is no [price] premium for wood certified under the FSC or Tree Farm system." The only benefit she identifies is that certified wood can jump to the front of the line for some purchasers.

She also highlights the challenges of fitting FSC to her forest. "The FSC rules are written for the South and East Coast," she explains. The combination of these factors means the rewards from FSC certification "haven't been what they expected."

These foresters are left with three choices. They can simply leave their forest the way it is, keeping the forest for the enjoyment it provides but giving up any economic benefit. Some choose this route, but it is expensive, and if the forest requires management or treatment of any kind, such as fighting pests or mistletoe, there is little hope to recover the cost.

Family foresters could reject FSC and seek other certification. This is the route Sherry took. The American Tree Farm System (ATFS) is crafted for small landowners, helping them keep the forest in their family by keeping it economically viable.

The ATFS certification was recently updated, following advice from "an independent panel of experts, representing academia, conservation organizations, federal and state governments, landowners, and foresters."[7] One of the benefits of ATFS, and SFI, is they both use consistent standards across the country. When consumers buy a product with those labels, they know what they are getting. Some environmentalists argue these standards are not strict enough, but with FSC's own inconsistent standards, it is hard to be certain about those purchases either.

The third route is to throw in the towel on responsible forest management and convert forestland into residential or commercial development. This approach can be a particular concern for many small-forest landowners. Most forestland owned by the federal government is far from population centers. In contrast, private forestlands are often closer to existing communities, increasing the pressure to convert by promising large financial rewards. This is an increasingly popular choice. One study focusing on Western Washington found, "Twenty-five percent of working forests in Puget Sound were converted out of forest to development and other uses between 1988 and 2004."[8] The financial rewards of selling to developers are compounded by tough limits on forestry. Family foresters find it makes more sense to sell and move than to fight. As a result, forest habitat is lost, creating the opposite outcome to what environmentalists intended when they created tough forestry standards in the first place.

All these competing factors are the reason foresters, biologists, hikers and others who care about the forest are so addicted to the word "balance." After the long and bitter fights over the spotted owl and other forestry-related environmental fights, there is a gradual movement among many people who care about forests toward recognizing that any solution that does not balance these factors will soon collapse, with serious and unintended consequences for the environment.

Certification systems strive to take account of all these influences, and some systems do a better job than others. Actually, the proliferation of certification labels is a good thing. The market for certified wood is still maturing, and although having a number of different labels can be confusing, it is already creating competition among them to demonstrate which is the most scientifically credible, offers a sustainable balance of benefits and can deliver on the economic rewards needed to encourage good stewardship of the land. Some certification systems will fail, and all of them are likely to change over time in response to these various pressures. But, market competition among the labels is certainly a good thing.

Thus far, FSC has gone too far in trying to avoid that competition, appealing to politics to short-circuit the process. That will not only end up harming foresters like Sherry Fox, it will end up harming the environment too. The best certification systems will be those that learn from the pressures they face and are adapted to actual, on-the-ground results. That will make those certification systems better and provide information consumers can be confident in so they can make accurate decisions that help the environment.

Old Saws About Old Growth

Imagine someone walking up to you and telling you these two things: "We are losing the last old growth forests in North America," and "Old growth is being used in everything from toilet paper to home construction." You might wonder how those two arguments can coexist.

On the one hand, we are concerned about the loss of beautiful old forests that provide critical wildlife habitat. In fact, some animals have a difficult time living outside those forests, making preventing the loss of such habitat even more important. The scarcity of old growth makes it extremely valuable, both in terms of providing wildlife habitat and as an economic commodity.

On the other hand, claims that old growth is being harvested for low-cost consumer products seem to be everywhere. When those who live near a forest want to block a pending timber harvest, they often will claim the area is precious old growth. Environmental groups have attacked some paper companies, claiming they destroy "ancient" forests to make toilet paper. Others claim old growth timber is used for housing construction.

So, which is it? Is old growth scarce and valuable or so cheap and plentiful it is used in everyday consumer products?

The fact is that old growth habitat truly is scarce. Heavy timber harvesting during the last century significantly reduced the amount of old growth forest. Centuries-old trees are extremely valuable due to the high quality of their wood and their extremely limited availability. So it makes little sense for environmentalists to claim that rare old growth trees are being used for some of the lowest-value products on the market, like toilet paper. The obvious conflict between these two viewpoints, however, does not occur to most people, and claims about the misuse of old growth timber are widespread.

There are more than a few of these "old saws" about old growth.

For instance, the green-building coordinator at the Washington State Department of Ecology once cited the need to protect old growth forests as a way to promote the use of FSC-certified timber in home construction. She argued that harvests following FSC's rules "**do not** contribute to the destruction of old-growth forests."[9] Lumber from old trees, however, is very expensive and is no better for home construction than lumber cut from second-growth forests that are more plentiful and far less expensive. A builder using old growth for home construction would be needlessly increasing costs with little, if any, benefit to the homebuyer.

In fact, there are few mills that can even process the large logs that come from old growth forests. As a result, it is difficult to find a price for lumber from old trees. Ask people who routinely sell timber in the Pacific Northwest and they won't even knew where to find a price for these logs. In Washington state, where there is still a significant timber-harvesting and -milling sector, we simply don't harvest old growth under FSC rules, or under any other set of rules for that matter.

Another claim made by groups like Greenpeace and the Natural Resources Defense Council that has received recent attention is that old growth forests are being cut down to make toilet paper.

This claim relies on semantic games. One article says that some pulp for toilet paper comes from "old, second-growth forests."[10] Second growth is not old growth, and the insertion of the word "old" is intended to confuse readers not familiar with forest science. The definition of old growth can be complex, but in this context it means forests which have never been harvested. Second growth is, by definition, not old growth. Further, old growth is defined as having trees that are an average age of at least 160 years old, and very few forests in the West were being harvested that long ago, meaning second growth forests have not existed long enough to become "old growth."

Another claim is that paper producers receive "as much as 22 percent of its pulp from producers who cut trees in Canadian boreal forests where some trees are 200 years old."[11] This sentence could not contain more caveats. Saying "as much as" indicates that the actual number is unknown, which the environmental groups who make this claim admit. The paper-making pulp itself is not from old growth forests, but is sold by producers who *may* cut trees somewhere else.

The age of "some" individual trees is not indicative of the quality of overall habitat, which is the critical issue for ecosystems. Indeed the term "old growth" is used by foresters not to describe individual trees, but an ecosystem of many trees. Some urban areas have trees over 200 years old; that does not make the neighborhood an old growth forest. Old forests can, of course, include many old, majestic trees. But old growth habitat can also be replicated in younger forests by thinning and creating a similar ecosystem. There are forests with old trees that are quite poor in their ability to support the creatures that need old growth forest.

Those who claim old growth forests are being harvested to make toilet paper intentionally or ignorantly conflate the actual science of old growth habitat.

But that is not the gravest error made by environmentalists who make these claims.

Trees in boreal forests are not harvested for pulp, which is a very low-value product. Pulp is a byproduct of making higher-value products like lumber. Wood scraps from that production would go to waste if it were not used to make pulp, chips or other wood-based products. In the way some environmentalists enthusiastically praise Native Americans for using every part of an animal, market competition has pushed sawmills to use every part of the tree. Some pulp comes from these wood scraps. If some of those scraps are from old growth timber, the trees were cut for a different, higher-value purpose, and using the scraps to make paper is the alternative to throwing them away.

Environmental groups would likely argue that old growth forests should not be harvested for any reason. That is fair enough. But claiming these forests are harvested to make toilet paper, which is perhaps the least valuable product in the process, is like claiming people drive their cars simply to enjoy the air conditioning.

Finally, some environmental activists claim that not using toilet paper from any non-recycled source would protect trees. Allen Hershkowitz of the Natural Resources Defense Council says, "No forest of any kind should be used to make toilet paper."[12] I suppose it depends on his definition of "forest," but this mindset may actually increase the loss of forest habitat. Hardwood tree farms, which are used by birds and other animals as habitat, exist due to the demand for pulp. If the demand went away, landowners would find other uses for their land, converting forestland to other profitable uses. Decreasing demand for paper products does not mean the forests will remain standing.

This is the real irony. While some people argue that we ought to only purchase products made with recycled paper, this does not mean the trees that would have been harvested will simply be left as they are. They may be replaced with other crops or land uses.

Using the protection of old growth to promote eco-fads (like FSC-certified wood, toilet paper made from recycled paper, etc.) is a common tactic when used to oppose all timber harvesting. Majestic old forests are a powerful visual image, and protecting them evokes strong personal emotions. Many of the claims about cutting old growth harvesting, however, are misleading. The value of old growth forests lies in their scarcity. That very scarcity makes it counterproductive to use high-quality trees from those forests for anything other than high-value products or products for which less expensive material is not available.

This is not a trivial issue for me. While at the Washington State Department of Natural Resources, I worked with others to craft the state's first ban on old growth harvesting in state-managed forests. It was important to protect the remaining high-quality, old growth habitat in the state. Further, there was little market for those trees even if we did harvest them. In this case, economic value and environmental value went hand-in-hand.

Many claims about old growth forests, however, are simply an attempt to oppose timber harvests in forests that do not actually constitute old growth habitat. Big, old trees often look much like big, young trees, and it is easy to mislead the public and others about the true age and environmental value of a particular forest. How a forest looks is more important to some people than how that forest actually functions in an ecosystem, which leads to inaccurate claims.

If there were no tradeoffs, that might not be a problem. In reality, as long as there is demand for construction materials, the best way to protect the environment is to use a material that is renewable and consumes the lowest amount of energy in its production. That material is wood.

Healthy Forests – Nature or Nurture?

The battle over old growth forests found its way to the debate about healthy forests.

In 2002, the Biscuit Fire in southern Oregon burned about half a million acres of forestland, including an area protected as wilderness. Once the fire was put out, a controversy erupted over how to restore the forest – which trees should be logged and which should be left standing – and over how to pay for the potentially enormous cost of restoration and replanting. The question of how to manage the site after the flames were out rekindled the discussion of forest management – before and after a fire.

There is one thing many people agree upon: giant fires like this are becoming more common. Some people blame increasing temperatures associated with climate change. Hotter summers mean drier forests and more fires.

There is another cause, however, that plays an important role in the frequency of wild fires: forest health.

For decades, after a timber harvest was complete, loggers would replant the species they believed would be most commercially viable in the future. In many cases this meant planting trees that were different from those that had grown there naturally. Additionally, these new forests were not subjected to the intermittent fires that would have occurred naturally. Over the millennia, fires swept through forests, creating large burn areas in some forests. In other forests, fires would burn more regularly, leaving the strongest trees standing while destroying smaller, competing trees and plants that claimed a share of the limited light, water and nutrients.

Replanted industrial forests, however, did not use fire to clear out forests in the same way. Replanted forests relied on regular thinnings, harvesting the smaller trees to leave strong, healthy ones behind. Too many trees fighting for water and nutrients leaves forests with tall, but thin, trees that struggle for every bit of water and sun. The result, too often, is a forest that is crowded and unhealthy. Thinning helps prevent that incendiary situation.

Ironically, this creates misleading statistics. Some people who support increased timber harvesting like to highlight the fact that there are more trees in U.S. forests today than there were decades ago. This statistic is often used to show that we are not losing forests in the United States. The problem is that more trees on fewer acres is actually a bad thing. The important point is not the number of trees, but the ratio of trees to acreage. Fortunately, in the last decade we have also seen an increase in the number of forested acres in North America. That is the key piece of information.

When trees do not have enough energy due to over-competition, they are less able to combat some of the threats they face. Trees prioritize their energy use, putting their growth first into building height and root structure, then to size and other priorities like reproduction. Toward the end of the list of priorities for trees is fighting pests by emitting sap to expel them. If you have ever seen amber jewelry with a bug trapped inside, this is exactly what occurred. The plant secreted sap to protect itself from the attacking insect, and later it hardened to amber.

If trees do not have enough energy, however, they cannot defend themselves, and invading pests can take hold. Infestations of beetles and other insects can kill large areas of the forest, leaving standing, dry, dead timber that is an invitation to fire.

This can occur where forestland was replanted but not thinned. It can also occur where the natural pattern of occasional forest fires has been interrupted. As the amount of forest habitat shrinks due to incursion of nearby homes, each bit of forest habitat becomes more valuable. As those built-up communities encroach, fires in the forest can spread quickly, risking homes and human lives in the process.

Federal forests often have the worst of both worlds. Thinning is not allowed or is discouraged in federal wilderness areas. Fire, which could also do the job, is also frowned upon because of the risk to nearby communities. As a result, forests become overstocked, with many small trees chocking up the land until they resemble standing matchsticks.

Some people in the environmental community argue that humans caused this condition. They are right.

Timber harvesting that occurred half a century ago, when forestry science was less mature, played a role in some places. Fire suppression also played a role, leaving too many trees on too few acres.

Since humans caused the problem, they argue, nature should be allowed to fix it. Here, they are wrong.

Even if Mother Nature were allowed to play its traditional role in creating forest health, the forests are not in a natural state, making any fire an unnatural event. In many cases these unnatural fires burn hot and can even sterilize the soil, making it difficult for new trees to return in the near term. Hot fires can also spread to forests that would otherwise be able to resist a fire. Once a fire begins, it can turn into a freight train, swiftly moving through areas of critical habitat.

While at the Department of Natural Resources, I worked as a public information officer on a fire team in north central Washington where the blaze had moved into an area designated as protected because of a spotted owl nest located there. The best guess of the biologists was that the nest site had been destroyed. As seductive as it might be to let nature solve the problem, letting fires burn in unhealthy forests is a bit like hoping that toxic waste sites will fix themselves naturally.

The answer is to allow managed thinning of these forests to return them to a more natural state. Thinning, however, is expensive. The low-quality timber retrieved may not even cover the cost of the thinning. In an industrial forest, thinnings are a cost of doing business, a planned investment in the forest to ensure the trees grow well and yield high-value timber.

In federal forests, however, there is a tremendous amount of work to do, and limited federal budgets do not allow the Forest Service to complete the work in a timely fashion, leaving large areas of unhealthy forest standing, creating all the fire risks that come with unhealthy trees crowded together. Since there is little harvesting in federal forests, money spent on thinning operations is unlikely to be recovered.

So what is the solution? The best answer is to allow some additional harvesting to help cover the costs of healthy forest management. This is where the fighting begins, and it is at the center of the debate over the Biscuit Fire.

In 2006, the magazine *Science* published a one-page story about new research on the aftermath of the Biscuit Fire, giving ammunition to those who oppose active management of forests before and after forest fires. The study, by an Oregon State University (OSU) masters candidate, said the negative environmental impacts of salvage logging after a fire compounded the impact of the fire itself. The author, Dan Donato, argued that post-fire salvage logging destroyed many of the naturally regrowing seedlings and the result was worse than if the burned area had been left to regrow on its own. Donato's implication was that salvage logging was being approved purely as a business decision and that the environmental impacts were being neglected.

That one-page article set off a firestorm of its own.

Other forest scientists quickly refuted a number of elements of the study. They noted that the salvage logging did not occur immediately after the fire, as planned, but was delayed. Michael Newton, professor emeritus at OSU noted, "Had the salvage logging taken place before the seeds had germinated, the seedlings would not have been injured. But it was delayed for three years by legal action." Ironically, environmental lawsuits delayed the logging, creating the circumstances environmental activists later decried.

That was not the only problem with the study. The actual research had not been completed at the time *Science* ran the piece, and there were considerations that had not yet been included. For instance, no data about the regrowth of shrubs, which can squeeze out tree seedlings, was provided. On government land, money from timber harvests is used in part to fund removal of shrubs to ensure speedy recovery of forestland. Without adequate funding, shrubs and other competing plants might have crowded out young trees, making it more difficult for them to reestablish the forest.

Others weighed in as well. Congressman Brian Baird, a Democrat from southwest Washington state, added his own criticism in a response published in *Science*. Congressman Baird noted that while the emphasis of the original article was only on the number of seedlings that had been destroyed where salvage logging had occurred, the mortality of seedlings on plots that had not been logged was also high and, in some cases, similar. This made it difficult to draw scientifically valid conclusions. As a result, Baird argued, the "results of this study should not be used to make broad inferences about the impacts of other post-fire harvest practices on forest health and recovery."[13]

Indeed, some of Donato's own professors at Oregon State University weighed in against his article, calling the reported results premature and inaccurate.

Increasing the skepticism about their research, Donato and his coauthors refused to release their data to Congressman Baird. They did not say there was not enough time to collect the data, only that they were not required to. This explanation not only violates a key tenet of scientific inquiry, but is an ironic suppression of their own data.

Some came to Donato's defense. Richard York, an assistant professor of sociology at the University of Oregon, attacked those who questioned Donato's results, including the leadership of OSU's forestry college, saying, "Although it is heartening that there are more than a few scientists, like Donato and Chapela, who are willing to go against powerful interests, attempts to suppress research findings that conflict with corporate agendas ought to spur the public to question how power is distributed in our world."[14] Although he had no experience in forestry science, he was quick to accuse those who doubted Donato's results of playing politics.

Ironically, just a few months after the political controversy, a study by Auburn University found that the OSU College of Forestry published more leading research and was cited more often by other researchers than any other forestry school in the country. The study confirmed OSU's reputation as a "research powerhouse," and backed up a 2002 study of academic leaders that called OSU the top forestry school. As much as York and others might like to claim that Oregon State was playing politics by being "willing to go against powerful interests," the evidence indicates the opposite. In fact, the original draft of Donato's piece specifically expressed the author's desire to influence the debate occurring in Congress regarding salvage logging. Recognizing that this comment might betray a political agenda, it was removed before publication.

Of course, there were also claims that old growth forests were being harvested as part of the salvage logging operation. But some of the "old growth" involved was only about 80 years old, far short of the 160-plus-years minimum age of naturally occurring old growth forests.

How do we sort through such a confused maelstrom? Politics clearly became a decisive part of the debate, with some people citing only the scientific findings they believed supported their desired outcome. This one fire generated claims of industrial and political interference, science released prematurely to influence a Congressional debate, sociology professors impugning the science of the deans of a much-admired forestry program, and assertions that old growth forests were being clear-cut. Much of this debate, however, only serves to, and is intended to, distract from the central question: How do we return forests to a healthy, fire-resistant state that more closely resembles natural patterns?

Ultimately, the debate comes down to the question of how best to manage unhealthy forests. It is clear the federal government does not have the funding to thin forests in danger of unnatural, catastrophic fire. It is also clear that managing a burned area, putting it back on the path to recovery, takes funding the government does not have. Given that circumstance, foresters generally agree that working with private timber companies is the only feasible way to do the thinning work that needs to be done. Ignoring that reality means choosing environmental ideology over the environmental reality that since humans created this problem, humans must play a role in returning the forests to a more natural state. Only then can we honestly consider returning limited fire to the forest and allowing nature to play the role it once did in areas of wilderness.

Forestry That Is For the Trees

Noted architect Frank Lloyd Wright framed it this way: "The best friend on earth of man is the tree. When we use the tree respectfully and economically, we have one of the greatest resources on the earth." Forests also offer imagery that is central to understanding our stewardship of the earth. This tension, between the benefits of using an energy-efficient and renewable resource and the negative images associated with that use, makes forestry a particularly powerful source of trendy environmental claims.

After all, who wants to destroy old growth forests to make toilet paper? Who wouldn't want to buy construction lumber that is "certified" to protect the environment? And given a choice between the humans who created unhealthy forests and a natural solution, it isn't easy to argue that we should rely on humans to get it right this time.

The reality, however, is that many of the claims we hear regarding the care of forests are incomplete or completely inaccurate. Old growth trees are simply too valuable to be used to make toilet paper. Certification systems like the Forest Stewardship Council reflect a political agenda, hiding unscientific value judgments and inconsistent standards behind an attractive label.

Even traditional fights, like those over spotted owl habitat, have become more complex. It now appears that another owl, the barred owl, represents a greater threat to the spotted owl than does logging. Indeed, the (Portland) Oregonian newspaper, which has often called for more protection for spotted owls from human activity, now recognizes that the natural threat from the barred owl is far more relevant, even asking, "Can a 12-gauge shotgun be a conservation tool?"[15] The Oregonian even went further, noting, "The new owl plan is in line with the emerging consensus that not only is there a role for commercial logging and thinning in public forests, there's an absolute need for it. For the first time since the spotted owl fluttered to the fore of the Northwest timber debate, there's broad agreement that forest thinning and timber production can be compatible with wildlife conservation and habitat restoration." This is a remarkable statement, one that just a few years ago would have been dismissed by environmentalists as nothing more than a defense of "corporate agendas."

But the old forest politics won't quickly be displaced by new science. Many people in the environmental community got their start fighting logging, and it will be difficult for them to recognize that the struggles of the 1980s are long-gone.

Clinging to those old slogans by promoting trendy certification systems and substituting politics for science, however, is the worst thing we can do for the forests and the planet. If we substitute high-energy-using concrete and steel for sustainable wood products, we do more harm. If we pick the FSC label over wood harvested to a higher environmental standard, but without the label, we do more harm. If we reject forest thinning or salvage logging in the hope that nature alone will heal unhealthy forests through massive, catastrophic fires, we do more harm.

The good news is that forestry offers the opportunity to be environmentally responsible while producing the goods, and jobs, we need. Forestry is one area where humans can work with nature to the benefit of both.

Chapter 9

The Power of Energy Eco-Fads

Imagine an increase in energy demand equal to what two and a half new countries the size of the United States would require in the next twenty years – with 750 million people enjoying one of the highest standards of living on the planet. That is the increase in energy demand the world expects to see in the coming two decades,[1] adding new energy consumption that is greater than the amount used worldwide in 1970.

Is it any wonder debates about where to get that energy are such a central part of the debate about humanity's impact on the planet? Is it any wonder that many people are seeking to profit by controlling or predicting where all of that energy will come from?

Politicians who want to ride the next surge of technological innovation while helping the planet have zeroed in on renewable energy as the latest form of economic and environmentally friendly development. Washington state congressman Jay Inslee has called for an Apollo-type program to promote more energy innovation. He says quite simply, "Clean and renewable energy technologies are the next wave of new industries that will create millions of new jobs."[2] He and other politicians hope to tap into new industries by favoring technologies like solar and wind power, encouraging innovation in targeted businesses and moving the world beyond carbon-emitting energy.

If we are going to take the next technological step, indeed leap, into the future, why think small? In Washington state, politicians and businesses saw no need to take small steps.

In 2007, Imperium Renewables announced it would build the largest biofuel refinery in the United States, on the Pacific coast of Washington state. Slated to produce 100 million gallons of biofuels a year, it would dwarf existing refineries in the U.S., and its production would be only a few million gallons a year short of the largest in the world.

Situated in the former timber-port town of Aberdeen, the plant could import the palm oil and other feed stocks it needed to create the fuel from global sources, and send the finished product by ship to customers overseas or on rail cars to buyers throughout North America.

The people of the one-time boom town were thrilled at the prospect of new jobs. For decades, Aberdeen had been a thriving timber community. When the spotted owl controversy shut down harvests in nearby forests, and the mills in town, local families were hit hard. The proposed biofuel refinery held the promise of economic recovery for a community that desperately needed it.

The refinery would also benefit from favorable treatment from the state. Permitting for the plant was approved quickly and state officials artificially created a profitable market, requiring gas stations to add biofuel to every gallon of gasoline and diesel sold in the state.

Later the refinery would find a profitable market in nearby British Columbia, where the government's "Low Carbon Fuel Standard" mandate gave the product a similar favorable market.

Good jobs. Abundant clean energy. Economic recovery for a depressed community. A leadership position in an expected growth industry. Unfortunately, it didn't work out that way.

Just a few years later, the biofuel refinery was running far below capacity. It employed only 30 people, instead of the hoped-for 50 workers. As gas prices fell, so too did demand for biofuel. Although the plant had the capacity to produce 100 million gallons annually, in 2010 the CEO was cheerfully noting that the plant had produced at nearly 50 percent of capacity in the first quarter. While offering a rosy outlook for the future, refinery owners still relied on special tax breaks from the federal government to make their business viable. "What the industry needs," CEO John Plaza told an industry newsletter, "is a two-fold support, a mandated floor, and incentives with tax policy to get the outcomes we're trying for."[3] He was saying that without federal mandates requiring consumers to buy a certain amount of biofuel (a "floor") and a public subsidy to help pay production costs, biofuel companies like his would continue to struggle.

What can one say about an industry that "only" needs government to force people to buy your product while subsidizing production to artificially lower the price? Pet rocks had a similar business strategy, but didn't hire the right lobbyists.

Washington state's biofuel manufacturers, however, are not the only ones promoting a renewable energy project that claims to be the "world's largest." In 2009, a group of investors announced with great fanfare a proposal to create the world's largest photovoltaic solar energy plant. Known as the "Teanaway Solar Reserve," the project would have an installed capacity to produce about 75 megawatts. Proponents told The Seattle Times, "The 'solar park' would produce enough electricity for 45,000 homes, and no greenhouse gases."[4] The project was welcome in Washington state where utilities are required by law to buy at least 15 percent of their energy from renewable sources, like solar power, by 2020. With customer demand required by law, these investors would know they had a virtually guaranteed market for the solar energy they produce.

And they promised to offer that energy at rock-bottom rates. Initially the project was estimated to cost "north of $100 million"[5] for a cost of $1,333 per installed kilowatt. Compared to the standard cost of around $7,000 per installed kilowatt for solar power, the price was tremendously inexpensive. How could anything possibly go wrong?

Here's how: First, as time went on, it became clear that "north of" meant something like "Alaska is 'north of' the equator." Instead of $100 million, the Northwest Power and Conservation Council estimated the actual construction cost would end up somewhere between $525 million and $750 million.[6] The group financing the project argued the cost would not go that high but did admit the cost would be in the $300-million range, going on to concede that "The final project cost numbers will likely change again."[7] While the proponents hoped to have the project up and running by the end of 2011, construction still had not begun at the beginning of that year. Indeed, in early 2011, the builders asked the Washington State Legislature for additional regulation, to improve the value of their project even further.

So, what happened to these two projects, one solar and one biofuel, both touted as the "largest" in either America or the world? The simple answer is reality happened. Both projects emphasized the eco-fad sex appeal of being on the cutting edge of the green energy wave. These projects were seductive to investors and politicians alike. Politicians of both parties lined up to offer support, touting the potential to create jobs and make Washington state a leader in this innovative new industry.

The promises, however, did not hold up. The same limits that applied to other manufacturers of biofuels and solar projects applied here, limiting the market and driving costs up.

What is especially striking is how quickly the projects ran into trouble. Imperium's plant was failing only two years after opening. The Teanaway Solar Reserve saw its initial construction estimate rise by 300 percent less than one month after it was announced. Innovation is difficult, especially at the level of the "world's largest." These projects remind us of the danger of jumping on board the latest energy eco-fad, hoping we can accurately predict the technologies that will satisfy the world's dramatically increasing thirst for energy. Planners tend to fight the last war rather than seeing what is ahead. Predicting what is to come is difficult, if not impossible.

When it comes to energy production, however, many people believe they can accurately see what is to come and are crafting regulations to steer events in their preferred direction. Given the magnitude of the projected demand for energy in the coming years, we are likely to see many more people who hope to meet that demand by promising to harness the power of the latest eco-fad.

To make wise decisions, we can't let the pursuit of subsidized profits trump science. Instead, we should encourage many flowers to bloom.

Expanding our options expands our horizons, opening new opportunities to sustainably provide the energy needed to lift people in developing nations out of poverty. When it comes to energy, however, we are narrowing our focus, putting our hopes in a few trendy options and placing our energy future on a platform with an increasingly narrow base.

Biofuel Follies

How political have alternative fuels become? Here is a short quiz. Who said the following?

> "It is not a good policy to have these massive subsidies for (U.S.) first generation ethanol. First generation ethanol I think was a mistake. The energy conversion ratios are at best very small. It's hard once such a program is put in place to deal with the lobbies that keep it going."[8]

Just a few years ago, saying such a thing would have branded you as a defender of big oil. The person who said this, however, won't be mistaken for a friend of the oil industry. It is none other than Al Gore. This, rightly, comes as a shock to many people who have listened to the former V.P. promote subsidies for corn-based ethanol and other biofuels over the years. Gore admits his previous support for biofuels had more to do with politics than with protecting the environment. "One of the reasons I made that mistake" of supporting ethanol, said Gore, "is that I paid particular attention to the farmers in my home state of Tennessee, and I had a certain fondness for the farmers in the state of Iowa because I was about to run for president."[9] He knew burning corn-based ethanol was not good for the environment, but he wanted to buy the votes he needed in his home state and in a state with critical presidential caucuses.

Gore now admits his short-term political interests created long-term problems for the environment. Instead of helping to eliminate subsidies when it became clear corn-based ethanol does not reduce carbon emissions, Gore sought to benefit politically from directing taxpayer subsidies to powerful agricultural interests, resulting in a policy that wasted scarce taxpayer funds on a program that is actually counterproductive for the environment.

Across the country, policymakers have promoted biofuels as a supposedly easy way to create jobs, develop a profitable industry, protect farmers and help the environment. Boosters have tried a range of strategies to make this idea work, from providing tax subsidies, to requiring motorists to purchase biofuels, to helping export biofuels produced in the U.S. These strategies have not only failed to achieve the results promised by politicians, they have often backfired, wasting money on bad ideas and creating entrenched special interests that fight to continue the bad policies long after everyone recognized that biofuels are a failure.

In 2010, the Congressional Budget Office (CBO) conducted an analysis of the cost of America's biofuel policy to help policymakers better understand how the policy affects the federal budget and the environment. CBO Director Doug Elmendorf outlined the many policies promoting biofuel production, writing on his blog that "Tax credits encourage the production and sale of biofuels in the United States, while federal mandates specify minimum amounts and types of biofuel usage each year through 2022."[10] These credits reduced tax revenue to the federal government by about $6 billion in 2009 alone.

Even in an era of trillion-dollar deficits, six billion dollars is quite a bit of money. What did we get for those tax credits? To reduce the use of one gallon of gas, and the carbon emissions associated with it, it cost taxpayers $1.78 for corn-based ethanol. Cellulosic ethanol, biofuel made from grasses or wood, costs taxpayers $3.00 per gallon – essentially doubling the price of a gallon of gas. Biodiesel was only slightly better, at $2.55 per gallon. These amounts represent only the additional subsidy, not the total cost of each gallon produced. In other words, the actual cost of each gallon of biofuel is twice, or more, the cost of traditional fuels.

Some people argue that to reduce our impact on the climate by cutting carbon emissions we need to spend money. That is true, but the relevant question is whether money is spent wisely. The CBO found that biofuel subsidies failed there as well. While the cost to reduce a ton of carbon in Europe was about $20, as measured on the European carbon market, the cost to reduce a ton of carbon in the U.S., by using biofuel subsidies, was dramatically higher: "about $750 per metric ton of CO_2e (that is, per metric ton of greenhouse gases measured in terms of an equivalent amount of carbon dioxide)[d] for ethanol, about $275 per metric ton of CO_2e for cellulosic ethanol, and about $300 per metric ton of CO_2e for biodiesel."[11] Even in the best case scenario, the tax subsidy for biofuels wastes $255 of every $275 spent. Corn-based ethanol wastes $730 of every $750 spent – about 97 percent! Wasting that amount of money not only fails to take advantage of the opportunity to make a positive impact on the environment, it is unsustainable. The trouble with costly government programs, as British Prime Minister Margaret Thatcher said, is that at some point "you eventually run out of other people's money."[12] If a policy is not economically sustainable, in the long run it is not environmentally sustainable.

The transit system for King County, Washington, learned this lesson the hard way. Officials who run the system, known as "Metro," announced in 2006 that their buses would run on biofuels. Saying "Metro is recognized as having one of the cleanest transit fleets in the nation," Metro officials claimed biodiesel "also provides significant reductions in greenhouse gases that cause global warming."[13] There were many other benefits – a list similar to that once touted by Al Gore. Metro's increased "consumption of biodiesel will help stimulate the production of farm commodities that are used to manufacture biodiesel, creating benefits for both the environment and economy."[14]

It only took a short time to learn the idea didn't work out that way.

Just one year after beginning the program and with little fanfare, Metro canceled the effort as biofuel prices skyrocketed. Metro and King County were required to reduce carbon emissions by 6 percent when they joined the Chicago Climate Exchange, but the cost of achieving that goal by switching to biodiesel was climbing. Biodiesel had doubled in price, and Metro called for an

---

[d] Carbon dioxide (CO_2) is not the only greenhouse gas, but all greenhouse gases are measured in comparison to CO_2, notated as CO_2e (equivalent). For instance, methane is considered to have about 25 times the global warming potential as CO_2, so reducing a ton of methane is equivalent to 25 CO_2e.

"indefinite pause" in their purchases, with the program's manager admitting he was "taking a hard look at it in terms of both its price and the science."[15] At a time when regular diesel was selling for $4.80 a gallon, biodiesel was running about $6.00 a gallon. With economic troubles looming on the horizon, Metro officials quietly dropped the program because it could no longer afford it.

Even if the agency had been able to continue purchasing biodiesel, Metro would have been unwise to do so. Not content with paying extra for biodiesel, the transit agency also decided to pay even more to receive fuel that was produced locally. Metro argued that although the local fuel would cost an additional 6 cents per gallon, the positive impacts would outweigh the additional cost. No longer would they have to ship the fuel from Iowa, saving transportation emissions. Even with those reductions, however, the additional cost yielded almost no benefit to the environment.

Although purchasing biodiesel locally added $120,000 to the annual cost, the buy-local strategy cut carbon emissions by a paltry 350 tons, costing $343 for every metric ton of reduced carbon emissions.[16] By way of comparison, Metro could have reduced the equivalent amount of carbon for just $1,225 by purchasing carbon credits on the Chicago Climate Exchange, of which Metro was a member. Metro wasted 99 percent of the taxpayer money it spent to reduce carbon emissions by purchasing local biodiesel. At the same time, the biofuel industry it hoped to foster was already failing.

It can be argued that spending more to buy local biofuel was money well-spent. Government purchases provide the seed money to develop an industry that will be part of the emerging and lucrative "green economy." The case of biodiesel, however, shows how the combination of government promises and regulations can have the opposite result.

Odessa, Washington, is a small farming town an hour south of the Grand Coulee Dam. With the promise of new markets, the farm co-ops in town launched Inland Empire Oilseeds in 2006, a company that would turn the canola grown in the region into biodiesel and sell it to buyers across the country. At first, the company did well, finding buyers for its entire capacity. In 2009, Inland Empire hired 24 people and shipped two million gallons of oil to its customers.[17]

Generous federal biodiesel subsidies helped keep their price competitive. Additionally, the National Renewable Fuel Standard, known as the RFS, required consumers to buy a certain amount of renewable fuels each year, guaranteeing a market for fuels that met the EPA's definition of renewable. That added a price premium of another 30 to 40 cents per gallon for fuels meeting the standard.

Inland Empire Oilseeds also received a loan from the State of Washington to build biodiesel plants in the state. General Manager, Steve Starr, explained that the loan was limited to creating biodiesel, so the company did not purchase the equipment necessary to produce cooking oil and other food products, putting all of their eggs into the renewable-fuel basket.

They soon found out that the problem with relying on the government is that you can't rely on it.

First, Congress let the federal subsidy for biofuels expire in early 2010. Losing the subsidy meant losing one dollar for every gallon Inland Empire produced – millions of dollars each year the small company would have to make up some other way. Congressional leaders promised the extension would come soon, but each passing month meant company executives had to find a way to keep its price low without the subsidy.

Inland Empire's owners provided loans to the company with generous terms, letting it hang on until the hoped-for subsidy returned. The loans piled up, however, and with the extension of the subsidy looking less likely every day, the company's owners began to become reticent about each new extension of credit.

Then, in July 2010, the EPA sounded the death knell for the company. In its revision of the RFS rule, called RFS2, the EPA excluded canola-based biodiesel. Inland Empire's product no longer counted toward meeting the federal mandates. At a stroke, EPA eliminated the market for their product. "Our sales went to zero overnight," Starr explained to me.

The company had no place to go. The restrictions imposed by their state loan prevented them from diversifying, so when the biofuel market went away, so did their business.

One week after EPA released the new standards Inland Empire Oilseeds stopped production.

Months later, EPA changed its mind, allowing canola-based biodiesel to count toward the RFS. The federal subsidy was finally renewed as part of the December 2010 budget agreement. By then, however, the company's owners were badly overextended and were uninterested in risking their financial stability on further government promises. The company is now trying to get into cooking oil production as a hedge against future instability.

When asked if they regretted launching the effort, the answer is unequivocal – "absolutely yes." They say it was a mistake to build a biodiesel-only plant, and Starr told me bluntly that "nobody is going to build a dedicated biodiesel plant in the country again."[18] Pinning all of the company's hopes on the promises of politicians and government is simply too risky.

Instead of building a lucrative new green economy, the broken promises of state and federal politicians turned financially sound farm co-ops into renewable-fuel market speculators. Co-op farmers were enticed by the promise of catching a new economic wave, only to see their business collapse when the subsidies became politically unsustainable. The "green" jobs created when the plant began production were lost.

Inland Empire Oilseeds' story is one of the more dramatic examples of the biofuel bust, but it is not unique. Imperium had similar problems. Nonetheless, politicians continue to promise support for the next green energy project, attempting to lure new startups into becoming reliant on those pledges.

But the problem with biofuels does not end there. There are growing questions about whether they deliver on their environmental promises as well.

When Metro canceled its biofuel program, agency leaders cited growing evidence that "biofuels may actually do more damage to the environment than fossil fuels."[19]

A year later, that evidence led the city of Seattle to alter its purchase of biofuels.

As at Metro, city officials said buying biofuels would cut carbon emissions. Their choice of biofuels, however, led to trouble, and in 2009 the city halted the purchase of soy-based biodiesel due to "concerns that the soy-based mix it was using was more harmful to the environment than regular diesel."[20] City officials learned that crop-based biofuels actually increased total carbon emissions because farmers planted crops on increasingly poor land, reducing forests and other cover, and because of the large amounts of energy used to convert crops into fuel. When all of these factors were accounted for, some expressed concern that soy-based biodiesel was environmentally counterproductive.

Officials at Metro and the city of Seattle found their efforts to become popular leaders in cutting greenhouse gases not only increased their own costs – costs that were not sustainable in the long run – but that jumping on the latest eco-fad actually led to negative environmental consequences. Attempts to stay ahead of the political curve led the two governments to commit themselves to untested technologies. The cost, in real dollars and lost opportunities, was so significant that the city leaders and transit agency managers abandoned their biofuel plans.

Elected leaders should certainly be held accountable for putting their desire to score political points ahead of environmental benefit, but they are not the only ones who have fallen for the biofuel fad. Their mistakes seem small when compared with the federal government's policy of promoting biofuel exports.

Those who believe biofuels are the next key fuel technology also argue that the U.S. should become the world's export leader. They say this technology would reduce America's dependence on foreign oil and would put fewer dollars in the pockets of regimes we oppose, like those in Venezuela and Iran. Additionally, why shouldn't we reap the economic rewards, in profits and jobs, of getting ahead of the development curve with biofuels? To aid that process, Congress decided to hand out subsidies to companies exporting biofuels overseas. At one dollar for every gallon exported, the subsidy was pretty significant – so significant that unintended consequences quickly followed.

It turned out the subsidy was so large that European biofuel manufacturers found they could ship their product across the Atlantic, mix it as biofuel in the U.S. so it qualified for the export subsidy, then ship it back for sale in Europe. The process was called "splash and dash." One European biofuel expert told a British newspaper, "You get the subsidy for the act of blending, so people are bringing boats of soy- or palm-based biodiesel from Europe and then mixing it with a bit of local biodiesel – or even fossil-fuel diesel – and then shipping it back."[21] An owner of a Scottish biofuel producer went on to put it in starker terms: "Environmentally it's a disaster." Some people claimed up to 10 percent of Europe's biofuel exports to the U.S. was part of the scheme, earning up to $300 million in American subsidies by 2008.[22]

When compared to the original intent, the results were a dismal failure. Instead of encouraging domestic biofuel production, supporting farmers and manufacturers, the costly federal subsidy helped European biofuel manufacturers pad their balance sheets. Rather than helping the environment by promoting an alternative to carbon-based fuel, it encouraged unnecessary shipping, emitting additional carbon into the atmosphere.

That is the risk we take when politicians attempt to achieve several goals at once, putting benefits for political constituencies ahead of environmental progress. This is what motivated Al Gore to support the ethanol subsidies he later opposed. At the time, pleasing farmers in Tennessee and Iowa was more important to him than protecting the environment, even while he continued to claim the policy was good for the planet. This is why we are not likely to see significant changes in biofuel policy in the near future. For politicians, admitting failure is not only embarrassing, it risks the political benefit they have gained by pandering to U.S. farmers and biofuel manufacturers.

It is simply easier to keep public money flowing to a failed program, and to compensate by spending additional tax dollars on another promising environmental technology, than it is to admit that the original idea was a mistake.

Free Energy, For a Price

As attractive as it is to be the "world's largest," the only word that may be more attractive is "free." That is the core appeal of wind and solar energy. Once wind turbines and solar panels are installed, you just sit back and reap the rewards, letting Mother Nature do all the work. No need to drill, mine, process, ship or even supply fuel. Even Abraham Lincoln saw the potential of wind energy, saying in 1860, "Of all the forces of nature, I should think the wind contains the largest amount of motive power—that is, power to move things. … As yet, the wind is an untamed, and unharnessed force; and quite possibly one of the greatest discoveries hereafter to be made, will be the taming, and harnessing of it."[23]

The problem is that the promise of free energy makes thoughtful consideration of the costs and benefits elusive. Behavioral economist Dan Ariely notes that people have a difficult time rationally judging the benefits of tradeoffs when "free" is involved. In his book, *Predictably Irrational*, Ariely tells of research where people took the less beneficial between two options because it was free. Ariely explains that "zero is an emotional hot button – a source of irrational excitement."[24] The lure of "free" energy has a similar effect on advocates who push for wind and solar.

Before going any further, it needs to be stated that wind and solar are likely to become a growing part of worldwide energy production, and that is not necessarily a bad thing. These technologies have a role to play and, as we shall see, some arguments made against them are overblown. As with biofuels, these technologies have promise, as long as we recognize their limits and keep our eye on their drawbacks as well as their benefits.

Unfortunately, an appreciation for the limits of these technologies is not reflected in energy policy. Politicians mandate the use of wind and solar power, fixing arbitrary targets that have more to do with the fact that we have five fingers (most renewable energy targets are divisible by five) than the legitimate potential of those technologies. Add in a dose of cross-state rivalry and you will understand the reasoning behind the renewable energy policies of many states.

The primary tactic used to promote renewable energy sources is a "renewable portfolio standard." The targets vary from state to state, but each one requires that a certain percentage of energy used in a state be produced from "renewable" sources. Since wind, solar and other renewables are expensive, environmental groups and politicians have decided the best way to promote them is to simply require utilities to buy the energy, regardless of cost.

What that means in practice varies. For instance, Washington state passed a law requiring utilities to supply 15 percent of energy from renewable sources by 2020. Ironically, according to the law, carbon-free hydroelectric power, which makes up more than 70 percent of the state's electricity generation, doesn't count.

Not to be outdone, Oregon officials announced they would set the target based on the catchy slogan "25 in 25" – 25 percent of energy would be renewable by 2025.

California would not allow itself to be out-greened, and in 2008 Governor Arnold Schwarzenegger announced an executive order moving the state's target to 33 percent by 2020. The state did, however, cast a wide net, counting "biomass, solar thermal, photovoltaic, wind, geothermal, fuel cells using renewable fuels, small hydroelectric generation of 30 megawatts or less, digester gas, municipal solid waste conversion, landfill gas, ocean wave, ocean thermal, or tidal current, and any additions or enhancements to the facility using that technology."[25] Despite the target being, in all likelihood, unachievable, it does have the rare quality of not being divisible by five.

Why the large difference between targets in different states? Is it a disagreement about the science of what is possible technologically? Do they represent differing assessments of what can be achieved economically? Not really. The reason for the differences is politics. There is a tremendous amount of uncertainty regarding the future of energy production, and this creates a vacuum that invites bold statements from politicians seeking to establish a popular image and show "leadership."

Political posturing over renewable energy comes with a big price tag.

In 2010, the average American family paid 11½ cents per kilowatt hour, (kwh) and the average industrial buyer paid 6.76 cents per kwh[26], using their leverage as a bulk purchaser. By way of comparison, wind power costs between 10 and 15 cents per kwh, with photovoltaic solar (the type of energy created by solar panels), running 32 cents per kwh for residential use and 17 cents per kwh for industrial[27]. In the right circumstances, wind can be competitive. Solar, on the other hand, averages triple the cost of current energy.

The actual cost of production is even higher. These market prices are artificially reduced by the government subsidies politicians provide to support renewable energy. The high cost of solar power is unlikely to come down in the near future. According to the Energy Information Administration (EIA) the cost of generating a megawatt hour (MWh, 1,000 kilowatt hours) of energy in 2016 from renewable sources will continue to be high. The EIA anticipates it will cost about $79 to generate a MWh using natural gas[28], the cheapest form of generation. By way of comparison, wind will cost an average of $149.30 per MWh and photovoltaic solar will cost an astounding $396.10 per MWh – five times the cost of natural gas. Despite the fact that the fuel for wind and solar is free, their cost of electricity production is still very high.

These averages do mask some circumstances where wind power might make sense. The EIA says the price of electricity generated by wind turbines can vary widely. Their energy outlook notes "regional wind costs range from 91 $/MWh in the region with the best available resources in 2016 to 271 $/MWh in regions where the best sites have been claimed by 2016."[29] In some places the current wholesale cost of wind is even lower. In Washington state, some wind energy contracts are $70 per MWh.[30] For windy locations the cost is competitive with natural gas and is actually lower than the future estimate for conventional coal, which is expected to cost $100.40 per MWh in 2016. Renewable energy should be used where it is appropriate, rather than treating it as a panacea that politicians should mandate across the board.

Some people concerned about carbon emissions, however, say this is a price worth paying. The cost, they argue, of the impact of carbon-based power sources on the climate will turn out to be much greater. This view is shortsighted. To most effectively reduce carbon emissions, we need to put our scarce resources where they will make the most impact. Solar, wind and other sources of renewable energy need to be understood in relation to all the ways we can reduce carbon emissions. Lavishing funding on solar power does not make sense if we could spend a smaller amount on another technology that yielded the same environmental benefit. Fortunately, there is a research group that looked at exactly this comparison.

The analysis consultant McKinsey Company compared a wide range of strategies designed to reduce carbon emissions, ranking them by cost per metric ton of CO_2e reduced. Some of the strategies McKinsey identified, like switching to compact fluorescent light bulbs, actually save money. Other strategies, like capturing and storing carbon emitted by burning coal, are more expensive. By comparing the cost to reduce each ton of CO_2e, we can be more certain that we are putting our money to the best use, making the greatest positive impact on reducing carbon emissions for each dollar.

It also allows us to measure our expenditures as time goes on by comparing the cost per metric ton to the European Carbon Market (ECX). As part of the Kyoto Protocol, European companies have to pay for the carbon they emit by purchasing a carbon credit for each ton of CO_2e. The European Union limits the total number of carbon credits, putting a cap on the annual level of emissions. This is the "cap" of cap-and-trade. The ECX is where the "trade" portion comes from. If a company does not use its carbon credits, it can sell them to other companies that need to emit more than their credits allow. Like any market, the price of credits fluctuates based on supply and demand. If a company finds it can purchase a carbon credit for $20 but the cost of the technology to reduce carbon emissions is only $10 per metric ton, it will purchase the technology. Likewise, if the cost to install the technology is $30 a metric ton, the company will simply purchase credits on the carbon market instead.

The ECX is not a perfect market. Governments set the total supply of carbon credits available, meaning the only real flexibility is on the demand side of the equation. Although cap-and-trade is often referred to as a "market-based" solution, government dictates still play the key role in setting the price.

Still, the European Carbon Market gives some indication of the reasonable price to reduce carbon emissions. Any project that spends more than what ECX is charging is probably wasting money because a similar amount of carbon reduction could be achieved simply by purchasing carbon credits on the market.

For much of the period during 2009-10, European carbon credits sold for about $20 a metric ton.[31] By comparing the estimates provided by McKinsey with the price of carbon credits on the ECX, we can arrive at a general judgment about which technologies make sense in reducing carbon emissions.

So, how do solar and wind power do?

By this measure solar energy is a fiasco, offering little environmental benefit for very high cost. McKinsey's analysis estimates it cost $210 to reduce one metric ton of carbon emissions using solar power in 2005.[32] This is about ten times the cost of carbon credits on the ECX, making solar energy an extremely expensive, and therefore ineffective, way to cut carbon emissions. What is worse, this number may actually be too low.

A study from the Center for the Study of Energy Markets, based in California, found that the price of carbon must rise to at least $300 per metric ton to make solar energy an environmentally efficient replacement for coal.[33] To replace natural gas, the cost would have to rise to at least $600 per metric ton.

Real-world experience shows even these numbers may be low. In Germany, where government subsidies led to a boom in the installation of solar panels, the results show how expensive solar energy is. A study by economists at Ruhr University in Bochum found using solar power in Germany to reduce carbon emissions "yields abatement costs that are as high as 716 euros per [metric ton]," more than $1,000 when the cost study was made in 2008.[34] At that cost, for every metric ton of CO_2e avoided by installing solar panels, we could reduce more than fifty metric tons using other methods. If waste of money is waste of resources, then this is environmental waste on a giant scale.

McKinsey projects these numbers will come down to $29 per metric ton by 2030.[35] That, however, is a long way off, and in 2011 building solar panels is a very poor way to protect the environment.

Wind power does better, but is still expensive on average. The basic problem with wind power is it is intermittent, and the energy generation cannot be predicted from one day to the next. Indeed when demand is highest in some areas, hot summertime days, the air is still and no wind is available to contribute to meeting the increased demand for electricity. As a result, wind energy must be "firmed" by using natural gas generating plants to back it up, so utilities can meet demand when the wind is not blowing.

Still, wind power fares much better than solar, costing an average of $134 to avoid one metric ton of carbon dioxide emissions.[36] The average is not always a useful metric, because the cost of wind energy can vary widely depending on location. In optimal areas, the cost could be half that amount. The German study confirms this range, reporting a cost of 54 euros per metric ton of carbon dioxide for wind power, about $87 at the time.[37] Still wind power is four to seven times more expensive than carbon credits, on average.

Politicians, however, see solar and wind power as the energy of the future – and they want to be seen as on board. While the fuel is free, they understand the energy is not, so they have generously provided tax subsidies for renewable energy. These subsidies do not reduce the cost of the energy, they just change who is paying for it. Additionally, the subsidies do not change the environmental inefficiency of the energy – the cost to reduce each metric ton of CO_2e is the same, but utilities simply pass some of the cost to taxpayers instead of to their ratepayers. As a result, politicians and environmental activists justify the cost as a way to create "green jobs" and accelerate the process of developing the technologies. The subsidies, however, have had some serious setbacks.

In California, solar-panel maker Solyndra received "some $500 million in federal subsidies and a campaign visit from Barack Obama before laying off 17% of its work force and giving up on a new factory that was supposed to create

1,000 green jobs."[38] In Oregon, state subsidies have been so generous they ended up costing the state about forty times what was expected, but the higher cost didn't necessarily create better outcomes. A report by The Oregonian newspaper in Portland found "a wind energy project that was handed tax credits totaling $40 million," despite the fact that "this project will generate less electricity than projects that received credits totaling around $4 million."[39] These public subsidies waste not only taxpayer money, but opportunities to make a real difference in reducing carbon emissions as well.

No energy source is a panacea, and wind power may be a reasonable option in the right location. The problem arises when politicians are less than discerning, offering subsidies for any wind or solar project, regardless of its efficiency or location.

Admittedly, I have focused on the environmental costs of alternative energy and ignored other potential benefits of solar and wind, like energy independence. Some people see the high cost of wind and solar as a way to reduce demand for petroleum products from countries that represent a threat to our national security. It is one reason conservative columnist Charles Krauthammer[40] and one of Ronald Reagan's chief economists, Arthur Laffer, favor policies that increase the price of carbon-based energy. Increasing the price of that type of energy would reduce demand for foreign oil imports while spurring innovation both to develop new sources of energy and to increase conservation. These considerations make wind and solar power more viable. They do not, however, make them free, and since so much of the justification of renewable sources of energy is based on their purported environmental benefit, they have a distance to go before the push for wind and solar power can be firmly moved out of the eco-fad category.

Some Trendy Opposition to Renewable Energy

Advocates of renewable energy are not the only ones relying on trendy arguments. Opponents of wind and solar power have also made some pretty silly arguments. For instance, some people who oppose wind energy say wind turbines kill "songbirds." A songbird, however, is often simply a robin or other common bird. These bird species are not threatened or endangered. Indeed, common housecats kill far more songbirds than do wind turbines.

Other opponents, including former Energy Secretary Spencer Abraham[41], cite a new illness they call "wind turbine syndrome" in arguing against the construction of wind farms. Some people argue the syndrome is a physiological disorder, and cite vague reports of symptoms like headaches and personal stress. Others, like Abraham, say it is an illness that "some people say drives them almost crazy."[42] The reports, however, all rely on a range of undefined symptoms. Wind turbines emit about 55 decibels of sound at a quarter of a mile away, equal to the sound in a typical office.[43] I can confirm that spinning wind turbines are fairly quiet. In 2008, I was videotaping a wind-power expert standing in front of a turbine. At one point I asked him to stop talking so the camera's microphone could pick up the sound of the turbine spinning only 50 feet away.

There are good reasons to question the value of solar and wind energy, but grasping at dubious arguments in an effort to hide what is often a NIMBY (not-in-my-back-yard) objection to these energy sources is more about politics than scientific facts.

Decisions about energy policy should be made based on sound principles of economics and science, with efforts to make new energy generation fit the community. As energy policy has become increasingly politicized, however, opponents see the push for renewable energy as a part of environmental activists' efforts at "remaking the economy of the nation, the whole globe." As a result, they sometimes grab on to emotionally satisfying, but dubious, claims. Sticking with the science provides more than enough reason to limit the use of renewable energy to locations where it makes sense and reject cookie-cutter approaches like the broad and heavy-handed mandate imposed by statewide renewable portfolio standards.

A Smarter Approach to Energy

In an area like energy policy where so many eco-fads abound, it is important to understand that not every new conservation technology fits that definition. One new technology favored by many looking to conserve energy shows how we can take positive environmental steps by harnessing the environmental conscience of millions of individuals just by providing a bit of useful information.

The Delaware Electric Cooperative (DEC) is a relatively small utility, even in Delaware, serving about 83,000 customers in the rural parts of the state. That has not prevented it from pioneering an innovative approach to conservation – one that utilities across the country are seeking to replicate.

Not far from where Benjamin Franklin lectured that "a penny saved is a penny earned," DEC is encouraging its customers, more than 90 percent of whom are residential, to put that maxim to work. Without a single major customer who could make significant energy reductions, the only hope was to find a way to encourage each of those many homeowners to reduce their energy use, especially at the time during the day known as the peak, when overall demand, and therefore prices, are highest.

The approach, advocated by DEC's President and CEO Bill Andrew, was to put the power in the hands of the utility's customers, giving them the information they needed to help cut demand when it would make the most difference for the utility's costs. The utility began a campaign called "Beat the Peak" designed to tell customers when small cuts in energy use would yield big savings.

Customers who signed up received a package containing three compact fluorescent light bulbs and an "in-home indicator," the size of an aspirin bottle, which they plugged into an outlet. The utility sends a signal to the in-home indicator, illuminating lights as a signal to customers. When energy demand is normal, the indicator's green light glows. As power demand rises, the utility sends a signal lighting a yellow light, encouraging customers to reduce discretionary energy use. When demand hits peak levels, the red light glows, encouraging homeowners to turn off as much energy as feasible. Although the utility strongly encourages customers to conserve during these peak periods, in the end the choice rests with the homeowner. Utility customers can turn off a lot, or a little, or nothing. It is their choice.

Despite relying on voluntary behavior, the results were substantial. "While similar co-ops in Virginia saw demand increase by 15 percent in November, we were $300,000 under demand – about 11 percent," says Andrew. The impact on rates has been significant. After only a year of the program, DEC lowered its rates by $10 million in 2010 and plans to reduce rates further in 2011.

These results are in large part due to the way the utility's customers have embraced the program. DEC set a goal of delivering 20,000 of the meters to their customers in the first year. "People thought we were crazy," said Andrew of the reaction of his colleagues to that aggressive target. By the end of the first year, however, the utility had run out of the meters and had to order another 10,000 of them. Nearly 40 percent of its customers now participate in the voluntary conservation program.

The effort demonstrates the power of information about prices, a key element of any free-market system. Although customers received some benefit at the end of each month by turning off unnecessary appliances and reducing household demand, the real payoff comes in the form of reduced utility rates. The success of the program results from harnessing the information each customer has about his or her ability to reduce electricity demand. Only I know what electric use is optional and what is necessary, and I can figure out ways to conserve energy that suits my lifestyle. No system imposed from the top has that capacity, which is why centralized approaches are less effective – they work against people instead of engaging them on a voluntary basis.

Delaware Electric Cooperative's system is one implementation of what people are calling the "Smart Grid," a system that takes advantage of new information technology to manage energy demand and provide incentives for individuals to become more efficient. DEC says its approach was built on the notion that "the customer is the most important part of a Smart Grid."[44] By putting customers at the center of the decision-making process, rather than dictating from above, simple signals yielded significant savings. The system used by DEC was relatively inexpensive – a software program that cost just over $1 million. Given the results, it was well worth the investment.

Others are looking at an approach that takes Smart Grid to another level.

Carl Imhoff is manager of the Electricity Infrastructure Market Sector at the Department of Energy's Pacific Northwest National Laboratory (PNNL), in Richland, Washington. Just a few miles from where the material for the first atomic bomb was created, PNNL is researching ways to make the electric grid more robust and improve its ability to adapt to the new demands it faces in integrating a wide range of energy sources and growing demand into the future.

Although the term "Smart Grid" has only become popular in recent years, the idea of making a dramatic leap forward in the grid's operation took shape in the mid-1990s. With new information technology, PNNL is working to offer electric customers the ability to respond to price signals and to give utilities more options at managing supply and demand. "We never had the ability to see those opportunities" before computers made them possible, explains Imhoff. "That's the magic of what is called 'Smart Grid,' the digitization of the power system."[45]

PNNL is focusing on three key elements of Smart Grid: sensing, two-way communication and distributed control.

Improved sensing allows managers of the electrical grid to keep the system running efficiently, incorporating intermittent sources of power like solar and wind, and keep the power flowing even when there are major outages at generating plants.

Two-way communication allows customers to receive price signals and send information to the utility. Combined with distributed control, the ability to turn appliances that have been chosen by the customer on and off, these elements of Smart Grid put free-market signals to work in a way that is more robust than the simple system offered in Delaware.

To test this approach, in 2005 PNNL launched a program called GridWise on Washington state's Olympic Peninsula to see what results could be achieved by implementing a small version of Smart Grid technologies. Equipment allowing two-way communications between the utility and the customer, sharing price and demand information every five minutes, was offered to 112 homes.

Based on settings chosen by the customer, the system could then turn off certain appliances, including clothes dryers and hot water heaters, or change the setting on the thermostat. During periods of high demand, the system could turn off the heating element of clothes dryers for three to five minutes. Appliances were designed to appear as if they were working normally so homeowners wouldn't wonder if their dryer was broken. The tumbler would continue to turn, but the heat would turn off temporarily when it received a signal from the Smart Grid.

Other appliances worked in a similar way – limiting the inconvenience, but reducing demand at key moments.

To determine how the system managed the appliances in their home, customers set a general level of price sensitivity using a tool on the Internet. Some told the system to cut energy costs as much as possible. Others indicated a desire to directly control their electricity use, preventing the system from automatically turning off appliances. The system worked much as a financial planner would manage a stock portfolio for a client. The GridWise system took guidance from the customer and managed electricity demand in response to the settings. And if customers wanted to override the system, they could do so.

As in Delaware, the goal was to improve energy conservation consistent with customer demands and guidance. "We wanted to see if we could leverage some simple incentive signals," says Imhoff.

The test began in 2006 and ran for two years. The results were exciting. Demand was reduced by 10 percent, yielding a rebate check for customers based on their level of participation in the program. Perhaps more important was the 15 percent reduction in peak demand. Utilities plan investments in energy generation and purchasing based on expected peak demand. By reducing peak demand, utilities can avoid making expensive investments and help keep utility rates low.

The ability of the system to work with customers' demands was critical to its success. Of those who participated, 93 percent said they would participate again in the future.

Like the development of the current electrical grid, completing the Smart Grid will be "a multi-decade journey," says Imhoff. But the benefits could be significant. In addition to keeping electricity rates low, Imhoff cites research that found implementing the Smart Grid nationwide could reduce CO_2 emissions by 12 percent by 2030.[46]

When Smart Grid is used to empower individuals, it can be a powerful tool to improve energy efficiency and reduce environmental impacts. Giving consumers control not only respects the individual freedom that is the foundation of the American system, it is more effective at finding ways to cut energy use in ways that are the least expensive and least intrusive.

Smart Grid offers the opportunity to make a dent in the debate about which is more important – personal freedom or the environment. By giving people incentives and information, the Smart Grid uses personal freedom and information to promote environmental sustainability. When it comes to energy policy, where eco-fads abound, Smart Grid is a technology that has earned its growing popularity.

We Were Wrong Last Time, But This Time We Are Right

In 1977, the Stanford Research Institute made a bold claim. Solar energy, it said, "is likely to dominate the space-heating market for new construction as soon as the year 2000."[47] Now eleven years beyond that date, solar power still represents a tiny portion, less than 1 percent, of electricity and energy generation. Predicting the path of future technology is difficult, but there are strong social incentives for politicians and others to claim they are on the cutting edge of the next great technology.

Politicians want to say they made development of the next great technology possible. The lure of claiming to have invented a powerful new technology, like the Internet, is great, even if it isn't true.

Environmental activists, hoping to speed up development of technologies that will provide significant reductions in environmental impact, place their hopes in energy production trends that seem promising.

False hopes and false starts, however, actually delay the development of key technologies. On paper, solar power has been the next great technology for nearly half a century, but the real-world results are disappointing, even with significant government support.

While politicians have been chasing their favored technologies, businesses and individuals have found their own ways of significantly improving energy efficiency. The result of these individual endeavors is astonishing. Since 1977, the amount of energy used per unit of production in the United State has been cut in half.[48] This remarkable accomplishment did not occur because government mandated the use of particular technologies. Nor did it occur by making giant leaps in technology that cut energy use in large amounts. The path was incremental and consistent, with small improvements every year, pushed by our natural desire to spend less on energy and keep more money in our pockets.

New technologies have been a part of that progress, but not always in the ways we expected. Biofuels have not lived up to their promise, despite fervent political support. Solar power is still a technology of the future. Wind power is closer to practicality, and actually competitive in some locations already, but it is still relatively expensive, on average. It is likely that all of these technologies will continue to develop, making them more practical tomorrow than they are today.

Competing technologies, however, will also emerge, perhaps surpassing the potential of those we see today. The key energy technology of the future could be superconductive wires that dramatically reduce the amount of energy lost during transmission, making current energy generation technology much more efficient.

As the lifeblood of our economy and lifestyle, energy production will continue to be a hot-button issue, and we will continue to grasp at the next emerging energy fad. The path toward energy efficiency, however, is more likely to be a slow and gradual climb that takes advantage of small improvements made by each one of us.

It is the reason that while many people are drawn to the allure of "free energy" drawn from the wind and the sun, the mundane but powerful information provided by millions of individuals through the Smart Grid is more likely to be the technology that moves us toward improved environmental sustainability.

Chapter 10

Climate Eco-Fads

"This program has done much better than we ever thought it would for the environment."[1] That was California's U.S. Senator Dianne Feinstein's assessment of the federal government's "Cash for Clunkers" program just a few months after it was enacted in 2009. Designed to encourage car owners to trade their old, gas-guzzling cars for new, fuel-efficient vehicles, the program was intended to help the ailing American automobile industry by subsidizing the purchase of new cars, with the requirement that each new vehicle had to be more efficient than the one it replaced.

Sen. Feinstein was not the only one bragging about the program's success. Congressman John Dingell of Michigan said the program would "result in meaningful reductions in vehicle fleet carbon emissions." Massachusetts Congressman John Olver said Cash for Clunkers would "pave the way toward a lower-carbon future."[2]

And *Time* magazine hyperbolically claimed, "Not even the most optimistic greens could have predicted that the federal government's cash-for-clunkers program would work this well."[3]

The program offered car buyers $3,500 toward the purchase of a new car or truck with gas mileage at least four miles per gallon (MPG) better than the car they traded in. If the efficiency improvement was 10 MPG, the rebate rose to $4,500. The program was so generous that demand spiked and it lasted only one week before authorized funding ran out.

By getting aging gas guzzlers off the road and replacing them with new cars, politicians and some environmental activists expected to see significant reductions in carbon emissions.

It didn't quite work out that way.

While the politicians focused only on the volume of cars being traded, assessing the program's benefit to the environment has more to do with how well it would reduce carbon emissions for the amount of money spent. In the case of Cash for Clunkers, the taxpayers spent billions to receive only tiny improvements in fuel efficiency.

Some quick calculations show that drivers who upgraded to a car four miles per gallon more efficient than their old car cut their carbon emissions by about 14 metric tons over the life of the vehicle. The federal government paid $3,500 to realize that emission reduction, for a cost of $250 per metric ton of CO_2. This is twelve and a half times more than it costs to reduce the same amount through the European Carbon Market.

The projection was slightly better when the owner upgraded by 10 MPG, receiving a $4,500 subsidy from the government. In that case, the cost per metric ton reduced fell to about $200 dollars, only ten times what it would cost in the European Carbon Market.

Other estimates show the results were worse yet.

A professor at the University of California-Davis estimated the cost would likely end up in the range of $365 for each metric ton of carbon emissions reduced[4] – eighteen times more expensive than in Europe.

Of course, Cash for Clunkers was also designed to bail out the American auto industry (it failed that test, too, given that more Japanese than American cars were purchased under the program[5]), so it is not accurate to count the entire cost of the program toward reducing emissions. The high cost and poor results of Cash for Clunkers, however, show that if the program made any sense at all, the environmental benefits accounted for about 6 percent of the program. Although it was sold as environmentally friendly, the program was the environmental equivalent of properly inflating the tires of a Hummer and then trumpeting its improved fuel efficiency.

How can such a significant policy failure be defended when a simple analysis before the program's enactment would have predicted the results? The bleak economic atmosphere during the summer of 2009 certainly contributed, with politicians looking for visible ways to spend money in hopes of helping American auto manufacturers. The overheated rhetoric and manufactured urgency of climate change also contributed to an atmosphere that discouraged clear thinking about the real costs and benefits of Cash for Clunkers.

By defining the issue as a "climate crisis," politicians and environmental activists can argue that we simply do not have time to think about the policy – only time to act. This makes the cause of climate change the perfect excuse for people seeking to quickly implement their favored policies and avoid public questions about the impacts of those policies. This narrow attitude was best expressed in the 1980s British TV satire, "Yes Minister," when one bureaucrat explained, "Something must be done. This is something. Therefore we must do it."

This attitude has spawned more than a few eco-fads designed to address the perceived risks of global warming. And because the issue is so large, the policies that emerge from these fads are often expensive, yielding extremely poor environmental results. If climate change is anywhere near the crisis some advocates claim it is, expensive failures are extremely bad for the environment. The larger the environmental challenge, the more important it is to get the policy right. As far as climate policy goes, that has not been the trend. Eco-fads have increasingly squeezed out effective, thoughtful, though less-flashy, policy approaches.

Electric Cars Were Never Killed

Few things in the debate about climate policy inspire as much hope and high emotion as all-electric cars. While many environmental activists believe electric vehicles could have already been developed with just a nudge from government policy, others argue the technology simply is not mature enough to be practical.

The debate was inflamed by the 2006 release of a documentary called "Who Killed the Electric Car?," which claimed to chronicle the development, and eventual cancellation, of the General Motors (GM) Saturn EV1 – an electric car sold in California. A limited number of the EV1s were leased and, eventually, GM confiscated the vehicles, destroying them despite a promise not to. Conspiracy theories immediately surfaced.

Environmental activists argued GM was hiding the truth – the truth that electric cars were technically feasible but less profitable. Automakers decided to kill the technology, the activists claimed, by hiring lobbyists to help them undermine California's tough zero-emissions car mandates that required car companies to offer zero-emissions vehicles as part of their fleets. The perception was that the ability to make an affordable, electric car was not a problem of technology but simply a lack of will.

This story, though attractive in its simplicity, has some serious flaws.

First, this view assumes the "Big Three" American automakers (GM, Ford and Chrysler) control the auto market. Some people claim they colluded to stop electric-car mandates, despite the availability of the technology and regardless of the pressure they felt from Japanese and European competitors. The conspiracy theory also discounts the possibility that GM simply made a bad economic decision, ascribing bad motives, not bad judgment, to the decision not to put more investment dollars into fuel-efficient vehicles. Indeed, the Chevy Volt, the car on which GM is staking much of its future, was originally developed as part of testing for the Saturn EV1. GM's decision not to sell a version of that test vehicle as a stepping stone to an all-electric vehicle was most likely a marketing failure rather than a failure of will.

Second, if car companies wanted to avoid building electric cars, why would they offer fuel-efficient hybrid vehicles during the same period of time? If the technology was available to build appealing cars that ran on batteries half the time, why would companies like Honda and Toyota not decide to go to all-electric, unless the technology was unavailable or cost-prohibitive? The clear answer is the technology of all-electric vehicles was simply not mature enough to make them a viable option for consumers.

It should be noted that although "Who Killed the Electric Car?" mentions the low cost to operate the car, the film fails to mention the cost of building the car – other than to speculate that if demand increased the per-unit cost would come down. This approach substitutes environmental wishful thinking for economic reality.

Electric cars, in fact, never really died. Electric car companies, like Tesla, were aggressively working to build a car that was usable, affordable and could travel hundreds of miles on a charge. The workable technology, however, eluded the company. Although the Tesla Roadster is a fast and attractive vehicle that travels more than 200 miles per charge, its market price is more than $100,000 and it only seats two, and snugly at that. Are we to assume that Tesla could have made a car with more room and better range at a fraction of the price, but the company artificially kept its price high for no reason? The simple conclusion is the technology is tougher to master than advocates think.

The very question "Who killed the electric car?" is faulty. The electric car was not killed, because as a viable consumer product it was never alive.

By way of contrast, hybrid vehicles are now the most prominent green-friendly car – despite the fact they did not initially benefit from preferential government subsidies and regulations. Honda and Toyota saw the opportunity to build market share by catering to people looking for fuel efficiency. That appeal has blossomed, with hybrids becoming the very symbol of fuel economy and environmental consciousness.

So strong is the appeal of hybrids that after more than a decade of trying to regulate zero-emissions vehicles into reality, California officials decided to back down and count hybrids as part of its vehicle-emissions reduction law. In March 2008, California's air regulators "gutted rules seeking to place tens of thousands of zero-emission vehicles on the road, instead ordering automakers to produce a fleet of cleaner-burning hybrids."[6] This was not the first change they were obliged to make. In 2003, "the Air Resources Board significantly scaled back the mandate and ruled that hydrogen cars, hybrids and cleaner-burning gasoline vehicles could meet the state's goals."[7] Despite the strong efforts of politicians to will electric cars into being, practical hybrids won the day. Hybrids are a response to consumer demand, a product of the free market that became the guiding environmental technology and the symbol of drivers who wanted to signal their environmental consciousness.

Despite two decades of inventive struggle, the lure of creating a practical electric car is still very strong. Even after California rolled back its electric car mandate, the state of Washington prepared to subsidize a network of electric charging stations. A law passed in 2009 requires the state to "implement an electric vehicle and alternative-fuel vehicle infrastructure program that accelerates planning and allocation of funding for pilot projects to demonstrate the feasibility of large scale deployment of charging and alternative fuels distribution infrastructure."[8]

That same year, as the federal government was preparing to take over General Motors, a former assistant commerce secretary in the Clinton administration encouraged politicians running GM to "insist on returns that benefit society as a whole" by requiring the company to "turn out a car that gets at least 100 miles per gallon—and to do it in three years."[9] To set this goal, the former secretary did not rely on his engineering expertise. He assumed he could impose his political goal, believing the achievement of a 100-MPG car is simply a matter of summoning enough willpower.

Whether electric cars meet this goal is in the eye of the beholder. A car that achieved 100 MPG could easily have a range of 1,000 miles between fill-ups. On the other hand, the range of two new all-electric vehicles is less than 100 miles. Trips within the range, however, use no gas.

GM's flagship vehicle, the Chevy Volt, can travel about 40 miles before it switches over and uses a gasoline engine to recharge the battery. Once it switches over to the gasoline mode, it will only achieve 32 – 36 MPG. More efficient than other vehicles its size, the Volt has a retail cost of more than $41,000.[10] Even at that price, GM admits it will lose money on every Volt it sells.

Nissan's Leaf, an all-electric vehicle, has a better range for every charge, but still has some significant limits. The range of the vehicle is about 100 miles between charges and the retail cost is more than $32,000. That does not take into account the cost of installing a charging station in your home – a cost shared by the owner and taxpayers who are subsidizing the installation of a limited number of stations.

People driving beyond the electric-powered range will need to find convenient recharging stations, and to allow for significant wait time while their batteries re-energize. The challenge of building a network of convenient charging stations is real. In 2003, California hoped to build a network of hydrogen filling stations to facilitate the creation of that alternative fuel. By 2010, the state expected to have 200 stations. When 2011 rolled around, however, only twenty stations had opened.[11] Providing electricity will probably be less daunting, but there are real costs, and the project will almost certainly prove more difficult than expected.

Certainly, electric vehicles are very attractive as a technology. A workable electric car would cut carbon emissions, reduce the cost of fuel, allow us to send fewer dollars to oil-producing countries that would like to harm us and, most important to some people, electric engines are powerful, responsive and fun. With such a significant potential payoff, it is understandable that politicians would be drawn to them.

Interestingly, after so much frustration and so many false starts, electric vehicles may actually be approaching viability. Despite a relatively high price and other limits, the cost of the Volt and Leaf are nearing the market cost of traditional gas-powered vehicles. But the key reason has little to do with political mandates.

Government policies assume innovation occurs in a straight line. Politicians provide subsidies to solve particular problems. Want an electric car? Provide subsidies to develop the car. That is not always the way creativity works, however, and some technologies emerge only after supporting technologies emerge first.

Steve Marshall, an electric-car expert at Seattle's Discovery Institute, believes electric cars are now at the threshold of the very breakthrough that has been predicted for two decades. The critical innovation that put us at the brink, he says, happened independently of electric car research – in laptop computers.

The rapidly growing demand for laptops pushed innovation in batteries, encouraging manufacturers to develop batteries that were lighter and held a charge longer. "The development of laptop computer batteries extended the range of electric cars, driving the price down," says Marshall. What California's requirements and political subsidies could not achieve, innovation in a relatively unrelated market did.

That is why a broad-spectrum approach to innovation is so critical. The fixation on one technology makes it more difficult for other, competing technologies to develop. Eco-fads lure us toward the trendy, specifically excluding other approaches, narrowing the options for technical solutions.

Who is to say the next great transportation technology isn't high-speed Internet access – allowing us to cut carbon emissions and fuel costs by telecommuting, for a fraction of the price of electric cars? Perhaps a more effective alternative fuel will be developed, allowing us to use current vehicle technology while achieving the energy-independence and carbon-emissions reductions goals. Perhaps improvements in battery technology, a reduction in the weight of vehicles and other improvements will allow electric vehicles to finally achieve the promise so many have hoped for.

Most likely, a combination of these approaches will provide the answer. Probably, the best solution will emerge as hybrids did: from innovators who found a solution that best suited the demands of consumers and wanted to improve their market position by providing a better way.

The electric car never died, it just has a lot of competition, which is a good thing for the environment and consumers.

Should We Follow LEED or Get Out of the Way?

If we can make our cars green, why stop there? Why not make buildings green? After all Scott Adams, the creator of Dilbert, made his home "green." "Let's say," Adams wrote in The Wall Street Journal, "you love the Earth. You see an article in a magazine about a guy who built a 'green' house using mostly twigs, pinecones and abandoned bird nests. You want to build a green home, too. So you find an architect, show him the magazine and say, 'Give me one just like this.'"[12] That's when the trouble starts.

When Adams finished his "green" home he was shocked to find his energy bill did not go down. Why? He found that installing big windows to add light undermines energy savings because windows are poor insulators. He also found that attempting to model the energy savings of a home before it is built is "as much guessing as engineering" – making it difficult to know how well energy-saving elements will come together. And he discovered something many politicians have not figured out yet – solar panels are expensive and inefficient. He put it more colorfully when he said, "Photovoltaic systems are a waste of money. ... In my defense, the price of your future photovoltaic system will never come down unless idiots like me pay too much today. You're welcome."

It seems counterintuitive that people, smart people, could attempt to build an energy-efficient building and fail so badly. But Adams' experience is not unique. Green buildings and the most popular set of green building standards, Leadership in Energy and Environmental Design (LEED), have fallen far short of their promises again and again.

The lure of green buildings among policymakers has been significant. According to the U.S. Green Building Council (USGBC), LEED mandates in the form of "legislation, executive orders, resolutions, ordinances, policies, and incentives are found in 45 states, including 442 localities (384 cities/towns and 58 counties), 35 state governments (including the Commonwealth of Puerto Rico), 14 federal agencies or departments, and numerous public school jurisdictions and institutions of higher education across the United States."[13] Washington state is among those jurisdictions, adopting legislation in 2005 that requires all state buildings and schools to meet LEED or a similar state version known as "High Performance Building Standards."

When the legislation was first proposed, advocates of the policy promised a range of benefits. Advocates promised green buildings would "reduce ongoing utility costs by 30%," "increase student test scores by 20%" and "reduce employee absenteeism by 15%."[14] Architects, who benefit from higher fees, joined environmental activists to encourage legislators to impose the new rules, echoing these claims. With these significant savings, they said, whatever additional costs were required to meet the new regulations would quickly be recovered in energy savings.

Advocates cited one success story in particular. Legislators were told Giaudrone Middle School in Washington state's Tacoma School District, built in 2003 using green building elements realized energy savings of 35%. At that rate of savings, they insisted the school would cut its energy costs by $30,000 a year.

There was only one problem: it wasn't true.

Giaudrone was not the only middle school opened in the Tacoma School District in 2003. Mason Middle School also opened that year, but without the green elements, providing a great opportunity to compare the energy performance of green and traditional buildings. Both buildings were in the same climate, roughly the same size, had the same types of rooms, would serve a similar number of students and were constructed and finished simultaneously – a near-perfect apples-to-apples comparison.

The results are clear. Unfortunately for green building advocates, the green school actually uses about 34 percent *more* energy per square foot than its traditionally built counterpart.

Supporters eventually admitted their original claims of large cost savings weren't true. They explained that the problem was faulty equipment that had been identified and replaced. The energy savings would materialize, they promised, in the next year. Indeed, for the 2005-06 school year, the green school narrowed the gap, using only 24 percent more energy per square foot. Despite being more than 50 percent off their original target, perhaps now they were finally on the right track? In 2006-07, the green school's inefficiency again shot upward. It used 46 percent more energy per square foot than the non-green school built in the same year.

Finally, after years of holding out hope that the green school would finally yield the savings its advocates had promised, the school district admitted the building simply was not going to save energy compared to a traditionally built school. In 2009, the district's facilities director admitted, "High performance schools are not cheaper to operate than a 1920, 1930s building."[15] Ultimately, the blame doesn't lie at the feet of the facilities director, who was simply trying to make the government-mandated standards work in his district.

The problems are a result of standards set primarily for political purposes. Indeed, other districts saw the same dismal results.

In Spokane, Washington, three elementary schools were built using the green standards. One of the schools, Lincoln Heights Elementary, was expected to yield big energy savings. In a video produced by the Washington State Department of Ecology, the district's facilities director claimed the district would probably "save about $40,000 a year in utility costs"[16] at Lincoln Heights. This was a strange claim to make. Total utility costs average only $70,000 a year for elementary schools in Spokane. Saving $40,000 would mean a savings of 57 percent – an unprecedented result.

Again, however, the claim wasn't true.

Lincoln Heights did use 20 percent less energy per square foot than the district average during the 2007-08 school year. The problem with this comparison, however, was that many of the schools in the district are very old, with some dating back to 1908. Comparing two schools built 100 years apart is not an appropriate way to assess the effectiveness of green schools.

Browne Elementary, built in Spokane in 2001 without the green elements, provides a better apples-to-apples comparison. Comparing the two schools, the same pattern emerged. The green school used 15 percent more energy than the non-green building. The worst-performing green school actually used 34 percent more energy per square foot than Browne. In fact, none of the three green schools performed better than the most recently built non-green school.

After these numbers came to light, the Department of Ecology quietly removed the video with the erroneous claim from its web page.

Other districts in Washington state have seen the same failure. Both of the newest green elementary schools in the Bellevue School District, near Seattle, use more energy per square foot than the district average. The same is true of schools in the Everett School District and Northshore School District in Western Washington.

Some districts are doing better. Three green elementary schools in the Lake Washington school district east of Seattle, for instance, have the lowest energy use per square foot in their district. The savings, however, are below what was promised by those who pressed the legislature to enact the green building regulations. The district estimates that meeting the green building regulations adds 6 percent to the cost of building a school. Since elementary schools in the district cost an average of $20 million to build, the regulations add about $1.2 million in costs. Even by saving $10,000 a year in utility costs, it would take more than 100 years for the district to recover the additional construction costs.

Even if the green schools do not save energy, as their supporters claim, perhaps there are other justifications? Advocates of the rules also claim the buildings have major health benefits, which could reduce absenteeism. An examination of student absentee rates casts doubt on this claim. In the three green elementary schools in Spokane, the average number of absences per student in the 2006-07 school year was 6.2 days. The average for the district as a whole was 6.15 days. The rate of absence for green schools was virtually identical to the district average – and, actually, slightly worse. The gap grew when looking at schools about the same size. The average absentee rate for schools of 400 students or fewer in Spokane fell to 5.85 days per year, making the absentee rates at green schools about 6 percent higher than comparably sized, non-green schools.

What's more, the lowest absentee rate among the green schools was 5.7 days, but two of the non-green schools had absentee rates significantly lower, at only

4.3 days per year. The impact of building a school to green building standards is simply overshadowed by other factors, making the standards an expensive and ineffective way to improve student absentee rates.

Finally, advocates claim green buildings improve the learning environment, leading to higher test scores. For example, a study for the Washington State Board of Education argued, "The benefits of daylighting in schools are well-documented. Research conducted by Heschong and Mahone demonstrate that high quality daylighting can be a significant factor in improving student test scores on standardized tests."[17] Setting aside the fact that "well-documented" is two studies by the same organization, the results do not show up when examining actual test scores in green schools.

Comparing test scores in the same district gives some indication of what difference a green school makes. Looking at rates in several school districts shows no distinct trend. In some green schools, students improved their reading scores more rapidly than the district as a whole, but math scores fell. Some schools saw improvement in all areas, while others saw reductions in all areas.

The challenge is compounded by the fact that scores vary widely from school to school. While 58 percent of students at Tacoma's "green" Giaudrone Middle School passed the reading test in eighth grade in the 2009-10 school year, the rate at Mason, the non-green school, was 74 percent. The gap in math scores was even higher, with 60 percent more students passing the test at the non-green school. Isolating the impact of the green schools is difficult given the large number of factors influencing the scores. The test data simply do not show consistent trends.

Why don't green schools actually achieve the promised results? There are a number of reasons.

The first reason is simply that school facilities directors were already using energy-saving technologies in new schools before the new state mandates took effect. Elements that did not make economic sense, like solar panels, are additions that may have been added to a school to meet the state requirements. Meeting the state standard, ironically, actually made the cost-to-benefit ratio worse. For example, many green schools in Spokane have extremely large bike racks because encouraging students to ride their bikes, instead of being driven by their parents, earns the school a point toward green certification. The bike racks sit mostly empty. The additional cost is necessary to meet the state-imposed standards, even if it is just wasted money. It adds cost but does nothing to reduce energy use.

Second, some of the requirements to meet the standards actually reduce the efficiency of buildings. As noted above, green-building advocates claim large windows improve school test scores. Others claim that larger windows cut energy costs by allowing more light into buildings. In 2010, Michelle Moore of the U.S. Green Building Council claimed that "by employing smart technologies like lighting sensors that don't use electric bulbs while the sunlight is lighting a classroom, you're able to save tremendously on energy costs."[18] By using larger windows, however, it becomes more difficult to control the temperature in the room because windows are poor insulators. On hot days, rooms become greenhouses. On cold days, heat escapes through glass surfaces. The costs of maintaining a steady temperature significantly outweighs any small amount of energy saved from daylighting. School directors understand this and are limiting the size of windows in the new schools, making them just large enough to meet the standards, but no larger.

The same is true regarding the claims that green buildings are healthier, bringing more fresh air into the building, avoiding an environment similar to some airplanes where the air becomes stale. This may improve the health of the building (although the absentee rates at green schools do not show it), but it increases costs by requiring the air conditioning system to bring more air in, heat that air to room temperature and then start the process all over again. The goal of bringing fresh air into the building more frequently is seriously at odds with the goal of energy efficiency.

Finally, contractors have learned which elements can help buildings meet the standards for the lowest cost – and energy-saving elements are not among the cheap options. One critique of LEED notes that "we've heard LEED consultants remark that you can 'certify a building without getting *any* energy points.' "[19] A study examining which points were popular in LEED-certified projects noted, "In many cases, projects can earn the first two to three energy use reduction points with relatively little changes [sic] to the existing design approach."[20]

Beyond that, earning energy-efficiency points can be expensive, including installing solar panels which are unlikely to ever pay for themselves. Schools in the Snohomish School District north of Seattle installed solar panels, in part to receive points toward green certification, spending $690,000 despite projections showing the panels would only save the district about $175,000 over the 25-year life of the panels.

Washington state has been a leader, although that may be a dubious title, in promoting green building. It is not alone, however, in seeing these same green-building shortcomings. In 2009, The New York Times reported the U.S. Green Building Council conducted a survey of certified buildings to see if they would meet Energy Star standards, which are based on actual building performance, not just projections. The results were sobering. The Times reported in the "study last year of 121 new buildings certified through 2006, the Green Building Council found that more than half — 53 percent — did not qualify for the Energy Star label and 15 percent scored below 30 in that program, meaning they used more energy per square foot than at least 70 percent of comparable buildings in the existing national stock."[21]

To put this in context, the average age of buildings in the "existing national stock" is 40 years. These serious failures demonstrate that for a significant percentage of builders, receiving green certification is only about being part of the latest trend and appearing green, not actually improving environmental sustainability.

For private companies using their own money to meet the standard, the problem is one of truth in advertising. When government officials require taxpayers to spend more to comply with regulations that do not save energy, the problem is more serious, because it takes money away from policies that might actually help the environment and devotes it to policies that only benefit politicians seeking to burnish their environmental image.

To its credit, the U.S. Green Building Council admits its LEED standard is not living up to its promise. In September of 2009, the USGBC sent an email to its members that included an article titled "An Aggressive Focus on Measurable Performance." The council noted that the past decade of its work "has meant great potential for increased efficiency and sustainability, but USGBC has recognized that there is a difference between intention and actual performance."[22] It began an effort to measure the results of buildings meeting USGBC's standard.

Others have taken a different route.

When it became clear the state of Washington's schools were not achieving their promised energy savings, the state's green-buildings coordinator for the Superintendent of Public Instruction dismissed the problem. In an internal email, she argued the state never promised the buildings would save energy, saying a report submitted to the legislature "was not trying to show energy savings."[23] Instead, she said the state only claimed "that the DESIGN INTENT for energy performance for the 11 schools who reported this information was to be on average 24% better than code." Whether the buildings lived up to that intention, apparently, was incidental.

Others have gone even further in distancing themselves from real-world results. Recognizing green certification does not always result in energy savings, one lawyer is now advising architects to protect themselves against making green buildings claims. The legal disclaimer makes it clear green buildings do not mean green results: "The Architect will exercise reasonable efforts to design and specify products and/or systems that achieve energy performance expectations or LEED Certification expectations that are expressly called for in this Contract, if any. The Architect does not, however, provide assurances that those performance or certification expectations will be met."[24] With the growing trend toward receiving green building status, there also appears to be a growing trend in emphasizing the "design intent" over actual performance. Design intent, however, does not reduce energy use or help protect the environment. LEED has become a classic eco-fad: something done for show that doesn't produce the promised results.

Calling an inefficient building "green" actually compounds the problem by attempting to cloak the environmental failure.

The reaction of some politicians has been even worse. Revealing that they care more about their own green image than the environment, some policymakers in Washington state have refused to recognize the failure of the green building standards they supported. Others have acknowledged that energy savings have not lived up to their hopes, but instead of looking to cut the taxpayers' losses, they have decided to double down by proposing to make the rules more restrictive. This response is environmentally counterproductive. While meeting higher levels of certification becomes increasingly expensive, the energy savings those increments yield become smaller and smaller because the easy energy savings have already been realized. By making certification more difficult to achieve, government officials are driving up the cost of buildings, all while receiving less for what they spend.

Green buildings are a potent example of how eco-fads can actually undermine efforts to make good environmental choices.

Creating Green Jobs as We Save the World

Even if green cars or green buildings do not deliver the promised benefits, there is a new reason many environmental activists use to justify these policies: creating green jobs. In uncertain economic times, those who advocate costly environmental regulation understand the public is nervous about any policy that may further damage the economy. Highlighting the creation of green jobs is a key part of trying to make green policies more palatable. When the promised jobs don't materialize, activists promise that next time will be different.

And advocates don't skimp on the promises.

In a video produced by the Washington State Department of Ecology, one environmental activist pledges green building regulations will "create tens of thousands of jobs in the green building and clean energy sectors so that we can prosper as, at the same time as we help save the world."[25] Who could argue with that statement, if it is true? Save the world and earn money doing it. Even if green buildings are not all they are supposed to be, what is the harm? We still help the economy, creating a new class of employment called "green-collar jobs."

The term "green-collar jobs" was coined by Alan T. Durning in his book of the same name. Written in 1999, it has a tone of easy come, easy go. Durning says, "The jobs-versus-environment drama has played out dozens of times in recent decades in the Northwest, usually according to the same script: representatives of declining resource industries predict economic catastrophe … politicians make bold proclamations; and then, when people have stopped paying attention, expansion in the Northwest economy quickly offsets lost resource jobs."[26] Durning was writing at a time when timber towns across Washington were failing as a result of the shutdown of forestry on federal land. Despite his cheery prediction, those lost jobs were not "quickly offset."

The coastal Washington town of Hoquiam, named for a Native American word meaning "hungry for wood," was hit hard. The left-wing magazine, *Mother Jones*, did not sugar coat it when it said, "Families were breaking up and moving out. There were suicides. It was really a hard time."[27] Hope, however, was on the way in the form of green jobs. In 2008, Durning's environmental Seattle-based think tank predicted Hoquiam's "economy is on the up" because an old timber mill "is now producing 100 percent recycled paper. The plant's energy source is 100 percent renewable…"[28]

Those high hopes, however, did not pan out. Hoquiam's population is smaller today than in 1999 when Durning wrote his book, and the percentage of people living below the poverty level has increased to more than one-in-five.[29] In addition to the failure of the nearby biodiesel plant mentioned earlier to create the promised jobs, in 2011 the recycled paper mill shut down permanently. The Seattle Times reported, "Grays Harbor Paper, a Hoquiam company that built a reputation for innovative green products, has announced a permanent shutdown resulting in the loss of nearly 240 jobs."[30]

The green economy has been a bust, and the promised green jobs have been economically unsustainable.

Hope, however, springs eternal, and the desire to improve the environment for, in Worldchanging blogger Alex Steffen's words, "absolutely no sacrifice whatsoever," is powerful. To bolster that hope, green job boosters point to the successful experience of others.

In 2009, president-elect Barack Obama echoed the message of many green-job advocates, pointing to Spain as the model for the green future. Visiting an Ohio company that produces components for wind turbines, he encouraged lawmakers to "think of what's happening in countries like Spain, Germany and Japan, where they're making real investments in renewable energy. They're surging ahead of us, poised to take the lead in these new industries."[31] One year later, Germany dramatically scaled back its green subsidies because it could no longer afford them. Spain's unemployment surged past 20 percent and the government slashed the green subsidies officials had claimed would usher in an era of green prosperity.

Indeed, Spain's experience offers dramatic testimony of the failure of the push for green jobs. Since 2003, Ernst & Young has published its estimate of the most attractive countries for investments in renewable energy. In 2006, things looked promising for Spain, as it occupied the top spot on Ernst & Young's list[32], thanks to a strong push by the Spanish government to create green jobs. By 2010, prospects were much more bleak. Spain had fallen all the way to number eight on the list and its national economy was in shambles – thanks in part to the very push for green jobs the government had hoped would create growth.

Economist Gabriel Calzada of King Juan Carlos University studied the impact of Spain's green subsidies on job creation and found the seeds of Spain's economic distress. By taxing productive businesses and diverting those funds to inefficient green businesses, he found mandatory policies to create green jobs "resulted in the destruction of nearly 110,500 jobs elsewhere in the economy, or 2.2 jobs destroyed for every 'green job' created."[33] Spain did not lose jobs despite the effort to create green jobs – it lost jobs because of those efforts.

Not surprisingly, advocates of such policies in the United States don't tend to mention the case of Spain anymore.

China is now the flavor of the month.

To some it might seem strange to model modern economic policy after a country that has a per capita wealth that is tied with Turkmenistan for 130th in the world.[34] But the dream of green jobs dies hard. Setting Ernst & Young's 2006 projection aside, advocates cite the 2010 version of the same report that put China in the top spot, leapfrogging the U.S.[35] This news led to real anxiety for some environmental activists, with one Seattle activist lamenting, "China wins again. It almost feels like we're not even playing the same game! Embarrassed yet? I am."[36]

There are many problems with focusing on China. The poverty in the world's most populous country (average Chinese citizens are one-seventh as wealthy as Americans) makes economic growth easier because there is so much room to grow. Since China is not a democracy, its government can artificially suppress living standards, hiding economic mistakes and imposing the costs on workers. Citizens of a democracy don't tolerate such practices, making the application of China's forced policies in the U.S. impractical.

Most importantly, perhaps, is that it is as foolish to claim China will succeed in creating an economically sustainable green economy today as it was to idolize Spain in 2006. Spain's unemployment rate in 2006, when it was named the top nation for renewable investing, was 8.6 percent. At the beginning of 2011, it was nearly 21 percent. With an economy that is much poorer and has more room to grow, China may not see that kind of dramatic failure, but success is more likely than it was in Spain. Pointing to China sounds more like scaremongering, using the specter of Chinese supremacy over the U.S. to argue for a dubious policy, than engaging in rational decision making.

To be sure, advocates of green jobs do not need to look overseas to find examples of how the push to create green jobs has not played out as expected.

The Pew Charitable Trusts looked across America for the states where "clean energy" plays a significant role in the economy. They declared Oregon the winner, noting green energy accounted for more than 1 percent of the state's economy.[37] The report cited this as good news, saying, "The clean energy economy, still in its infancy, is emerging as a vital component of America's new economic landscape," and declaring green jobs "an increasingly important part of the nation's economic recovery." The states leading the way to this new economy, the organization argued, could expect to reap large rewards.

Timing being everything, Pew's could not have been worse. As the report came out in June of 2009, Oregon's unemployment rate hit 11.6 percent, more than 2 percent above the national average. Whatever role green jobs played in Oregon's economy, they certainly were not leading it down the path of recovery.

Why have efforts to create green jobs backfired so badly?

One reason is the line of thinking behind green jobs that actually rewards doing less with more. In an article called "Calculating the benefits of a green recovery," The Seattle Times cited an economic study that found government projects that "aim to reduce greenhouse gases, improve transit and rail service, enhance energy efficiency and encourage renewable energy," actually "produced more 'job hours' than tax cuts or traditional infrastructure spending."[38] In other words, green projects require more work per dollar generated. This sounds good, but it is actually bad for workers and the economy.

The reason is that green projects are less productive, requiring more work to produce the same amount of energy. Green energy advocates actually tout this, noting that "renewable energy technologies create more jobs per average megawatt (MW) of power generated"[39] than their nongreen counterparts. This is akin to advocating that we ban tractors to create more jobs for family farmers. It would take more labor to produce the same amount of food, the cost of food would rise, everyone, including the workers, would be poorer, but we would have more jobs. Banning tractors would also promote a greener world by reducing fuel consumption, right?

It is strange that people would think having to split the same amount of money among more workers would make them better off. To create good jobs, we need to put people where they can add the most value for their skills, instead of finding ways to make people work harder to produce less.

Another reason the effort to create green jobs has backfired is because, as with so many other green policies, the politics of the issue are more important than the practical results.

In Washington state, the Department of Employment Security released a report in 2010 showing the number of green jobs had increased significantly in recent years, jumping from 47,000 to 99,000 in just over 12 months. The governor was quick to claim victory, stating in a press release, "I'm delighted that our efforts to increase green jobs are working."[40] Indeed, a government policy was responsible for the increase in the numbers – a change in how the state counted green jobs. The new study used a more expansive definition of what counts as a green job, so the apparent growth was nothing more than a statistical trick. The report itself cautioned the change in methodology made it impossible to determine the real number of green jobs, even going so far as to admit toward the end that, "it seems unlikely that a large proportion of the increase in green jobs is due to new hiring."[41] For political purposes, that caution was thrown to the wind. After all, the report was never intended as a planning document. Its real value lay in the political opportunity to issue a press release to claim success in moving the state toward the "green economy."

Are green jobs all bad then? Of course not. What the state of Washington's study did find is that green jobs have always been there, the state is only recognizing them now. Jobs that improve energy efficiency, reduce resource use and lower costs are green and create wider prosperity. Green jobs turn bad when we sacrifice prosperity and environmental progress for the sake of creating jobs in a particular, politically trendy category.

Some people might argue it is worth paying more to produce green energy since it reduces environmental impact. That is a consistent viewpoint, but the argument in favor of green jobs is that they are good for the economy and create more prosperity, which they clearly don't. What's more, a true environmental ethic requires that we do more with less, not less with more.

Green jobs are a trendy eco-fad and, as in Spain, that popularity is likely to be the green sector's worst enemy. At some point, if we ignore the costs of following the fad, the chickens come home to roost and the real harm to the economy and the environment is revealed.

The Adjective that Makes Every Effort Noble

Green cars. Green Buildings. Green Jobs. Adding that one little word "green" before anything suddenly changes it for the better, adding promise, hope and images of a better future.

It can also have a more sinister purpose – discouraging us from looking more closely at the projects that have acquired that bewitching adjective. To question cars is admirable. To question green cars shows you don't care about the planet. What kind of person would argue against green buildings or green jobs? The word "green" makes a good bludgeon to use against people who question politicians using taxpayer dollars to support projects of dubious science and economics.

Standing up to the presumption of green is difficult. People want to be green, so they go along with these trends, letting "green" act as their guide.

In the case of green cars, consumers rejected the option due to the price. No matter how much they might have wanted to buy a zero-emissions vehicle, they chose hybrids as an affordable and effective alternative. With green buildings and green jobs, the adjective became a political symbol, rather than a reflection of results. And once "green" became associated with those projects, it made it harder to undo them once it became clear they were more harmful than helpful.

Indeed, the political failure to separate good green projects from those that fail has undermined the credibility of people who argue that climate change is the most urgent issue we face. The more important the issue, the more important it is that we get the solutions right. When we do not take the effectiveness of the solution seriously, it leads some of us to wonder whether the problem is really as serious as environmental advocates say it is.

Although there is still much to learn, even scientists who call themselves climate skeptics or climate realists argue that human-caused CO_2 emissions can influence Earth's temperature, creating risk of some harmful impacts. The trends we have seen so far have been at the low end of the projections, but dealing with the potential environmental risk in a thoughtful way makes sense.

If using the word "green" becomes a way to harness the power of fads to impose, and then protect, bad policy ideas, then we can't claim to truly care about climate change.

Chapter 11

Green Living Eco-Fads

They compete with the Toyota Prius as the most powerful and common symbol of environmental consciousness. Their power as a fashion statement is as significant as their actual value. They have become de rigueur for shoppers who want to make a statement. Reusable grocery bags are now offered by many grocery stores, often colored green with the logo of the store printed on the outside. They promise a range of benefits to the environment.

Reusing bags means less trash. It means using less energy and petroleum and less water in the manufacturing process. Substituting reusable bags for plastic bags means less trash ends up in the oceans. Substituting reusable bags for paper ones means cutting down fewer trees and using less energy. That is why one reusable-bag seller claims, "Every study ever done shows reusable bags as by far the best choice for the environment."[1]

Grocery-store owners like reusable bags. Rather than offering shoppers one-time bags for free, stores typically sell reusable bags to their customers, recovering the cost of production. And what company could complain about charging people to carry around a bag with the store's logo on it? Tommy Hilfiger, Ralph Lauren and others have made a killing doing that very thing with clothing.

Users of "green" grocery bags, however, got a bit of a jolt in 2010 when they learned the bags are not as benign as environmentalists claim.

The New York Times reported that recent studies found some of the bags contained high levels of lead, which could result in a range of health problems. "The recent studies ... found that the lead in some bags would pose a long-term risk of seeping into groundwater after disposal; over time, however, paint from the bag could flake off and come into contact with food," wrote The Times.[2]

Another study found that since the bags are reused, but typically not washed, they can become incubators for germs, bacteria and attendant health risks.[3]

Having been bombarded with so many questionable claims about eco-friendly products, some of the shoppers interviewed by The Times were not surprised at the finding. "Green is a trend and people go with trends. People get them as fashion statements and they have, like, 50 of them. I don't think people know the real facts."[4] There is a growing recognition that the fashion of being green is interfering with the higher goal of helping the planet. The challenge for many people is what to do about it. How do we tell the good from the bad as we make dozens of small decisions each day that we hope will add up to making a positive difference for the environment?

The question also is whether the primary goal is truly to be green or simply to receive the social rewards of appearing green. Indeed, one company now sells a reusable bag with the not-so-subtle (and perhaps satirical) message printed in large letters on the side: "My reusable bag makes me better than you."[5] Economists understand people react to incentives, whether those are in the form of money or social benefits. Green consumer goods attempt to harness those social benefits, offering them as an added incentive and providing product differentiation between the green products that will elevate one's status among peers and the traditional products that could brand one as a know-nothing pariah.

It is next to impossible to know everything about the products we buy, so getting it right every time is unlikely. If we remember to discern emotion from fact in those purchases that make the greatest difference to us, consumers can take an important step toward avoiding the pitfalls certain "green" marketers are trying to lure us into.

As important as it is to know which environmental claims are false, it is just as important to understand the tradeoffs of making particular environmental choices. We may reduce the amount of trash we produce yet increase health risks or the level of lead in the environment. These tradeoffs are inherent in our efforts to live a truly green lifestyle. As long as we understand the choice we are making, we can make the decisions that move each of us toward the lifestyle we want to live and to the legacy we want to leave behind us.

Ban the Bag!

One primary reason so many people have purchased the "green" reusable grocery bags is the desire to reduce the environmental impact of plastic bags.

When plastic bags were introduced, their durability was a major selling point. In an age when recycling and biodegradability are favored characteristics, a product that is built to last forever may actually be seen as having a long-term, negative impact on the planet.

Grocery stores often prefer plastic bags because they are less expensive and use less energy to produce. They also consume less energy to recycle. Using less energy contributes to the bag's lower cost and means reduced impact on the environment.

Despite that, plastic bags have been fingered for a wide range of environmental crimes.

Although many people recycle the bags or use them again for other purposes (dog owners know what I'm talking about here), many of the plastic grocery bags used by consumers eventually end up in landfills. The city of Seattle estimates each consumer uses 485 plastic bags a year.[6] When multiplied by all of the people in Seattle, the mind conjures images from the movie "Wall-E," with huge mounds of discarded plastic products overwhelming landfills.

That, however, is not even the worst environmental impact some people associate with plastic bags. The bags that are not sent to landfills might end up as litter, with all too many of them making their way to our oceans where they persist, impacting wildlife and plankton. Environmental activists have claimed that the sheer volume of this kind of trash has created a massive garbage patch in the Pacific Ocean, with some estimating it has grown to twice the area of Texas. Some estimates claimed the sheer size of the patch has had a massive impact on wildlife, with some arguing that "the bags kill more than 100,000 marine mammals and one million seabirds every year."[7] Even if landfill space is not in short supply, and even many people who oppose plastic bags acknowledge it isn't, this significant impact on wildlife certainly justifies significant steps to reduce plastic bag use.

The question is how to weigh the various costs and benefits of plastic bags. A number of communities have proposed adding a tax for every bag used or else banning them altogether. The hope is that people will turn to other alternatives, like reusable bags, or cut down on the number of bags they use. The benefits of this approach, however, have been mixed at best, with even environmentalists scratching their heads about how to find the right balance.

Since plastic bags were developed because they use fewer resources, and hence are cheaper, getting rid of plastic bags would not reduce the use of water and energy significantly. When the Seattle City Council proposed taxing plastic bags, The Seattle Times tallied the overall reduction in resource use that would result. The city expected to spend $10 million, projecting that water use for bag production would be reduced by thirty-nine million gallons each year and would cut CO_2 emissions by 6,000 tons per year. These numbers sound large, but actually the impact is quite small.

As mentioned earlier, the cost to reduce one ton of CO_2 on the European Carbon Market is about $20. Reducing 6,000 tons of CO_2 would cost about $109,000, or 1 percent of the cost of the bag tax.

The numbers for conserving water are similar. Each day, Seattle uses about 130 million gallons of water. Reducing water use by thirty-nine million gallons a year is less than one one-hundredth of 1 percent of water used in Seattle, or less than one-third of one day's consumption. So, the amount of water saved by this tax would be infinitesimal. How much is that amount of water worth? Using residential rates, which have the highest marginal rates, the cost of thirty-nine million gallons (5,213,904 cubic feet) is between $169,452 and $553,716 depending on the amount used, assuming use during peak times.

In other words, the bag tax would cost $10 million to gain environmental benefits that could be acquired for as low as $278,452. This assumes people do not replace plastic bags with something else, which they often do.

Those costs, however, do not take into account the impact of plastic trash that reaches the ocean. Recent research, however, demonstrates the impact of plastic floating in the ocean has been dramatically exaggerated. A study by Oregon State University (OSU) noted that the actual size of the garbage patch is "less than 1 percent of the geographic size of Texas."[8] What's more, the amount of plastic in the ocean does not appear to be growing, and has apparently stabilized since the mid-1980s. OSU scientist Angel White says this doesn't mean we should ignore the problem. "There is no doubt that the amount of plastic in the world's oceans is troubling, but this kind of exaggeration undermines the credibility of scientists," White said.

The impact on marine mammals was similarly exaggerated. The real impact is much, much smaller. The Sunday Times of London explains how the numbers came to be exaggerated:

> "This figure is based on a misinterpretation of a 1987 Canadian study in Newfoundland, which found that, between 1981 and 1984, more than 100,000 marine mammals, including birds, were killed by discarded nets. The Canadian study did not mention plastic bags. Fifteen years later in 2002, when the Australian Government commissioned a report into the effects

of plastic bags, its authors misquoted the Newfoundland study, mistakenly attributing the deaths to 'plastic bags.'"[9]

Even a Greenpeace biologist lamented the distortion of the data, telling The Times, "It's very unlikely that many animals are killed by plastic bags. ... We are not going to solve the problem of waste by focusing on plastic bags."

The environmental impact of plastic bags, however, is not zero, and some people say despite the exaggeration, there is still reason to do something. The question is: What should we do?

One problem is that when plastic bags are removed as an option, people turn to alternatives that have a similar impact. When a tax on plastic grocery bags took effect in Ireland, makers of other types of plastic bags saw significant increases in their sales. One manufacturer crowed, "We've experienced a growth of 300 – 400%. It's been phenomenal. You can trace it back to when the bag levy came in."[10] Rather than reuse the plastic bags from the grocery store, people bought plastic bags to fill those needs, making the overall benefit of the bag tax negligible.

Furthermore, given the energy and resource benefits of plastic bags, how much do we really gain by banning or discouraging their use?

Does it make sense to stop using plastic bags? Should we forget the reusable bags and just accept that some small amount of environmental impact is going to occur? There is no perfect answer. Plastic bags are a visible, but probably a negligible, symbol of environmental pollution. The threat from lead in reusable bags is likely to be extremely tiny, and if you use them consistently, the amount of energy and resources consumed by the bags you use will likely be smaller than if you used disposable paper or plastic.

What this really means is that the passion about discarded plastic is misplaced. Spending tremendous amounts of time and money to address a relatively small problem by creating solutions that make only marginal improvements is strong evidence that an eco-fad is at work. Reusable bags are not necessarily bad, but they do not deserve their position as an environmental status symbol.

Buy Local ... 'Cause Others Are Scary

"Local is so 2008? Yes, and it is also so 1908, 1608 and 508 B.C. Until the last 100 years or so, the 'alternative food crowd' encompassed nearly all of humanity."[11]

In her glowing tribute to the local food movement, syndicated columnist Froma Harrop notes that buying local is nothing new – people were doing it for thousands of years until humanity figured out how to preserve food for shipping. Known as the "locavore" movement, it can inspire some heated emotions.

Portland, Oregon, chef Eric Bechard put his fists where his locavore words were when he attacked the organizer of a culinary contest, fracturing his leg, for allowing the winning chef to use pigs from Iowa and Kansas.[12] When was the last time a kitchen cook-off ended with police, Tasers and pepper spray?

The agenda is not limited to food. The "buy-local" movement also encourages consumers to shop at local bookstores, local grocery stores and other small stores, buying products produced and grown locally.

A big part of the push is the belief that by lowering the number of miles a product travels, we can reduce its carbon footprint and the impact on the planet. Advocates have even created a metric called "food-miles," measuring how far the finished product travels before it hits our plates. Advocates argue that "cutting down on the fuel used to transport food could help slow global warming, and a local food system makes it easier to police for food safety, puts more money into the local economy and fresher, better-tasting food in your mouth."[13]

A guest-opinion column in the Seattle Times written by a King County employee added his voice, claiming, "Transportation of food requires copious amounts of fossil fuels and other resources that contribute to global warming and pollution, so the lower the food mileage we rack up, the better."[14] The logic goes, the shorter distance your food travels, the less fuel burned to transport the food and the lower the carbon footprint of the delicious heirloom tomato you are putting in your mouth.

Despite the popularity of this concept, few people who have actually studied the issue believe food-miles are a useful metric. In fact, the research shows measuring food-miles is counterproductive.

The primary fallacy is the emphasis on the distance the final product travels to the consumer, rather than the cost of the various inputs to a product. Rich Pirog, a researcher in sustainable agriculture at the University of Iowa, notes that food-miles are "not a reliable indicator of environmental impact. What one would want to do is look at your carbon footprint across a whole food supply chain."[15] Consider this comparison between Idaho and Maine potatoes, grown on opposite sides of the U.S.:

"Take the case of the well-traveled Idaho potato and its closer-to-home cousin from Maine. For a consumer on the US East Coast, the Maine potato seems the winner in the local food derby. But Maine potatoes get to market by long-haul truck while Idaho's go by train, a more energy-efficient mode of transportation, so they have a smaller carbon footprint even with a larger number of food-miles."[16]

On a global level, another study found that New Zealand sheep had a smaller carbon footprint than sheep raised locally in other parts of the world. This was true even when New Zealand sheep were shipped to the other side of the world in Great Britain. Scientists found "that lamb raised on New Zealand's clover-choked pastures and shipped 11,000 miles by boat to Britain produced 1,520 pounds of carbon dioxide emissions per ton while British lamb produced 6,280 pounds of carbon dioxide per ton, in part because poorer British pastures force farmers to use feed."[17] Even if some locally grown lamb did have a smaller carbon footprint than New Zealand-grown lamb, buying based on food-miles alone would not be useful in determining the actual carbon footprint.

An agricultural expert in King County, Washington, highlighted the difficulty in measuring environmental impact with miles. The expert noted that dairies were leaving King County, in part due to land regulation, but also due to the fact that it is cheaper to ship milk than hay – making it more efficient, and energy friendly, to locate dairies close to where hay is grown. At the time, the King County Agriculture Commission was considering promoting locally produced milk, with the benefit to the environment being one justification. Ultimately the commission realized trucking hay over the Cascade Mountains from the eastern part of the state to King County would use more fuel than shipping milk over that same route. Buying local King County milk, therefore, would actually be the environmentally unfriendly thing to do.

These sorts of calculations are complicated and they often lead to counterintuitive results. While food-miles advocates examine the final distance the food travels, they do not look at the miles traveled by all of the product inputs, which can make a bigger difference. Actually, transportation is a pretty small part of the energy used in food production. One study found that only 11 percent of CO_2 emissions associated with food production are from transportation.[18] Making buying decisions based on this small part of the equation is like judging a present based on its gift wrap.

Consumers who are truly interested in reducing their CO_2 footprint with their food purchases need to look beyond food-miles and simplistic "buy-local" campaigns.

Not surprisingly, many buy-local campaigns have more to do with local businesses trying to gain a competitive advantage over others. When they say "buy local," often what they really mean is "buy from me."

A 2009 story in a Seattle news blog highlighted the growth of buy-local campaigns across the Pacific Northwest. One of the activists featured was a bookseller in Bellingham, Washington. His commitment to "buy local," however, appeared to be based solely on his desire that people buy from him rather than from online giant Amazon (a company also located in the Northwest) or Barnes & Noble. On the bookstore's web page, he listed his five favorite books. None of them were written by a local author and certainly none of them were printed locally. Ultimately, his commitment to the buy-local effort amounted to encouraging people to buy books that were written and printed elsewhere and shipped to him, rather than buying books that were written and printed elsewhere and shipped directly to your home or to a major bookseller.

Some people claim buying from a local, and small, retailer has other benefits, arguing the service provided when buying goods locally is superior to buying from major retail outlets. Others say that local food is fresher and, consequently, tastes better. This may be true. These considerations, however, have nothing to do with the politics of buying local. They are standard, consumer preference issues, compelling businesses to provide better goods and services for those buying their products. In those instances where better food can be had by shipping it from somewhere else (compare a pineapple from Hawaii to one grown in Oregon), justifications based on service or quality could dictate we buy from overseas rather than locally. Buy-local advocates, however, do not agree with that conclusion, making it clear that arguments about service, taste or quality are not really the reasons they promote local purchases.

This is where buy local can even become a bit ugly. What could possibly have compelled the chef in Portland to resort to violence to keep products from other states out of the culinary contest? Did he see them as inferior or dangerous? Certainly he would say no, and yet something drove him to fracture the event organizer's leg. This is clearly a movement that is driven by a strong dose of emotion, and is predicated on separating "us" from "them." The concept of separating groups into local and foreign has not always been a positive impulse, to say the least.

And because the calculations related to the energy use and environmental impact of food-miles can be complicated, too many advocates of the buy-local movement rely on the simplistic approach that local is good and foreign is bad. In this case "foreign" may mean it is only from another part of their own state or region.

Sometimes buying local manifests itself in some truly absurd thinking. Some people seem to believe buying local will allow us to magically cut costs simply because our neighbors want to charge less – presumably to be nice to their neighbors. In Washington state, one community justified creating a publicly owned utility, at significant ratepayer expense, in part by claiming that a local public board and local maintenance would mean lower rates and better service than that currently being provided by maintenance people from a private company who lived a few miles away in the next county.

Unfortunately for them, the laws of economics do follow county lines, and the costs of organizing and running the utility were far higher than advocates claimed, despite the "local" management. Ultimately, salaries still need to be paid and equipment and energy still need to be purchased. Buyers demand the same, or greater, level of service they did when the utility was privately owned. These constraints meant the geographic location of the utility board and managers had very little to do with how well and at what cost the utility actually provided the services.

When judging the merits of local purchase, considering why we want to buy locally is the key. If locavores believe locally grown food has a smaller environmental impact – using food-miles as a surrogate for total energy use – they will probably be unhappy to learn their approach is actually counterproductive.

If the reason has more to do with good taste and the quality of service, then the justification has nothing to do with locality, but with the qualities we find attractive in any product, no matter what its source. A locally grown vine-ripened tomato may taste better than one picked green and shipped across the country. Coffee that has traveled thousands of miles, on the other hand, may taste far superior to beans grown locally. Judging on flavor does not lead us to conclude that local is better.

Even when these facts become clear, however, too many people continue to cling to a belief in buying locally. They may argue they trust people in their local community more than people who live at greater distances.

Are people from my community really more trustworthy than people in a town several miles away, or in another state or even another country? Is there any reason people in Detroit should trust people in Los Angeles more than people from Toronto, since those people just across the river are, after all, Canadians? Indeed, we could turn that example on its head and argue Canadians just a few miles away are more local than Californians who are so distant. There is no clear answer indicating geographic distance has anything to do with the quality of the people producing the goods and services. Distance should have little to do with how we treat others.

Buying local should not become a thoughtless and simplistic surrogate for things we really care about. Caring for the planet and the people on it obliges us to follow the science and respect others we share the earth with, no matter how far from us they happen to be.

Shining the Light on Earth Hour

Not all our consumer behaviors are intended to have a direct impact on environmental health. Indeed, environmental activists often encourage actions they admit are purely symbolic. The best example in recent years is "Earth Hour" – an hour in March when people across the planet are asked to turn out their lights to symbolize concern over the impacts of global warming. It is hard to fault such awareness-raising events, since the costs incurred are purely voluntary.

In addition to the symbolism, however, the World Wildlife Fund actually claims Earth Hour has a positive environmental impact, significantly reducing carbon dioxide emissions by this one simple act.

For instance, the Earth Hour Wikipedia page[19], which supporters use to highlight a range of purported benefits, says, "Vietnam electricity demand fell 500,000 kWh during Earth Hour 2010," and "The Philippines was able to save 611 MWh of electricity during the time period, and is said to be equivalent to shutting down a dozen coal-fired power plants for an hour." It also claims, "Toronto saved 900 megawatt-hours of electricity. 8.7% was saved if measured against a typical March Saturday night." These statistics are meant to encourage us to imagine what could happen if we simply took these kinds of actions on a more regular basis, significantly cutting energy use and helping the planet.

There is less than meets the eye with some of these statistics. For instance, Vietnam's electricity reduction saved about $27,000, or one-third of one penny for every person in the country. Even in a country where the average wage is only 31 cents an hour, this represents a 1 percent difference. Additionally, it wasn't Toronto that reduced energy use during Earth Hour by 900 MWh, but the entire province of Ontario, which represents about 40 percent of the Canadian population. Some people will find it shocking that part of the information on Wikipedia might be inaccurate or exaggerated, but these are emblematic of what happens when ideas move beyond substance to eco-trendiness.

Additionally, the question is whether these data, assuming they are accurate, are typical or consistent. By way of comparison, I looked at energy use during Earth Hour 2010 in Washington state to see if trends were consistent with these results. By looking at electricity data from various parts of the state, I found that energy use actually increased during Earth Hour compared to similar Saturdays, and to the Friday and Sunday before and after the event.

For instance, when looking at energy use during that entire weekend, the data showed that energy use went up on all three days during the 8 p.m. hour, fell during the 9 p.m. hour on Friday and Sunday, but not on the Earth Hour Saturday. During Earth Hour, use actually increased by more than 1 percent compared to the Friday before and the following Sunday.

To see whether this was simply a result of Saturday energy use being larger than the other days of the weekend, I also compared the energy use during Earth Hour to the same hours on the previous and following Saturdays. The results were the same, with the energy use during Earth Hour 2010 exceeding that of other Saturdays.

Could it be that weather played a role? Probably not. The temperatures were not significantly different on these three Saturdays.

So what is going on here? There are a couple of potential explanations.

It could be that Earth Hour 2010 in Washington state was an aberration, with some other unseen factor causing energy use on Earth Hour to exceed that same hour on comparable Saturdays, as well as on the day before and after. This is possible, but the obvious reasons, such as a change in temperature and weather, can likely be ruled out.

On the other hand, we could be seeing a real-life manifestation of what happened in the University of Toronto study that found people who buy green products are more willing to engage in moral compromises in other areas. People, having turned off their lights, might do other things that end up using more electricity, like watch TV (in the dark), run the dryer or put food in the oven to be enjoyed when the lights come back on. Such activities could be justified by the feeling that people are already doing their part by turning off the lights, ignoring the electricity used by the things they do instead of using light.

In fact, people may do other things that have greater environmental impacts that do not show up in the data. For instance, driving to a restaurant to eat dinner while the lights are off at home might actually emit more CO_2 into the atmosphere than staying at home with a few lights on.

It is hard to know precisely why electricity use increased during Earth Hour 2010 in Washington state. In all likelihood, a combination of factors led to the failure of the effort to reduce electricity use. There can be no question, however, that the symbolic effect of Earth Hour is undermined if the result is an increase in energy use.

It is a good reminder that, with so many actions being claimed as "green," we need to look beyond the packaging.

The Tradeoffs and Weaknesses of Buying Organic

Before many of the green products we see on the shelves today were conceived, there was organic food. Organic food has been marketed for decades, offering consumers a pesticide-free food alternative. From concerns about DDT, Alar and genetically modified foods, some consumers worry that chemicals on food are reaching our bodies and harming our health. Sorting out these charges can be difficult, and some of them, like the Alar scare, have shown to be seriously overblown or false.[20]

Still, for many people, the increased cost of organic food is a small price to pay for a bit of extra peace of mind. There are some important things to keep in mind when choosing organic.

First, what is organic? As noted, the FDA has standards defining what can be labeled "organic." Complying with these standards, however, can be expensive and is often more suited to major agricultural corporations than family farms. It can be hard to buy organic and support small farmers at the same time, if that is your choice.

Second, there are tradeoffs. For example, California's legislation on organic food runs squarely against one of the most iconic political movements in state history – the United Farm Workers movement of Cesar Chavez. One of the most significant improvements in the working conditions of the field workers during the farm-labor campaign of the 1960s and '70s was the banishment of the "short-handled hoe." The hoe was used to remove weeds from around crops. Farmers argued longer handled hoes were imprecise, leading to crop damage that drove up the price of remaining crops. For the farmworkers, however, using the short-handled hoe meant working in a stooped position for hours. Among those who used it, the short-handled hoe earned the nickname "el brazo del diablo" – the arm of the devil. Chavez himself used the hoe when he was a young farmworker, and in 1969 said if growers "had any consideration for the torture that people go through, they would give up the short-handled hoe."[21] The hoe was banned in 1975, marking a great victory for the farmworkers' movement. In 1985, when government rules were drafted to allow the re-introduction of the hoe, the outcry was so great, the proposal was dropped.

Organic growers, however, are exempted from the short-handled hoe ban. Since organic food is already more expensive than crops grown using pesticides, producers argue they need to reduce crop damage by requiring use of the more precise short-handled hoes. As a result, organic foods receive a specific exemption in California's agriculture laws, allowing the use of the tool which was placed upon Chavez's coffin during his funeral as a symbol of his struggle and triumph.

This has led some activists on the left to "challenge assumptions that organic represents a more socially sustainable agricultural-production system and suggest that the organic boom, in and of itself, holds little promise for California's farm workers."[22] In its effort to reduce the use of chemicals that may impact the environment or human health, organic agriculture in California took a step backward in the treatment of farmworkers.

Finally, some organic practices that appear environmentally friendly actually are not. Some people argue grass-fed beef is more natural and better for the environment than shipping corn to feed cattle. After all, the grass is under the livestock's feet – no transportation required. Michael Pollan noted that "growing meat on grass can make superb ecological sense: so long as the rancher practices rotational grazing, it is a sustainable, solar-powered system for producing food on land too arid or hilly to grow anything else."[23] Why screw up a system that nature organized?

Actually, there is an important reason. According to Dr. Jude Capper, assistant professor of dairy sciences at Washington State University, the answer is that feeding corn to cattle is better for the environment. In an interview with consumer reporter John Stossel, Dr. Capper noted that a richer diet allows the cows to grow more quickly, meaning they have less time to cause environmental impact. Capper told Stossel, "There's a perception out there that grass-fed animals are frolicking in the sunshine, kicking their heels up full of joy and pleasure. What we actually found was from the land-use basis, from the energy, from water and, particularly, based on the carbon footprints, grass-fed is far worse than corn-fed."[24] The reason is simple. The faster the animals grow, the less time they have to consume water and other resources, not to mention the less time they have to digest food and "emit" methane, a potent greenhouse gas.

People may feel better about eating beef from free-range cattle that lived longer, perhaps happier, lives. That should not be confused with the impact those animals have on the resources they use during their longer lives and the ultimate impact they have on the environment. When it comes to those calculations, faster-growing cattle are better for the planet. That is the tradeoff, and different people will come down on different sides of the decision.

Choices and Falsehoods

Whether deciding to eat organic, buy local or use your own grocery bags, the best decision often depends on your personal values. When making these types of consumer decisions, there is a natural desire to find the "right" answer, but frequently the answer depends on the questioner's viewpoint. For people concerned about the impact plastic may have on the environment, biodegradable paper or reusable bags are probably the best choices. If you are concerned about the working conditions of farmworkers, organic may not be the best choice. Others may make the opposite choices, using plastic bags because they require less energy, and buying organic vegetables due to their concern about health and the impact of pesticides on the environment.

Of course we need to make sure we know the facts about the decisions we make so we can be true to the values we hold. Asking for grass-fed beef as a way to reduce environmental impact can be the wrong decision. As with many eco-fads, consumers are bombarded with information that is inaccurate or, at the very least, difficult to decipher. Nobody can have all the information necessary to make the best decision every time. The best we can do is to try to gather good information about the decisions that are most important to us.

Whatever our choices, however, there will be tradeoffs, and expecting to find the one way to achieve "green living" is a fool's errand. The good news is that as consumers demand more options consistent with their values, the number of options will multiply, providing goods and services to help us live well and live right by the planet.

Chapter 12

Avoiding Eco-Fads

With a population of half a billion people, and growing, India in 1968 was the very symbol of environmental peril. Everywhere Paul Ehrlich looked he saw poverty and squalor. Hundreds of millions of people using resources, like water and land, which were already scarce and would only become more scarce as India's population climbed. Writing in "The Population Bomb," Ehrlich claimed India was emblematic of the coming resource calamity that faced the entire world. At the time, he said, "I have yet to meet anyone familiar with the situation who thinks India will be self-sufficient in food by 1971," and he even went on to say, "India couldn't possibly feed 200 million more people by 1980."[1]

In viewing poverty, Ehrlich saw resource destruction and a greater threat to the planet as a whole. The poverty was to be decried, a side effect of a system of consumption that inevitably led to collapse.

Forty years later, the National Geographic Society believes India has enjoyed an amazing turnaround. Despite seeing the population double to more than 1.1 billion since 1970, that country now ranks as the world's "greenest" society, according to National Geographic Society's calculations. How did India achieve this? The Times of India explains the National Geographic Society's logic:

> "That cold water bath many Indians have because there's no electricity … that 'matka' they use because they can't afford a fridge … and the long walk they take to work and back because private transport is expensive and public transport shoddy. There's an upside to the hard life. Indians may be green with envy at the consumption-driven lifestyle in the West, but their own frugal ways and modest means have catapulted them to

the top spot in the world's Green index, making them the most environmental-friendly denizens of Planet Earth."[2]

The very squalor that served as a warning to Ehrlich forty years prior is now presented as evidence the Indian people are, in fact, living in harmony with the planet. Exhibit A for planetary destruction in 1968 turned state's evidence in 2009, arguing that others should follow India's lead for the sake of Mother Earth.

The facts in both cases are the same, but the environmental and policy conclusions are the exact opposite. Actually, the facts were not the same. From Paul Ehrlich's point of view, India's situation became dramatically worse. Not only has India's population doubled, the economy, measured on a per capita basis, has grown nearly thirtyfold. If the measure of environmental success is a small population with low consumption, India, in 1968, when Ehrlich examined it, was dramatically more "environmentally friendly" than it was in 2009, when it was declared to be the planet's "greenest" society.

What is going on here?

This is the power of eco-fads writ large. Instead of examining India through the lens of science and economic dynamism, both Ehrlich and the National Geographic Society chose to define "green" in ideological ways, first determining what they believed green should look like, then highlighting countries meeting that definition. They did not test their conclusions against objective results, preferring to stick with a prefabricated conclusion. This defines the phrase "form over function," which is at the heart of fashion and is the driving force behind eco-fads.

Fashion is based not on practical results but on appearance and whether the thing being judged conforms to a particular understanding of what is in vogue. Soon, however, the definition changes, giving way to a new approach based on another view of what is "in." One year hats for men are required fashion. Another year they are out of style. One year, poverty is emblematic of environmental destruction. Another year it is the symbol of environmental consciousness.

Of course, both Ehrlich and the National Geographic Society will claim their views, though reaching opposite conclusions, are based on science and other objective standards.

Ehrlich created an equation, IPAT, to argue that his conclusions were based in an almost mathematic logic. Our impact on the earth (I), in his calculation, was the sum of population (P), affluence (A) and technology (T). That the calculation yielded wildly inaccurate results did not undermine its validity in his eyes – after all, it was science.

The National Geographic Society ranks countries based on how much beef people eat, the number of cars they drive, the type of energy they use for home heating, and the like.[3] For each of these categories the National Geographic Society cites scientific evidence of the relative impact on the planet. That rating system, however, should lead them to conclude that the India of 1968 was even greener yet, with fewer people eating beef, driving cars and using fossil-based energy, or using any energy at all for that matter.

It does not seem to occur to either Ehrlich or the National Geographic Society that their calculations are based in a trendy misunderstanding of environmental friendliness, namely the assumption that using fewer resources is inherently better for the earth. This idea is not science, but ideology. By defining "environmentally friendly" to mean low levels of resource use, the key decision about measuring environmental impact has already been made. The only "scientific" part of the assessment is determining how to count the impacts which had already been determined, pre-science, to be detrimental.

Sticking to this kind of trendy ideology is not always benign. Imagine the cost of implementing Paul Ehrlich's population and resource control proposals in 1968. The result would have been famine, human suffering and widespread despair.

The National Geographic Society's focus on resource use also has negative consequences because it sends the wrong signals about how to make real improvements in environmental quality. Calling India the greenest country in the world does not alter the fact that in some of the most tangible and important measures of environmental quality, the subcontinent fares quite badly.

A 2007 study by a prominent cancer institute found, "Some 70% of people in the city of Calcutta suffer from respiratory disorders caused by air pollution."[4] Worse, in 2009 New Delhi was determined by some estimates to have the worst air quality in the world.[5] That is not the end of problems for New Delhi residents – the water in the Yamuna River is so polluted that levels of fecal coliform are "100,000 times the safe limit for even bathing."[6] Knowing that they live in the "greenest" country is probably little comfort to Indians dealing with these health threats.

Compare the safety of "green" India with the record of the United States. The U.S. ranks at the bottom of the National Geographic Society's survey of green countries, but the objective environmental record in the U.S. is much better than India's. Air quality in the United States is excellent, where the average level of pollutants in major cities like Miami and San Francisco is lower even than cities like Boise.[7] While weather plays a significant role in air pollution data, the fact that a city like San Francisco, with a population greater than 800,000 people, can have better air quality than Boise, which is one-quarter the size, indicates humans are playing a diminishing role in environmental impact. Indeed, New York City's median air quality index for 2008 was only slightly worse than Boise.

When it comes to air quality, there simply is no comparison between India and the United States. Ignoring this reality should lead us to question the value of National Geographic's ranking system. Their index is more a measurement of which countries fit their preconceived notion of green rather than an objective test of how the environment is actually faring.

Add this to income and life expectancy disparities between India and the United States, and National Geographic ends up giving the "green" lifestyle a pretty bad name.

If policymakers use National Geographic's guidelines to shape policy, the environment will be no better off in the future and, in fact, many policymakers will head in the wrong direction as they focus on the wrong metrics. Measuring resource depletion may be the popular thing – in 2008 as it was in 1968 – but it is pretty hard to claim it is the right thing for the planet or the people who inhabit it.

Environmentalism Isn't Trendy, Environmental Policies Shouldn't Be Either

The cost of environmental trendiness is compounded when we consider that concern for the environment is not, in and of itself, an eco-fad. It is now widely recognized that a healthy environment is good for people. There is a strong moral case to be made for caring for the planet, reducing the impact humans have on the creatures that share the planet with us. While species extinction is, and always will be, a part of nature – it is a key part, not just a side effect, of natural selection – that does not mean we should recklessly engage in unnatural selection without regard for the impact on the health of the earth.

Political liberals and conservatives agree on this point, actually. Liberals express their reverence for nature by working to protect natural lands, enjoying the outdoors by hiking and mountain climbing and raising alarm bells about threats to wildlife. Conservatives value the planet by working as farmers and foresters, ensuring the earth's bounty will continue for the benefit of next generation. They hike and hunt and fish. Conservatives are often found in the most rural parts of the country, foregoing both the benefits of city life and the noise of the concrete jungle to be close to the land and to nature.

They may express their relationship to the environment in a different way, but liberals and conservatives place a value on nature, working to preserve its bounty for the future.

So if environmental consciousness is not a fad, why would we turn to fads when trying to formulate actions and policies designed to make that consciousness tangible? The divergence of our stated concern for the environment, and the unserious way we demonstrate that concern, is the clearest signal of the power of eco-fads to entice and lead us in the wrong direction.

Avoiding the Lure of Eco-Fads

Getting green right is not easy. Politicians, businesses, activists and others have strong incentives to convince you their path to environmental sustainability is the right one. They have the time, the money, the knowledge and support to back up that desire.

You, on the other hand, are much more limited in your time and resources. For most of us, sorting out the eco-fad from the environmental reality is a serious challenge.

The good news is that, ultimately, you have the power. You control your purchasing habits, how you vote and where you decide to expend your environmental protection effort. Following a few guides, we can improve our environmental purchasing and reward office-holders who make truly good environmental policies (and, just as importantly, punish those who do not). A few guides can help us make decisions that are good for the environment, not just our self-image.

It is critical, first, to recognize when the emotional benefits of environmental policies or purchases have become more important than the actual scientific benefits of those actions. We need to ask ourselves, are we doing this because it is good for the environment or because it feels good? As the researchers at the University of Toronto found with the students who bought from the "green" online store, if being green becomes about conferring emotional benefits, it will cloud our ability to make good decisions, leading us to make inappropriate moral compromises.

When environmentalism shifts from a good-faith effort to help the planet and becomes a symbol of social status, the environment suffers. Despite that damage, we see this trend everywhere. Politicians choose policies based on political benefit and popularity. Businesses tout products with dubious environmental benefits, putting more time into developing a green image than technologies and products that actually benefit the environment. Scientists succumb to a myopic view of the world, filtering information through the lens of their own field of study and values, arguing that their view of the science trumps all other interpretations.

And each of us, seeing our peers and celebrities go green, looks to follow suit and send signals about our worth as a person – and seek to reinforce a positive self-image in our own mind.

The emotional benefits of following popular trends are significant. If we mistake chasing those benefits for clear thinking, however, we are fooling ourselves.

Perhaps the worst part of substituting emotional benefits for actual environmental benefits is that it closes our mind to new information. Admitting that we have made the wrong environmental choice also means losing the accrued positive social and personal benefits that choice offered over time. John Charles, the former head of the Oregon Environmental Council who became a strong advocate of free-market approaches to environmental sustainability, said he lost many of his friends when his political views changed. Not only was the change difficult for him personally, he also paid a social price. His peers had invested so much emotional energy into their environmental views that a difference of opinion became personal.

If we become too emotionally invested in a particular approach, we build barriers to contradictory information because it threatens the very image of who we are. It would be foolish to argue people make the right decision every time. Yet, some people behave that way when it comes to the environment. They carefully filter out any new facts that indicate they may need to reexamine their opinions – popular opinions that have helped us gain the respect of our peers and ourselves.

Emotion can be a positive force. Caring for others and future generations is praiseworthy, and these emotions underlie the desire to make environmentally responsible decisions. Our emotional commitments can certainly be a force for good.

Emotions, however, are a poor guide when it comes to making rational decisions about purchases and public policy. When we find ourselves unable to change our minds without invoking a strong emotional reaction, the balance has moved too far away from science and sound decision making.

Second, not everything is equally important. Some decisions will make a significant difference while others are of marginal or negligible value.

Further, what is important is different for each of us. Fishermen will be more concerned about sustainable fisheries than hikers who prioritize wilderness preservation. Some people will decide that climate change is such a significant threat they overlook safety concerns about carbon-free nuclear power, while others will argue the risks from nuclear power are too high.

Trying to achieve the perfect result in setting priorities and making decisions according to those priorities is a losing cause. It is simply too difficult to understand all of the costs and interactions of our decisions. We do not have the time or ability. There is even a well-established phrase that recognizes the difficulty in getting it right every time given the human limits of time and focus: "rational ignorance." It is irrational to believe we can know everything. The more rational approach is to reduce the problem to something we can manage.

The best approach is to pick your priorities and get them right. Each little thing you may do wrong can be more than offset by getting a few big things right.

Even people who believe they have set priorities can find eco-fads undermining their approach. Many who claim to care about air quality ignore the rapid decline in pollution in the U.S., pointing instead to rising rates of asthma in a statistical sleight of hand. If outdoor air quality plays only a minor role in asthma rates, as it appears to, focusing on asthma will lead in the wrong direction – both in terms of improving air quality, and controlling and curing asthma. Yet, because American air quality has improved so significantly, some environmental activists ignore the data, encouraging policymakers to focus on statistics that exaggerate the real threat from air quality, taking focus and resources away from problems that are more serious.

It is not merely enough to identify those things that are important to you. You must also understand the nature of the threats and find the right balance.

It is critical, also, that we look for data that contradicts our view. This is not merely a good idea. The influential scientist Karl Popper believed it is the very essence of the scientific method. Attempting to falsify a hypothesis is a more robust approach to learning the truth than attempting to prove a favored theory is correct. It is a difficult thing to do. Everyone wants to be right. Forcing ourselves to find data that contradicts our ideas is difficult. But doing so shows respect for the truth and for protecting the environment. What could say more about our commitment to leaving a positive environmental legacy for the future than risking our own ideas for the sake of that future?

Recognize that you will make mistakes. You will buy the wrong product. You will vote for the wrong candidate. You will find that changing circumstances make the decision that was right yesterday wrong tomorrow. This can be a good thing. Focusing on the dangers of air pollution makes less sense today than it did in 1970, when air pollution was much worse. Adapting to the new concerns is not a repudiation of the importance of addressing air quality. It is simply the recognition that new information has changed the nature of the decision. Failing to adapt under those circumstances is a signal that advancing environmental quality is not the real goal.

Finally, not all environmental solutions are created equal. Consider this choice. Would you:

1. Buy 700 acres of forest for use as parkland, or

2. Eliminate the CO_2 from 96,153 cars for an entire year.

You can get either for $10 million, yet the scale of impact is pretty different. Given that difference, even if you are committed to creating parks, you may decide that the value of offsetting the carbon emissions from those cars is the better approach. That type of thinking, however, is all too rare when it comes to judging environmental policy.

Often environmental activists convey the message that cost is unimportant because, after all, it is only money, and we are trying to save the planet here. Money, however, is nothing more than a representation of available resources, and for a movement concerned about scarce resources it makes no sense to ignore resource use simply because it is represented in the form of money. Wasting money is wasting resources, and making sure our consumer purchases and public policies make the most of those resources is not merely thrifty, it is environmentally responsible.

Putting a cost to environmental benefits helps us understand the magnitude of the problems we face and the scale of the benefit we are providing. Prices provide necessary context that may be missing. If you could spend $100,000 to save one million gallons of water a year, would you do it? What if you knew that this amount of water costs only about $4,300? It would take you more than 23 years to recover the cost. That price is not merely a financial representation, but an indication of the scarcity or availability of water. If we are concerned about saving water, this price is a pretty good indicator of how to go about it, since with increasing scarcity comes increasing prices.

True concern about the environment requires us to be mindful of the costs and benefits of the decisions we make. Tradeoffs are a part of life, and ignoring them does not make them go away. There is a tendency to believe the environment is too important to be sidetracked by mere economic considerations. Our true situation is just the opposite. We can be careless only when the cost and environmental stakes are low. Why treat the environment like an impulse buy?

Like Bjørn Lomborg's Copenhagen Consensus, if we look at the costs and benefits of each priority, we will make better decisions when facing environmental choices. In the same way the McKinsey report ranks carbon reduction projects by their cost per ton of carbon avoided, we can examine how effectively each approach moves us toward our chosen environmental goal.

There will be times when we decide the environmental benefit of a policy is so negligible we will move on to other priorities, like providing aid for the poor, paying for our children's education, or saving for a family vacation.

In the absence of a tangible measurement like price, however, such decisions are little better than arbitrary guesses. Without that economic information, social and emotional influences are likely to play a disproportionate role in decision making because all choices will seem equal. If we are choosing between two policies of unknown actual environmental benefit, but one comes with a cool hat that says "I care about the planet," we are likely to go for the one with the hat.

People often complain about using such a sterile and calculating approach to addressing an issue they care about. Nobody said doing the right thing would be easy, and complaints about the need to keep an eye on the bottom line are often the result of a desire to do what feels good, and to set aside restrictions that keep us from getting that emotional benefit. An eye on the economics is something that no serious environmentalist should forego.

Environmentalism Without Eco-Fads

For some people the fact that symbols of environmental concern are ubiquitous is a good thing. They argue it is evidence of the growth of environmental awareness. That is true to some extent. But awareness is giving way to empty symbolism, as environmentalism becomes little more than a social badge of honor. Importantly, the power of green symbolism can have negative consequences for the environment.

Politicians promote the biofuels eco-fad that damages the environment and wastes resources. Scientists give misleading guidance, promoted by the limits of their own perspective and limited expertise outside their field of specialty. Reporters hype each new environmental threat, no matter how improbable, to make their journalistic reputation, satisfy a personal agenda or get credit when a predicted risk actually materializes, by claiming they saw it coming all along. Companies peddle the latest environmental threat, offering solutions they can profit from.

We are all susceptible to these temptations. We choose reusable bags instead of plastic bags when that decision may actually increase the amount of energy we use. We choose concrete over wood to save trees, not considering that concrete is not renewable or energy-efficient. We support politicians who impose "green" building standards that end up backfiring, increasing energy use. We buy solar panels to promote renewable energy, when virtually any other power source would be more efficient, less expensive and better for the environment.

We confuse personal benefit with environmental consciousness. Nobody would claim the environment was made better simply because they profited from a sale. Those same people, however, believe that doing something that makes them feel good must also make the planet a better place for future generations of wildlife, birds, fish and people.

At one time, the public recognition of environmental threats was a positive force for sustainability. Indur Goklany, who served as chief of the Technical Assessment Division of the National Commission on Air Quality, calls the time when environmental threats are first understood the "period of perception."[8] A country's wealth combines with the realization that we are having a negative impact on environmental quality, generating efforts that reverse the damage. That perception leads to action. In the United States, that action combined with the natural, free-market drive to eliminate waste, resulting in remarkable improvements in air and water quality.

After time, however, the medium has become the message, as environmental awareness itself has been turned into a social commodity. Appearing green to others outweighs the concerns that sparked the initial perception of environmental damage. The very environmental awareness that was so critical to making initial progress is now overshadowing the science and economic information that is critical to making further progress.

This is the key question as we look to take the next steps along the path of environmental sustainability: Can we prevent eco-fads from becoming the dominant force in environmental decision making?

The answer to that question will have a great deal to say about the public policies we choose and the success or failure of those efforts.

References

Chapter 1: The Rise of Eco-Fads

1 Charles Mann, "The Test Tube Forest," *Business 2.0*, February 2002, p. 66

2 Ibid.

3 Baseball Almanac, "Hank Aaron Quotes," http://www.baseball-almanac.com/quotes/quoaar.shtml.

4 Paul McDougall, "Global Warming Skeptics Plot 'Carbon Belch Day,'" *Information Week*, May 27, 2008, http://www.informationweek.com/news/global-cio/compliance/showArticle.jhtml?articleID=208400325.

5 Editors, "Talk Back," *Business 2.0*, March 2002, p. 13

Chapter 2: What is an Eco-Fad?

1 Energystar.gov, "Light bulbs (CFLs): Energy Star," *Energystar.gov*, http://www.energystar.gov/index.cfm?fuseaction=find_a_product.showProductGroup&pgw_code=LB.

2 EPA, "Mercury Releases and Spills | Mercury | US EPA," http://www.epa.gov/mercury/spills/.

3 Wendy Kaufman, "The Prius Rules Hybrids — but Is Interest Falling?," *National Public Radio*, http://www.npr.org/templates/story/story.php?storyId=12523027.

4 Michael Strong, *Be the Solution* (Hoboken, NJ: John Wiley & Sons, 2009), 68.

5 Alexis Madrigal, "Dog Unto Others: Canines have a sense of fairness," *Wired*, December 8, http://www.wired.com/wiredscience/2008/12/dogenvy/.

6 Bryan Caplan, *The Myth of the Rational Voter*, (Princeton, NJ: Princeton University Press, 2007) 137.

7 Ibid., p. 138

8 Nina Mazar and Chen-Bo Zhong, "Do Green Products Make Us Better People?," *Research Report – Psychological Science*, http://papers.ssrn.com/sol3/papers.cfm?abstract_id=1463018.

9 Ibid.

10 Rebecca Tuhus-Dubrow, "Buy Local, Act Evil?," *Slate.com*, http://www.slate.com/id/2237674.

11 Lisa Stiffler, "Bill orders firm steps to make state 'greener'," *Seattle Post-Intelligencer*, February 19, 2008, http://www.seattlepi.com/local/article/Bill-orders-firm-steps-to-make-state-greener-1264919.php#ixzz1Q1DWhWRG

12 Alex Steffen, comments before the Seattle City Council, April 12, 2010

Chapter 3: The Illogical Common Sense of Eco-Fads

1 Cass Sunstein, *Worst Case Scenarios*, (Cambridge, MA: Harvard University Press, 2007), 128.

2 William Nordhaus, *A Question of Balance*, (New Haven, CT: Yale University Press, 2008), 15.

3 Ronald Bailey, *Eco-Scam: The False Prophets of Ecological Apocalypse*, (New York: St. Martin's Press, 1993).

4 Nassim Nicholas Taleb, *The Black Swan*, (New York: Random House, 2007), 75.

Chapter 4: Why Politicians Promote Eco-Fads

1 Greg Nickels, "More than symbolism at stake when cities tackle climate change," *The Seattle Times*, October 31, 2007, http://seattletimes.nwsource.com/html/opinion/2003983806_nickels31.html.

2 City of Seattle, "Climate Progress Report: meeting Kyoto and beyond," December 8, 2009, http://www.seattle.gov/news/detail.asp?ID=10390&Dept=40.

3 Craig Welch, "Seattle meets goal to reduce greenhouse-gas production," The Seattle Times, December 9, 2009, http://seattletimes.nwsource.com/html/localnews/2010457770_citycarbon09m.html.

4 City of Seattle Office of Sustainability and Environment, "2005 Inventory of Seattle Greenhouse Gas Emissions: Community & Corporate, Final Draft," October 2007, http://www.seattle.gov/climate/docs/2005%20Seattle%20Inventory%20Full%20Report.pdf, 15.

5 Jay Manning, Washington State Department of Ecology, email to Ted Sturdevant and Keith Phillips, May 07, 2009

6 Bonner Cohen, *The Green Wave*, (Washington, D.C.: Capital Research Center), 2006, 158.

7 Trade Commission of Spain, "Vice President Al Gore Touts Spain's Leadership in Energy and Infrastructure," March 18, 2009, http://www.businesswire.com/portal/site/home/permalink/?ndmViewId=news_view&newsId=20090318005802&newsLang=en.

8 Cristina Blas, "Spain admits that the green energy as sold to Obama is a disaster," La Gaceta de los Negocios, May 21, 2010, http://pajamasmedia.com/blog/leaked-spanish-report-obamas-model-green-economy-a-disaster-pjm-exclusive/2/.

9 Nina Shapiro, "King County's "Green Cab" Experiment Goes South," *Seattle Weekly*, April 29, 2009, http://www.seattleweekly.com/2009-04-29/news/king-county-s-green-cab-experiment-goes-south/.

10 Jerome Groopman, *How Doctors Think*, (New York: Houghton Mifflin Company, 2008), 169.

11 City of Seattle Department of Transportation, "Seattle Department of Transportation: Car Free Day Events," http://www.seattle.gov/transportation/carfreedays.htm.

12 Brandon Houskeeper, "Car-free Days are Seattle's Latest Eco-fad, but are there any real benefits?," *Washington Policy Center*, September 2008, http://www.washingtonpolicy.org/Centers/environment/envwatch/September2008EnviroWatch.pdf.

13 Amos Tversky and Daniel Kahneman, "Loss Aversion in Riskless Choice: A Reference-Dependent Model," *Quarterly Journal of Economics*, 106 (1991):4.

14 Stephen J. Dubner and Steven D. Levitt, "Monkey Business," *The New York Times Magazine*, June 5, 2005, http://www.nytimes.com/2005/06/05/magazine/05FREAK.html?pagewanted=all.

15 Bruce Bueno de Mesquita, Alastair Smith, Randolph M. Siverson, and James D. Morrow, *The Logic of Political Survival*, (Cambridge, MA: The MIT Press, 2003).

16 City of Seattle, "Carbon Neutral Seattle – Logo Contest," http://carbonneutral.seattle.gov/logo-contest/.

17 Alex Steffen, comments before the Seattle City Council, April 12, 2010.

18 Alex Kirby, "Climate Crisis near 'in 10 years'," *BBC News*, January 24, 2005, http://news.bbc.co.uk/2/hi/science/nature/4202649.stm.

19 Alastair Jamieson, "Barack Obama has four years to save the world from climate change, warns Prof James McCarthy," *Telegraph.co.uk*, February 12, 2009, http://www.telegraph.co.uk/earth/environment/climatechange/4598999/Barack-Obama-has-four-years-to-save-the-world-from-climate-change-warns-Prof-James-McCarthy.html.

20 Bill McKibben, "The Tipping Point," *Yale 360*, June 3, 2008, http://e360.yale.edu/content/feature.msp?id=2012.

21 Paul Greenberg, "Hot Planet, Cold Facts," *The New York Times*, April 29, 2010, http://www.nytimes.com/2010/05/09/books/review/Greenberg-t.html.

Chapter 5: The Profitable Business of Eco-Fads

1 TerraChoice, "TerraChoice 2010 Sins of Greenwashing Study Finds Misleading Green Claims on 95 Percent of Home and Family Products," *TerraChoice*, October 26, 2010, http://www.terrachoice.com/files/TerraChoice%202010%20Sins%20of%20Greenwashing%20Release%20-%20Oct%2026%202010%20-%20ENG.pdf.

2 Ecofabulous, http://www.ecofabulous.com

3 John Mackey, *Be the Solution*, (Hoboken, NJ: John Wiley & Sons, 2009), 82.

4 Ibid, p. xii

5 Daniel McGinn, "The Greenest Big Companies in America," *Newsweek*, September 28, 2009, 44.

6 General Electric, "ecomagination 2009 Annual Report," http://files.gecompany.com/ecomagination/ge_2009_ecomagination_report.pdf, 49.

7 General Electric, "GE:ecomagination," http://ge.ecomagination.com/report.html.

8 Amanda Little, "GE Kicks off ambitious green initiative," *Grist*, May 10, 2005, http://www.grist.org/article/little-ge/.

9 Jeff Immelt, "Global Environmental Challenges," speech to George Washington School of Business, May 9, 2005, http://www.ge.com/files/usa/company/news/global_environmental_challenges.pdf.

10 General Electric, "ecomagination 2009 Annual Report," http://files.gecompany.com/ecomagination/ge_2009_ecomagination_report.pdf, 3.

11 Jeff Immelt, "GE 2008 Annual Report," February 6, 2009, http://www.ge.com/ar2008/letter.html.

12 United States Climate Action Partnership, http://www.us-cap.org/.

13 Adam Smith, *The Wealth of Nations*, (London: J.M. Dent and Sons, 1957), 117.

14 Timothy Carney, "Obama's hidden bailout of GE," Washington Examiner, March 4, 2009, http://www.washingtonexaminer.com/politics/Obamas-hidden-bailout-of-General-Electric_03_04-40686707.html#ixzz12aUccxJR.

15 FilterforGood, "Filter For Good: Surfrider," *Filterforgood*, http://www.filterforgood.com/surfrider/.

16 Penn and Teller, "Bullshit!," Feng Shui/Bottled Water (TV episode 2003 #1.7).

17 Arrowhead, "Arrowhead – The Eco-Shape Bottle, TV Commercial & Features, Doing our Part | Nestle," http://www.arrowheadwater.com/DoingOurPart/EcoShapeBottle.aspx.

18 Wired, "Make a Lighter, Stronger Plastic Bottle," *Wired*, February 23, 2009, http://www.wired.com/culture/design/magazine/17-03/dp_bottle#ixzz13EAU9DL2.

19 Starbucks, "Organic Shade Grown Mexico | Starbucks Coffee Company," *Starbucks*, http://www.starbucks.com/coffee/whole-bean-coffee/latin-america/organic-shade-grown-mexico.

20 Tim Harford, "Tim Harford – Article – Business Life: Fair Trade or Foul," April 28, 2008, http://timharford.com/2008/04/business-life-fair-trade-or-foul/.

21 Lorraine Mitchell, "Dolphin-Safe Tuna Labeling," Agricultural Economic Report 793, December 2000, 22.

22 Ibid.

23 Ibid.

24 Mitchell, p. 23

25 Stephanie Simon, "The Secret to Turning Consumers Green," *The Wall Street Journal*, October 18, 2010, http://online.wsj.com/article/SB10001424052748704575304575296243891721972.html.

26 Ibid.

27 Terrachoice, 2010

28 Alexis de Tocqueville, *Democracy in America*, (London: Penguin Books, 2003), 782.

29 Todd Myers, "Offering Environmental Salvation...For A Price," *Washington Policy Center* blog, October 18, 2010, http://www.washingtonpolicy.org/blog/post/offering-environmental-salvationfor-price.

30 Chris Horner, *Red Hot Lies*, (Washington, D.C.: Regnery Publishing, 2008), 252.

31 Kirsten Gillibrand, "Cap and Trade Could Be a Boon to New York," *The Wall Street Journal*, October 21, 2009, http://online.wsj.com/article/SB10001424052748704500604574481812686 144826.html.

32 Christina Williams, "Northwest businesses call for Senate action on climate change," *Sustainable Business Oregon*, June 3, 2010, http://sustainablebusinessoregon.com/articles/2010/06/northwest_businesses_call_for_senate_action_on_climate_change.html.

33 Randy Woods, "The 2009 Green Washington Awards," *Seattle Business*, October 2009, 35.

34 Heather Rogers, *Green Gone Wrong*," (New York: Scribner, 2010), 25.

Chapter 6: The Media and Eco-Fads

1 John Charles, "A Bias Crisis in Journalism," *Brainstorm*, February 2005, http://www.brainstormnw.com/archive/feb05_feature.html.

2 Charles, "Shading the Truth Green," *Brainstorm*, January 2004, http://www.brainstormnw.com/archive/jan04_feature.html.

3 Charles, 2005

4 Ibid.

5 Ibid.

6 The Washington Post, "Greenpeace just kidding about Armageddon," *The Washington Post*, June 2, 2006, http://www.washingtonpost.com/wp-dyn/content/article/2006/06/01/AR2006060101884.html.

7 Erica Barnett, "Are the Terrorists Right?" *The Stranger*, March 4, 2008, http://www.thestranger.com/seattle/Content?oid=526435&mode=print

8 David Postman, "Did the Eco-Arsonists Win?," *The Seattle Times*, March 25, 2008, http://blog.seattletimes.nwsource.com/davidpostman/2008/03/did_the_ecoterrorists_win.html.

9 Mark Nowlin and Lynda Mapes, "Building a Greener House," *The Seattle Times*, March 11, 2008, http://seattletimes.nwsource.com/ABPub/2008/03/11/2004276500.pdf.

10 Sandi Doughton, "The truth about global warming," *The Seattle Times*, October 11, 2005, http://seattletimes.nwsource.com/html/nationworld/2002549346_globewarm11.html.

11 Charles, 2004

12 Scott Bauer and Dinesh Ramde, "Feingold labels himself underdog against newcomer," *The Washington Post*, September 9, 2010, http://www.washingtonpost.com/wp-dyn/content/article/2010/09/09/AR2010090904824_pf.html.

13 Kristen Millares Young, "Seattle's plans for future shaped by climate change still in infancy," *Seattle Post-Intelligencer*, April 1, 2008, http://www.seattlepi.com/local/357223_port01.html.

14 Lisa Stiffler, "Sound Warning: Scientists say the region is already feeling climate change," *Seattle Post-Intelligencer*, October 18, 2005, http://www.seattlepi.com/local/244995_soundclimate18.html.

15 Lisa Stiffler, "Sea Level rise of 6 inches by 2050 in Puget Sound," *Seattle Post-Intelligencer*, January 17, 2008, http://blog.seattlepi.com/environment/archives/129696.asp.

16 Robert McClure, "I'm a person for Puget Sound," *Seattle Post-Intelligencer*, May 3, 2007, http://blog.seattlepi.com/environment/archives/114909.asp?source=rss.

17 Discovery Communications, "Discovery Communications Adsales – Networks – Planet Green – Research," *Discovery Communications*, http://adsales.discovery.com/networks/planet-green/research/.

18 The Seattle Times, "Local News – About This Project – Seattle Times," *The Seattle Times,* http://seattletimes.nwsource.com/html/localnews/2003660504_webclimateabout09.html.

19 Ibid.

Chapter 7: The Difference Between Science and Sex Appeal

1 Kari Norgaard, "Kari Norgaard, assistant professor of sociology and environmental studies," *Whitman Magazine,* March 2009, http://www.whitman.edu/content/magazine/in-their-words/dearmrpresident/norgaard.

2 James Hansen, *Storms of My Grandchildren,* (New York: Bloomsbury USA, 2009), xi.

3 Roger A. Pielke Jr., *The Honest Broker: Making Sense of Science in Policy and Politics,* (New York: Cambridge University Press, 2007), 44.

4 Hansen, p. x.

5 Thomas Kuhn, *The Structure of Scientific Revolutions,* (Chicago, IL: University of Chicago Press, 1962), 78.

6 Pat Michaels, *Climate of Extremes,* (Washington, D.C.: Cato Institute, 2009), 201.

7 Stephen Jay Gould, The Structure of Evolutionary Theory (Belknap Press of Harvard University Press, 2002) pp. 763-4

8 Eastangliaemails.com, "East Anglia Confirmed Emails from the Climate Research Unit – Searchable," *Eastangliaemails.com,* http://eastangliaemails.com/emails.php?eid=295.

9 Daniel Sarewitz, "How science makes environmental controversies worse," *Environmental Science & Policy,* 7 (2004): 392,, http://cspo.org/documents/environ_controv.pdf.

10 Russ Roberts, "Gordon on Ants, Humans, the Division of Labor and Emergent Order," *Econtalk,* http://www.econtalk.org/archives/2007/08/gordon_on_ants.html.

11 Kuhn, p. x

12 Intergovernmental Panel on Climate Change, "Guidance Notes for Lead Authors of the IPCC Fourth Assessment Report on Addressing Uncertainties," *Intergovernmental Panel on Climate Change,* http://ipcc-wg1.ucar.edu/wg1/Report/AR4_UncertaintyGuidanceNote.pdf, 3.

13 Ian Ayres, Supercrunchers, (New York: Bantam, 2007), 112.

14 Ayres, p. 115

15 Ayres, p. 116

16 Chris Andreae, interview with Paul Ehrlich, co-author with Anne Ehrlich of "The Dominant Animal: Human Evolution and the Environment," December 1, 2008, http://kboo.fm/node/10746.

Chapter 8: Forestry Eco-Fads

1 Gordon Robinson as quoted in Patrick Moore, *Trees Are the Answer,* (Vancouver, BC: Beatty Street Publishing, 2010), 32.

2 Moore, 33.

3 Garrett Hardin as quoted in Moore, 33.

4 Bruce Lippke, "Building Materials and Climate Change: The Unseen Connection," *California Forests* (California Forestry Ass.), Vol. 10 No. 1 (2006): 12-13, http://www.ruraltech.org/pubs/pubs_list/2006/pdfs/lippke_calforests_winter06.pdf.

5 Michael E. Conroy, "Can Advocacy-Led Certification Systems Transform Global Corporate Practices? Evidence and Some Theory," *Political Economy Research Institute,* University of Massachusetts Amherst, (September 2001):3, http://scholarworks.umass.edu/cgi/viewcontent.cgi?article=1014&context=peri_workingpapers.

6 Sustainable Forestry Initiative, "The Sustainable Forestry Initiative: Objectives and Principles," *International Federation of Inspection Agencies,* http://www.ifia.com/SFI/SFIObjectivesPrinciples.htm.

7 American Tree Farm System, "American Tree Farm System: Certification 2010-2015 Standards of Sustainability," *American Tree Farm System*, http://www.treefarmsystem.org/cms/pages/26_130.html.

8 Peter Goldmark, "DNR and the State of Puget Sound: Why forest conversion matters to all of us," February 25, 2010, *Washington State Department of Natural Resources*, http://www.dnr.wa.gov/AboutDNR/FieldNotes/Pages/20100215_goldmark_pugetsound.aspx.

9 Rachel Jamison, "Green Buildings Can Boost Industry," February 14, 2008, *The Daily Olympian*, http://www.forestrycenter.org/headlines.cfm?refID=101627.

10 Leslie Kaufman, "Mr. Whipple Left It Out: Soft Is Rough on Forests," *The New York Times*, February 25, 2009, http://www.nytimes.com/2009/02/26/science/earth/26charmin.html.

11 Ibid.

12 Ibid.

13 B.N. Baird, "Comment on 'Post-Wildfire Logging Hinders Regeneration and Increases Fire Risk'," *Science*, Vol. 313 no. 5787 (August 2006): 615, http://www.sciencemag.org/content/313/5787/615.2.full.

14 Richard York, "Corporate Forestry and Academic Freedom," *Siskiyou Project*, January 24, 2006, http://www.siskiyou.org/news/in_the_news/corporate_forestry.cfm.

15 The Oregonian Editorial Board, "Owl vs. Owl," *Oregon Live*, February 19, 2011, http://www.oregonlive.com/opinion/index.ssf/2011/02/owl_vs_owl.html.

Chapter 9: The Power of Energy Eco-Fads

1 U.S. Energy Information Administration, "International Energy Outlook 2010," July 2010, http://www.eia.doe.gov/oiaf/ieo/pdf/0484(2010).pdf, 1.

2 J U.S. Representative Jay Inslee, "Jay Inslee – Apollo Energy Fact Sheet," http://www.jayinslee.com/index.php?page=display&id=31&sub=1.

3 Jim Lane, "The New Imperium: A Major Player in Biodiesel 1.5 aims for Biofuels 2.0," http://biofuelsdigest.com/bdigest/2010/08/03/the-new-imperium-a-major-player-in-biodiesel-1-5-aims-for-biofuels-2-0/.

4 Sandi Doughton, "Group hopes to build 75-megawatt solar park near Cle Elum," *The Seattle Times*, July 10, 2009, http://seattletimes.nwsource.com/html/localnews/2009443136_solar10m.html.

5 Teanaway Solar Reserve, http://teanawaysolarreserve.org/fact.html.

6 John Stang, "Kittitas Solar Plant could be super expensive," *Seattle Post-Intelligencer*, August 2, 2009, http://www.seattlepi.com/local/408805_solarplant3.html.

7 Teanaway Solar Reserve, ibid.

8 Gerard Wynn, "U.S. corn ethanol 'was not a good policy' - Gore", *Reuters*, November 22, 2010 http://af.reuters.com/article/energyOilNews/idAFLDE6AL0YT20101122?sp=true.

9 Wynn, ibid.

10 Doug Elmendorf, "Using Biofuel Tax Credits to Achieve Energy and Environmental Policy Goals," *Congressional Budget Office Director's Blog*, July 14, 2010, http://cboblog.cbo.gov/?p=1161.

11 Elmendorf, ibid.

12 Margaret Thatcher Foundation, "TV Interview for Thames TV This Week: 1976 Feb 5 Th," http://www.margaretthatcher.org/document/102953

13 Govlink, "Biodiesel partnership," *Govlink: a multi-jurisdictional website hosted by King County in Washington State*, August 25, 2006, http://www.govlink.org/biodiesel/.

14 Ibid.

15 Angel Gonzalez, "Biofuel backlash: High prices, pollution worries hit consumers," *The Seattle Times*, June 8, 2008, http://seattletimes.nwsource.com/html/localnews/2004464783_biofuels08.html.

16 Todd Myers, "Inefficient King County Biodiesel Effort Leaves the CO_2 of 4,319 Cars in the Atmosphere," *Washington Policy Center*, May 2007, http://www.washingtonpolicy.org/publications/environmental/inefficient-king-county-biodiesel-effort-leaves-co2-4319-cars-atmosphere.

17 Bert Caldwell and John Stucke, "Odessa refinery helping meet demand for biofuel," The Spokesman-Review (Spokane, WA), January 10, 2010, http://www.spokesman.com/stories/2010/jan/10/a-local-growth-industry/.

18 Conversation with the author, March, 2011

19 King County Councilman Reagan Dunn, *KingCounty.gov*, "Dunn calls for study to examine potentially harmful biofuel impacts," May 8, 2008, http://www.kingcounty.gov/council/news/2008/May/RD_biofuel.aspx.

20 Chris Grygiel, "City of Seattle halts biodiesel purchases, looks for greener fuel," *Seattle Post-Intelligencer*, June 19, 2009, http://www.seattlepi.com/local/407384_fuel19.html.

21 Terry Macalister, "Demands for crackdown on biofuels scam," *The Guardian*, April 1, 2008, http://www.guardian.co.uk/environment/2008/apr/01/biofuels.energy.

22 Keith Johnson, "U.S. Biofuels Subsidies: Not for Farmers, but for Europeans," *The Wall Street Journal Environmental Capital Blog*, http://blogs.wsj.com/environmentalcapital/2008/04/01/us-biofuels-subsidies-not-for-farmers-but-for-europeans/.

23 Abraham Lincoln, "Lecture on Discoveries and Inventions," 1860, http://american_almanac.tripod.com/lincoln.htm.

24 Dan Ariely, *Predictably Irrational*, (New York: HarperCollins Publishers, 2008), 49.

25 State of California, "SB 107. Renewable energy: Public Interest Energy Research, Demonstration, and Development Program," 2006, http://www.energy.ca.gov/portfolio/documents/sb_107_bill_20060926_chaptered.pdf.

26 U.S. Energy Information Administration, "Electric Power Monthly - Average Retail Price of Electricity to Ultimate Customers: Total by End-Use Sector," November 15, 2010, http://www.eia.doe.gov/cneaf/electricity/epm/table5_3.html.

27 Solarbuzz, "Solar Electricity Prices," *Solarbuzz*, November 2010, http://www.solarbuzz.com/SolarPrices.htm.

28 U.S. Energy Information Administration, "2016 Levelized Cost of New Generation Resources from the Annual Energy Outlook 2010," January 12, 2010, http://www.eia.doe.gov/oiaf/aeo/electricity_generation.html.

29 Ibid, 3.

30 Author's interview with Robert Kahn, Executive Director, Northwest & Intermountain Power Producers Coalition, November 30, 2010.

31 European Carbon Market, https://www.theice.com/productguide/ProductGroupHierarchy.shtml?groupDetail=&group.groupId=19.

32 McKinsey and Company, "Reducing U.S. Greenhouse Gas Emissions: How Much At What Cost?," December 2007, http://www.mckinsey.com/clientservice/ccsi/pdf/us_ghg_final_report.pdf, 25.

33 Severin Borenstein, "The Market Value and Cost of Solar Photovoltaic Electricity Production," January 2008, http://www.ucei.berkeley.edu/PDF/csemwp176.pdf, 25.

34 Manuel Frondel, Nolan Ritter, Christoph M. Schmidt and Colin Vance, "Economic Impacts from the Promotion of Renewable Energy Technologies: The German Experience," Ruhr Economic Papers #156, 2009, http://ideas.repec.org/p/rwi/repape/0156.html, 13.

35 McKinsey, 59.

36 Peter Lang, "Cost and Quantity of Greenhouse Gas Emissions Avoided by Wind Generation," February 16, 2009, http://carbon-sense.com/wp-content/uploads/2009/02/wind-power.pdf, 10.

37 Frondel et al., 13.

38 George Gilder, "California's destructive green jobs lobby," November 16, 2010, http://online.wsj.com/article/SB10001424052748703305404575610402116987146.html.

39 The Daily News editorial board, "Time to take a hard look at cost of tax incentives for green jobs," *The Daily News* (Longview, WA), November 11, 2009, http://tdn.com/news/opinion/article_18174928-5e62-54f7-bdc9-629974ee8fc1.html.

40 Charles Krauthammer, "The Net-zero Gas Tax," *The Weekly Standard*, December 26, 2008, http://www.weeklystandard.com/Content/Public/Articles/000/000/015/949rsrgi.asp?pg=1.

41 Red County Editors, "Energy Myth: Renewable Energy is Always Popular and Safe," *Redcounty.com*, November 16, 2010, http://www.redcounty.com/content/energy-myth-renewable-energy-always-popular-and-safe.

42 Ibid.

43 Department of Energy, "New England Forum: Wind Turbine Sound," August 3, 2010, http://www.windpoweringamerica.gov/ne_issues_sound.asp.

44 Rob Book, presentation to American Legislative Exchange Council, December 2, 2010.

45 Conversation with author, December 12, 2010

46 Pacific Northwest National Laboratory, "Smart grid could reduce emissions by 12 percent," January 28, 2010, http://www.pnl.gov/news/release.aspx?id=776.

47 TriviaLibrary.com, "Solar Energy Future Development," *TriviaLibrary.com*, http://www.trivia-library.com/b/solar-energy-future-development.htm.

48 Energy Information Administration, "Table 1.5 Energy Consumption, Expenditures, and Emissions Indicators, Selected Years, 1949-2009," U.S. Energy Information Administration / Annual Energy Review 2009, http://www.eia.doe.gov/emeu/aer/pdf/pages/sec1_13.pdf

Chapter 10: Climate Eco-Fads

1 Bryan Walsh, "Cash for Clunkers: How Big an Environmental Boost?," *Time*, August 5, 2009, http://www.time.com/time/printout/0,8816,1914602,00.html.

2 Declan McCullagh, "'Cash for Clunkers' Does Little to Help the Environment," *CBS News*, August 5, 2009, http://www.cbsnews.com/8301-503983_162-5217824-503983.html.

3 Walsh, 2009.

4 Christopher Knittel, "The Implied Cost of Carbon Dioxide Under the Cash for Clunkers Program," Center for the Study of Energy Markets, Working Paper 189, August 2009, http://www.ucei.berkeley.edu/PDF/csemwp189.pdf.

5 Irwin Stelzer, "Seven Lessons of Cash-for-Clunkers' Failure," *Washington Examiner*, August 27, 2009, http://washingtonexaminer.com/print/op-eds/2009/08/irwin-stelzer-seven-lessons-cash-clunkers-failure.html.

6 Associated Press, "Carmakers Can Breathe Easy, California Reduces Emissions Mandate," March 28, 2008, http://www.foxnews.com/story/0,2933,342132,00.html.

7 Ibid.

8 Washington State Legislature, SB 5735, Adopted April 14, 2009.

9 Douglas Olin, "Earn the Bailout, Detroit," *Los Angeles Times*, November 12, 2008, http://www.latimes.com/news/opinion/la-oe-olin12-2008nov12,0,7834379.story.

10 Gm-volt.com, "Popular Mechanics Finds Chevrolet Volt Gets 32 MPG City and 36 MPG Highway in Extended Range Mode," *Gm-volt.com*, October 10, 2010, http://gm-volt.com/2010/10/10/popular-mechanics-finds-chevrolet-volt-gets-32-mpg-city-and-36-mpg-highway-in-extended-range-mode/.

11 California Fuel Cell Partnership, "Station Map | California Fuel Cell Partnership," http://www.cafcp.org/stationmap.

12 Scott Adams, "How I (Almost) Saved the Earth," *The Wall Street Journal*, August 21, 2010, http://online.wsj.com/article/SB10001424052748704868604575433620189923744.html?KEYWORDS=dilbert.

13 U.S. Green Building Council, "USGBC: Government Resources," http://www.usgbc.org/DisplayPage.aspx?CMSPageID=1779.

14 Washington Conservation Voters, "Priorities for a Healthy Washington: High Performance Green Buildings," January 2005.

15 Susannah Frame, "Investigators: Green school claims oversold," *KING TV*, November 13, 2009, http://www.king5.com/news/investigators/Investigators-Green-school-claims-oversold.html.

16 Frame, ibid.

17 O'Brien & Company, "Washington Sustainable Schools Program Phase 2 Pilot Project Final Report," January 27, 2005, 31.

18 Fox News, "It's Not Easy Being Green," April 23, 2010, http://video.foxnews.com/v/4163643/its-not-easy-being-green/.

19 Auden Schendler and Randy Udall, "LEED is Broken...Let's Fix It," *iGreenBuild.com*, 2005, http://www.igreenbuild.com/cd_1706.aspx.

20 Lisa Fay Matthiessen and Peter Morris, "Costing Green: A Comprehensive Cost Database and Budgeting Methodology," Davis Langdon, July 2004, http://www.usgbc.org/Docs/Resources/Cost_of_Green_Full.pdf.

21 Mireya Navarro, "Some Buildings Not Living Up to Green Label," *The New York Times*, August 30, 2009, http://www.nytimes.com/2009/08/31/science/earth/31leed.html?_r=4&hpw.

22 U.S. Green Building Council, "USGBC Update - The Future of Green Buildings: An Aggressive Focus on Measurable Performance," September 2009, email to author.

23 Patricia Jatczak, "RE: Spokesman Review article: 'Green' school rules need to be suspended," March 3, 2009, email.

24 Susannah Patton, "Green Construction Brought Into Question," *The Zweig Letter*, November 15, 2010, Issue 887, 4.

25 Washington State Department of Ecology, "Green Building: Jobs of the Future," 2009, http://www.ecy.wa.gov/programs/swfa/greenbuilding/pdf/GreenBuilding_video_transcript.pdf.

26 Alan Durning, "Green Collar Jobs," *Seattle: Northwest Environment Watch*, 1999, 5.

27 Jennifer Vogel, "Small-town America's Green Lifeline," May/June 2008, Mother Jones, http://motherjones.com/environment/2008/05/small-town-americas-green-lifeline.

28 Kristin Kolb, "Smells Like Green Spirit," *Daily Score Blog*, April 29, 2008, http://daily.sightline.org/daily_score/blogall_view?topic=greenbiz&b_start:int=60.

29 U.S. 2010 Census, "Hoquiam city, Washington – Fact Sheet – American Fact Finder," http://factfinder.census.gov/home/saff/main.html?_lang=en.

30 Hal Bernton, "Grays Harbor Paper shuts plant; 240 jobs lost," *The Seattle Times*, May 26, 2011, http://seattletimes.nwsource.com/html/businesstechnology/2015159995_papermill27.html.

31 Gabriel Calzada Alvarez Ph.D., "Testimony Before the House Select Committee on Energy Independence and Global Warming," September 24, 2009, http://globalwarming.house.gov/files/HRG/092409Solar/calzada.pdf.

32 Ernst & Young, "Renewable Energy Country Attractiveness Indices," Spring 2006, http://sefi.unep.org/fileadmin/media/sefi/docs/archive/EY_CAIndices_Spring_06.pdf, 4.

33 Gabriel Calzada Alvarez Ph.D., "Study of the effects on employment of public aid to renewable energy sources," King Juan Carlos University, March 2009, http://www.juandemariana.org/pdf/090327-employment-public-aid-renewable.pdf.

34 Central Intelligence Agency, "The World Factbook – Country Comparison: GDP - Per Capita (PPP)," https://www.cia.gov/library/publications/the-world-factbook/rankorder/2004rank.html.

35 Ernst & Young, "Renewable Energy Country Attractiveness Indices," November 2010, Issue 27, http://www.ey.com/Publication/vwLUAssets/Renewable_energy_country_attractiveness_indices_-_Issue_27/$FILE/EY_RECAI_issue_27.pdf, 11.

36 Anna Fahey, "China Wins – Again," *Sightline Daily*, October 20, 2010, http://daily.sightline.org/daily_score/archive/2010/10/20/china-wins-again.

37 Pew Charitable Trusts, "The Clean Energy Economy: Repowering Jobs, Businesses and Investments Across America," June 2009, http://www.pewcenteronthestates.org/uploadedFiles/Clean_Economy_Report_Web.pdf.

38 Jon Talton, "Calculating the benefits of a green recovery," *The Seattle Times*, May 22, 2009, http://seattletimes.nwsource.com/html/soundeconomywithjontalton/2009251471_calculating_the_benefits_of_a.html.

39 Aaron Lehmer, "Renewable Energy Development Creates More Jobs than Fossil Fuels," Ella Baker Center for Human Rights, http://www.greenforall.org/resources/summary-of-research-on-the-job-creating-potential/download.

40 Governor Christine Gregoire, "Gov. Gregoire announces Washington state economy is getting 'greener,'" March 18, 2010, http://www.esd.wa.gov/newsandinformation/releases/archives/2010/wa-state-economy-is-getting-greener.php.

41 Washington State Employment Security Department, "2009 Washington State Green Economy Jobs," March 2010, http://www.workforceexplorer.com/admin/uploadedPublications/10258_Green_Jobs_Report_for_Web_2009.pdf, 32.

Chapter 11: Green Living Eco-Fads

1 1 Bag at a Time, http://www.onebagatatime.com/planet/environmental-impact/paper-bags/.

2 Michael Grynbaum, "Even Reusable Bags Carry Environmental Risk," *The New York Times*, November 14, 2010, http://www.nytimes.com/2010/11/15/nyregion/15bags.html?_r=4.

3 Theresa Marchetta, "Reusable Grocery Bags Breed Bacteria", news report aired in Denver, CO on September 27, 2010, http://www.thedenverchannel.com/news/25181234/detail.html.

4 Grynbaum, ibid.

5 Entertainment Earth, http://www.entertainmentearth.com/prodinfo.asp?number=AU11948.

6 Seattle Public Utilities, "City of Seattle Disposable Shopping Bags Green Fee and Expanded Polystyrene (EPS) Foam Food Container Ban Frequently Asked Questions (FAQs)," June 18, 2008, http://www.cityofseattle.net/util/groups/public/@spu/@csb/documents/webcontent/spu02_014614.pdf.

7 Alexi Mostrous, "Series of blunders turned the plastic bag into global villain," *The Sunday Times of London*, March 8, 2008, http://www.timesonline.co.uk/tol/news/environment/article3508263.ece.

8 Oregon State University, "Oceanic "garbage patch" not nearly as big as portrayed in media," Press Release, January 4, 2011, http://oregonstate.edu/ua/ncs/archives/2011/jan/oceanic-%E2%80%9Cgarbage-patch%E2%80%9D-not-nearly-big-portrayed-media.

9 Mostrous, 2008.

10 Carrier Bag Consortium, "The Holes in the Argument for a Carrier Bag Tax," http://www.carrierbagtax.com/downloads/CBC2ppLeaflet61.pdf.

11 Froma Harrop, "A locavore's logic," *The Seattle Times*, July 21, 2009, http://seattletimes.nwsource.com/html/opinion/2009510582_harrop22.html.

12 William Yardley, "The pride and prejudice of 'local'," *The New York Times*, July 8, 2010, http://www.nytimes.com/2010/07/09/us/09local.html.

13 John B. Saul, "The Bounty Around Us," *Pacific Northwest Magazine*, August 19, 2007, http://seattletimes.nwsource.com/html/pacificnw08192007/2003837335_pacificplocal19.html.

14 Tom Watson, "Eating local means figuring out your 'food-miles'," *The Seattle Times*, April 19, 2009, http://seattletimes.nwsource.com/html/pacificnw/2009076639_pacificfootchoices19.html.

15 Deborah Zabarenko, "Do food-miles make a difference to global warming?," *Reuters*, October 17, 2007, http://uk.reuters.com/article/idUKN0521281920071017.

16 Ibid.

17 James McWilliams, "Food that travels well," *The New York Times*, August 6, 2007, http://www.nytimes.com/2007/08/06/opinion/06mcwilliams.html.

18 Christopher L. Weber and H. Scott Matthews, "Food-Miles and the Relative Climate Impacts of Food Choices in the United States," *Environmental Science & Technology* 42, no.10 (2008): 3508–13.

19 Wikipedia, "Earth Hour," http://en.wikipedia.org/wiki/Earth_Hour

20 See, for instance, Jane Brody, "Personal Health; Health Scares That Weren't So Scary," August 18, 1998, http://www.nytimes.com/1998/08/18/science/personal-health-health-scares-that-weren-t-so-scary.html.

21 Susan Ferriss and Ricardo Sandoval, *Fight in the Fields: Caesar Chavez and the Farmworkers Movement* (New York: Harvest Books, 1997), 207.

22 Christy Getz, Sandy Brown and Aimee Shreck, "Class Politics and Agricultural Exceptionalism in California's Organic Agriculture Movement," Politics Society, 36: 478 (2008), 500.

23 Michael Pollan, "Power Steer," *The New York Times Magazine*, March 31, 2002, http://michaelpollan.com/articles-archive/power-steer/.

24 John Stossel, "Natural is not always better," *Creators.com*, November 17, 2010, http://www.creators.com/opinion/john-stossel/natural-is-not-always-better.html.

Chapter 12: Avoiding Eco-Fads

1 Ronald Bailey, "Billions Served: Norman Borlaug interviewed by Ronald Bailey," *Reason Magazine*, April 2000, http://reason.com/archives/2000/04/01/billions-served-norman-borlaug.

2 The Times of India, "Indians are world's 'greenest': Survey," *The Times of India*, May 14, 2009, http://timesofindia.indiatimes.com/articleshow/msid-4527041,prtpage-1.cms.

3 National Geographic Society, "Greendex 2010: Consumer Choice and the Environment – A Worldwide Tracking Survey," June 2010, http://images.nationalgeographic.com/wpf/media-live/file/GS_NGS_2010GreendexHighlights-cb1275487974.pdf.

4 Subir Bhaumik, "Air pollution suffocates Calcutta," *BBC*, May 3, 2007, http://news.bbc.co.uk/2/hi/south_asia/6614561.stm.

5 Bruce Einhorn, "World's worst air is in New Delhi," *Bloomberg Businessweek*, March 12, 2009 http://www.businessweek.com/blogs/eyeonasia/archives/2009/03/worlds_worst_air_is_in_new_delhi.html.

6 Arvind Padmanabhan and Rajeev Ranjan Roy, "Delhi's water crisis is set to explode," IANS (Indo-Asian News Service), July 28, 2008, http://www.thaindian.com/newsportal/health/delhis-water-crisis-is-set-to-explode_10077209.html.

7 U.S. Environmental Protection Agency, "AirData," http://www.epa.gov/air/data/index.

8 Indur M. Goklany, *The Improving State of the World* (Washington, D.C.: Cato Institute, 2007), 105.

INDEX

ABOUT THE AUTHOR

With more than a decade of experience in environmental policy, Todd Myers serves as Environmental Director at the Washington Policy Center in Seattle. He previously served on the Executive Team at the Washington State Department of Natural Resources. Myers has a Bachelor's Degree in Politics from Whitman College and a Master's Degree in Russian/International Studies from the Jackson School of International Studies at the University of Washington. He and his wife Maria live in the foothills of the Cascade Mountains in Washington state.

Washington Policy Center (WPC) is an independent, non-profit, think tank that promotes sound public policy based on free-market solutions. WPC improves lives of Washington state's citizens by providing accurate, high-quality research for policymakers, the media and the general public.

Headquartered in Seattle, with offices in Olympia and Eastern Washington, WPC publishes studies, sponsors events and conferences and educates citizens on the vital public policy issues facing our region. WPC has an annual budget of $2 million and a full-time staff of 16. Broadcast, print, and online media throughout Washington and across the nation cover WPC's work regularly and seek out its policy experts for analysis and commentary. In addition, lawmakers routinely invite WPC to testify before legislative committees.

Created in 2003, WPC's Center for the Environment brings balance to the environmental debate by promoting the idea that human progress and prosperity work in a free economy to protect the environment. The Center publishes studies and articles on a wide range of environmental subjects and has been used in local and national media outlets including The Seattle Times, BBC, Fox News, NPR and the New York Daily News.